HUNTERS GUIDE

TO
PROFESSIONAL OUTFITTERS

WORLDWIDE 1989 EDITION

PUBLISHED ANNUALLY BY:
SHERMAN HINES PHOTOGRAPHIC LTD.
17 Prince Arthur Avenue
Toronto, Ontario, Canada
M5R 1B2

1989 ed., 1st
Includes index.
ISBN 0-940143-16-X

Design: Sherman Hines
Production: Stephen Ewins and Chris Belfontaine
Advertising: Sherman Hines and Chris Belfontaine
Statistics: Chris Belfontaine
Publisher: Sherman Hines
General Manager: Stephen Ewins

DISTRIBUTION:

Africa, Europe & United States
Safari Press
Box 3095
Long Beach, CA
USA 90805
Fax: (213) 594-9613

Canada
Sherman Hines Photographic Ltd.
17 Prince Arthur Avenue
Toronto, Ontario, Canada
M5R 1B2
Fax: (416) 964-1553

Printed and bound in Hong Kong
by Everbest Printing Co.
Printing enquiries please call:
(416) 967-4319

We have compiled our outfitter's list by means of extensive research and the names and addresses are accurate to the best of our knowledge. We are not responsible for any mistakes or omissions. To make a correction to any listing, please contact the editor of Hunters Guide at 17 Prince Arthur Ave., Toronto, Ontario, Canada M5R 1B2.

If you are a professional outfitter and your name is not listed in the free directory, please send your name and address on your letterhead to Hunters Guide.

Photograph Credits

Front cover photo:
Courtesy Cotton Gordon Safaris, Ltd.
Endpapers:
"Fall Roundup" by Hayden Lambson
Page 3:
Bullet courtesy Federal Cartridge Co.
Page 24, 25:
Courtesy Don McVittie
Page 28 - 31:
Courtesy Campbell Smith
Spread Page 62 :
Ron Nemetchek, North River Outfitting
Page 94:
Yellowknife Inn
Page 154, 237:
Sammy Cantafio
Dall Sheep Page 196:
Ken Whitmire
Page 224, 226:
Courtesy Art Alphin
Moose Page 241:
Rick Furniss

Photos by Sherman Hines:
4, 6, 8, 10, 12, 14, 16-21, 24, 65, 67, 70, 75, 80-82, 92, 93, 96-99, 111-118, 122, 132, background 134, 143-147, 152, 153, 158, 159, 161, 163, 183-195, 202, 203, 216, 217, 220, 221, 228, 229, 234-236, 240, 248, 249, 256, 257, 270, 271, 274, 275, 278-290, 299, 314-316, 320-322, 328

Special Thanks to:
Boyd Deel, North-Western Safaris
Ken du Plessis, Faunafrika Safaris
Gilbert Paul, Ernst Dedekind Safaris
Gerhard Steenkamp, Game Hunters' Safaris
Jimmie Rosenbruch, Glacier Guides
Don Lindsay, IPHA
Ray Simpson, Collingwood Bros.
Lynn Castle, Denali Wilderness Lodge
SATOUR:
Dr. Danie Hough
Gunther Dettweiller
Dick Garstang
Tom Elder
SAA:
Steve Donnelly
Gavin van der Merwe

How to use this book

Hunters Guide to Professional Outfitters is your primary source of information to plan your next major hunting or fishing trip.

Begin with the Table of Contents to determine, first of all, your geographic preference. This book offers full-page advertisements from some of the world's finest outfitters, in Africa, North America, Australia, South America or Europe. Once you've found the type of hunting or fishing you desire, call, fax or write to the outfitter to make your arrangements; be sure to mention the *Hunters Guide*! Next, turn to the sections on booking agents, supplies, taxidermists, rifles, ammunition and so on, to find those additional services necessary to make your hunt completely satisfying.

In the Directory section at the back of the book, you will find an extensive listing of outfitters from around the world. This section is listed alphabetically so that you can find your chosen outfitter as easily as possible.

For more detailed information on any of the advertisers or directory entrants, just clip and fill out a reader service card from the page at the back of the book and mail it to the outfitter/supplier of your choice.

Remember, this book is an annual publication. Each year it will grow to include more and more services catering to hunters and fishermen. As it does, it will become even more useful to you. You can obtain each year's edition by contacting the publisher for a direct mail order or subscription, through a bookstore, or you can drop by our booth at some of the major hunting shows and exhibitions.

Outfitters and Suppliers:

If you would like to advertise in this book or have your name added to the Directory, we'd be pleased to hear from you. Contact Sherman Hines and we'll provide you with all the information you need.

Hunters Guide to Professional Outfitters
17 Prince Arthur Avenue
Toronto, Ontario, Canada
M5R 1B2

Sections

Contents

1	**Big Game Outfitters**

Africa

Australia / New Zealand

Europe

North America

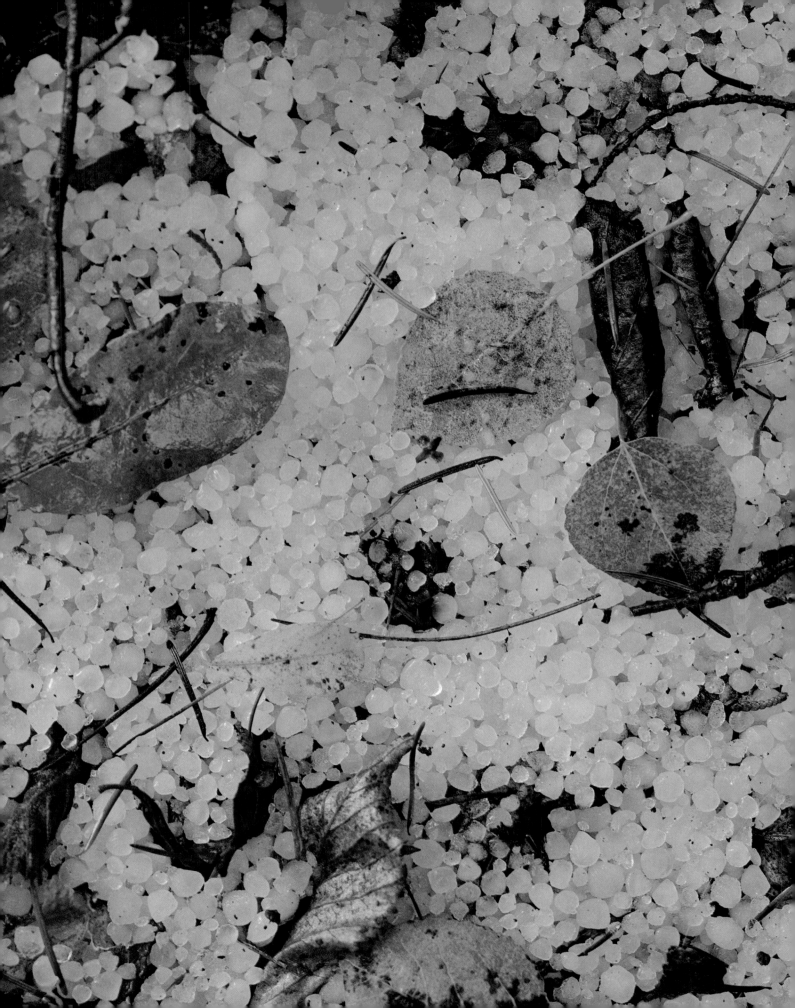

South America

2   Upland Game and Waterfowl Outfitters

11 Airlines and Travel

12 Outfitters Directory

Editorial

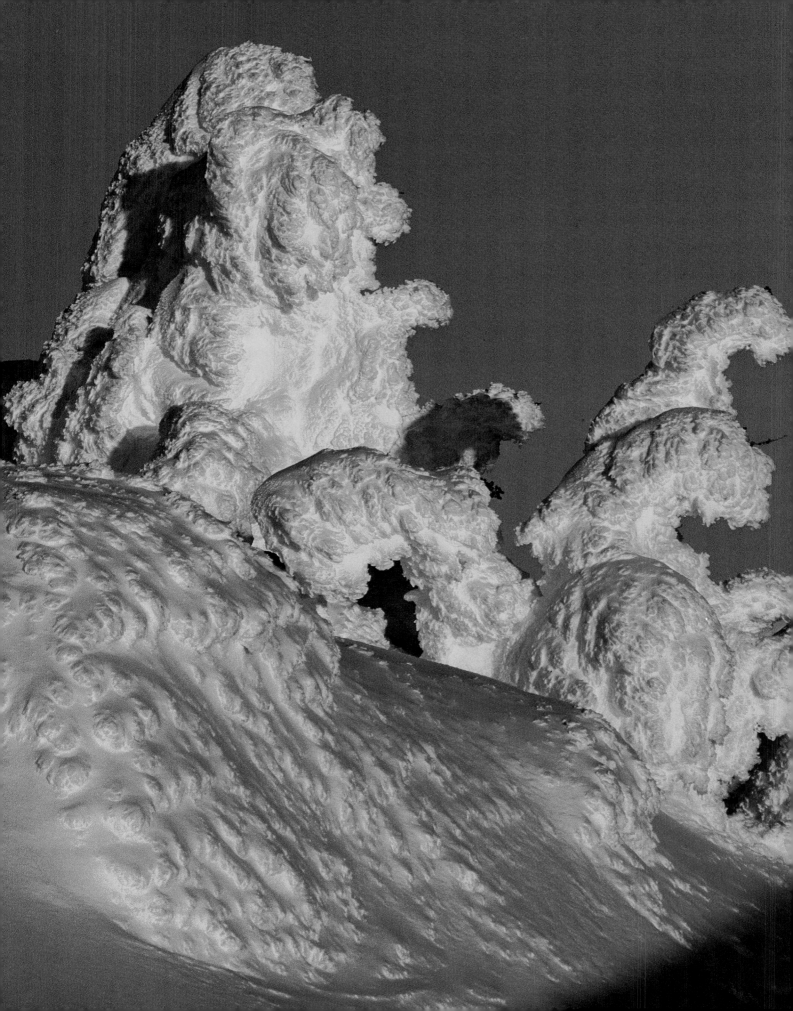

A message from the publisher

I am very excited about this year's Hunters Guide to Professional Outfitters.

The response to the premiere edition was all that I hoped for, and as a result of the tremendous surge of interest by outfitters and trade to the market's only book of this kind, the 1989 Hunters Guide is almost twice as big as the 1988 book.

I am totally committed to making this book the most complete, carefully researched, up-to-date, essential source book in existence for hunters all over the world. In the near future, serious sportsmen will regard *Hunters Guide* as a staple as important to the success of their hunt as is their rifle.

The response by hunters is proof: in its first year, readership of the *Hunters Guide* was 50,000 to 60,000. I've had reports from outfitters that this book in their trophy rooms and hunting lodges has upwards of 100 readership during one season!

This year, you'll find pages on virtually every popular hunting area in the world, along with something new — articles of interest that I thought were worth reprinting for you. Of course, you'll find once again a whole range of suppliers, from airlines to get you to your hunt right through to artists who create art for you as an investment or a reminder of your trip.

So, enjoy this book, and if you like, send me your comments on it. This book is meant for you, the serious sportsman, and I want it to reflect your needs and interests. Or come and visit our booth at the following shows in 1989: Booth #1955 at the Shot Show, January 12 to 14 in Dallas; booth #510 at the SCI convention, January 18 to 21 in Reno; booth #266 at the FNAWS convention, February 15 to 18 in Reno; and booth #808 at the Rocky Mountain Elk Foundation Exposition, March 2 to 5 in Seattle.

Good hunting in 1989!

Sherman Hines

What it means to be a hunter

The cottontail rabbit made me a hunter. I successfully stalked him when I was 11 years old, and countless feelings flowed through me as I lifted his lifeless body. I was proud, because I knew my Dad, uncles, and Grandpa would beam in approval when I showed them my prize. I was happy with my hunting skills -- sneaking up on the rabbit and dispatching it with a single humane shot was a challenge that I'd successfully met. The fact that I'd done it alone, without the help of Grandpa's beagles, was a most satisfactory and heady feeling. But I was sad, knowing that the rabbit would never again sit next to the stone wall under the bramble patch, and it was with a bit of remorse that I looked back at the cottontail's newly vacated resting spot as I carried him out of the woods. I was too young to know that animals never die peacefully, and that I, as a hunter, exacted a much more humane termination of a creature's life than nature's other options. A week after the hunt, I noted with delight that another rabbit took up

residency in the bramble patch, learning the eternal lesson that the bounty was being replenished, as it always is.

Some years later, while glassing a Dall ram in Alaska's splendid Wrangell Mountains, I thought about the cottontail. In many ways, that important rabbit hunt wasn't much different than the one I was involved in. To be sure, the circumstances were not similar, but the basic objectives were there. The Wrangells offered a magical arena in which to pursue the quarry, as did the little woodlot in New York that was surrounded by crowds of humans. The ram, like the rabbit, yielded a challenge of getting within range and making a clean kill, and if I scored, I'd have the same sense of pride as well as memories of a hunt never to be

As hunters, we are unlike any other group in society. A fisherman can practise catch and release, allowing his quarry to live another day. A logger can cut a tree down and know that its fibre will make lumber and pulp, two essential materials for civilized man. A miner can rip apart a mountain, knowing that his product will make steel for an automobile, or copper for an electrical wire, or gold for a ladies' ring.

But we, as hunters, are alone in our sport. There are no spectators or apparent benefits to society other than the money we spend on a particular hunt, thus contributing to the livelihood of other people. Our decisions must be quick and correct, and we must survive in an environment that could easily become lethal. We are chastised by others who do not understand, cannot understand, the motivation behind our sport -- the delicious sights, sounds and smells of the outdoors, the experience of a new adventure, the making of new friends, the quest of a wild animal. The nonhunter cannot know that the kill, if one is made, is only a small part of the pursuit. We can stand proud, knowing that we deeply respect the wild things, as well as the magnificent outdoors that we have passionately come to love.

Jim Zumbo is editor-at-large for OUTDOOR LIFE magazine.

Big Game Outfitters 1

PROFESSIONAL HUNTERS' ASSOCIATION OF SOUTH AFRICA

The Association's Aims and Objectives

To conserve game and flora

To safeguard the client and particularly the non-resident hunter

To promote the ethical conduct of hunting and to countenance only the fair chase

To maintain a high standard of professional service by members

Hunting with an association member assures your protection and enjoyment

Hunting in
South Africa

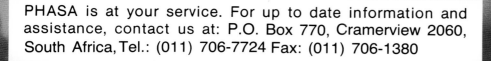

ZULULAND SPECIES
NYALA
KUDU-SOUTHERN
REEDBUCK-COMMON
REEDBUCK-MOUNTAIN
IMPALA-SOUTHERN
GREY DUIKER
RED BUSH DUIKER
CAPE BUSHBUCK
STEINBUCK
BLESBUCK-COMMON
ZEBRA
WATERBUCK-COMMON
BLUE WILDEBEEST
WARTHOG
BUSHPIG
OSTRICH
JACKAL

* When Available

CAPE SPECIES
KUDU-CAPE
BUSHBUCK-CAPE
BLESBUCK-WHITE
BLESBUCK-COMMON
SPRINGBUCK-CAPE
SPRINGBUCK-WHITE
SPRINGBUCK-BLACK
VAAL RHEBUCK
SOUTHERN MOUNTAIN REEDBUCK
WHITE TAILED GNU
CAPE GRYSBUCK
*BONTEBUCK
CAPE ELAND
GEMSBUCK
ZEBRA
RED HARTEBEEST
GREY DUIKER
STEENBUCK

SPECIES AVAILABLE - TRANSVAAL
LEOPARD
KUDU-SOUTHERN
ELAND-LIVINGSTONES
NYALA
BUSHBUCK-LIMPOPO
ZEBRA-BURCHELLS
WATERBUCK-COMMON
IMPALA-SOUTHERN
KLIPSPRINGER
BLUE WILDEBEEST
GEMSBUCK
RED HARTEBEEST
WARTHOG
BUSHPIG
BLESBUCK-COMMON
MOUNTAIN REEDBUCK-SOUTHERN
JACKAL
GREY DUIKER
STEENBUCK
*SABLE ANTELOPE
COMMON REEDBUCK
BABOON
SHARPS GRYSBUCK
HYENA
*GIRAFFE

•JOHNNY VIVIER(Professional Hunter)
•LEW HARRIS(Professional Photogapher)

P.O. BOX 514, HARRISMITH, 9880, R.S.A.
TEL. FROM USA: DIAL 27-01436-22924 ALL HOURS

JOHNNY VIVIER
HUNTING SAFARIS
SOUTH AFRICA

North-Western
Safaris
South Africa

North-Western Safaris offer hunting in all four Provinces of South Africa for the complete range of Southern African species. No effort is spared in securing the best possible trophies for clients.

North-Western Safaris
South Africa

North Western Safaris
Private Bag X2626, Potgieterus 0600
Transvaal, Republic of South Africa

IN U.S. CONTACT: North-Western Safaris
Box 5909, San Jose, Ca 95150
408-866-4672

Leopard
Eland
Kudu
Waterbuck
Blue Wildebeest
Zebra
Bushbuck
Gemsbuck
Cape Hartebeest
Klipspringer
Blesbok
Impala
Grey Duiker
Steenbuck
Crocodile
Bushpig
Warthog
Mountain Reedbuck
Buffalo
Lion
Sable Antelope
Nyala
Common Reedbuck
Suni
Red Duiker
White Rhino
Springbuck
Black Springbuck
White Springbuck
White Blesbuck
Bontebok
Red Lechwe
Vaal Rhebuck
Fallow Deer
Cape Grysbuck
White-tailed Gnu
Caracal
Serval
Baboon
Jackal

**NORTH WESTERN
TRANSVAAL**

**NORTH EASTERN
TRANSVAAL**

CAPE PROVINCE

ZULULAND

THE HUNTING SAFARI BROCHURE

TAWICO

YOUR HUNTING SAFARI IN TANZANIA

Your hunting safari will be organized by the Tanzania Wildlife Corporation. The Corporation's team of experienced administrative and field staff are there to ensure that your trip does not become a hit-and-miss affair. They will plan your itinerary, take care of your itinerary airline bookings, local charter flights, hotel and lodge arrangements, ground transport, camping arrangements, and the preservation and processing of your trophies. On your safari you will be guided by a reliable Professional Hunter in a 4-wheel drive vehicle and an experienced Game Scout who is familiar with the terrain, a driver and a gunbearer. Camp equipment in the field is comprehensive and specially trained staff is at your service at all times to ensure that you are adequately served during your field trip. A safari is planned as far as possible to suit the individual requirements of each client as such no two safaris are exactly alike.

Price Schedule and Conditions

All safaris start and end in Arusha, except for the Selous Game Reserve where the starting and ending point shall be Dar [Es] Salaam. Quotations are inclusive of the day a safari starts and the day it is completed.

A deposit of 40% of the total cost of the safari is required before confirmation and deposit once paid is not refundable. A safari is considered confirmed only on receipt of the deposit. The balance to be paid one month before commencement of the safari. Payment must be made direct to the Tanzania Wildlife Corporation and must be in any currency convertible in Tanzania Shillings either by Cashiers Cheques, Telegraphic Transfer, Bank Draft, Travellers Cheques or Cash. Under any circumstances, Personal cheques are not accepted. Payments may be made to our bankers:

The National Bank of Commerce,
Uhuru Branch,
SOKOINE ROAD,
P.O. Box 3004,
ARUSHA,
TANZANIA
Tel. No. 3751
Telex No. 42133 NBCARS
To our Account Number 58292

CENTRAL AFRICAN REPUBLIC

ROBIN HURT SAFARIS LTD.

USA OFFICE: Sporting International Inc., 7701 Wilshire Place Drive, Suite 504, Houston, Texas 77040
Tel: (713) 744-3527 Tlx: 9108811101 Fax: (713) 895-8753 Att: Walter Fondren
NAIROBI OFFICE: Sporting International (Nairobi Office), Box 24988, Nairobi, Kenya
Tel: 882268/882826 Tlx: 25583 HURT KE Fax: 882939 Att: Mrs. Janet Hurt

Hunting Zambia

A golden ball that is a fading sun sinks beyond the western horizon as safari chairs are arranged about the fire by a white-coated waiter. Another places snacks on a covered table, finishing the preparations for "sundowners". This is a scene that is played out daily in each safari camp in Zambia, one of the last countries to offer old-time bush safaris. Zambia offers no farm or ranch hunting but is a country of bush, from flat valleys to rolling hills that turn blue in the sunset.

Zambia is vast, lightly populated and unspoiled by what many term progress. It is a land of great rivers: the mighty Zambezi with its spectacular Victoria Falls, the Kafue and its floodplains, and the sluggish Luangwa with its teeming wildlife. There are the great lakes: Tanganyika, Bangweula and Kariba. This magnificient country is much the same today as it was when first seen by the great explorers such as Livingstone and Stanley.

Formerly named Northern Rhodesia, Zambia gained independence in 1964. Some 75 different tribes make up the country's population, speaking more than 40 different dialects. (English is the official language.) The country is situated on the great plateau of central Africa and is bordered on the north by Zaire and Tanzania, on the east by Malawi, the southeast by Mozambique and Zimbabwe, the south by Botswana and a small strip of Namibia, and on the west by Angola. Average temperatures in the capital city of Lusaka are 75 degrees May to August, 85 degrees September to November and 78 degrees December to April. The rainy season normally lasts from early December through late March. While Zambia has no closed hunting seasons, safaris are normally from mid-May through November.

There are four major hunting areas. The Luangwa Valley and the Kafue are the most prominent, with the Bangweula and Kafue Flats being more specialized. There is growing interest within the National Parks and Wildlife Service in opening other areas in western Zambia as well as along the Zambezi. Some hunting blocks have also been established south of Lake Tanganyika and have been in operation for the past few years.

Cotton Gordon

COTTON GORDON SAFARIS, LTD.

Hunting Zambia

MEMBER

- International Proffessional Hunters Association
- Proffessional Hunters Association of Zambia
- Dallas Safari Club
- Sarfari Club International
- Game Conservation International

Tarryall River Ranch • Lake George, Colorado 80827 • Area Code 719-748-3255

Cape Buffalo

Eland

Klipspringer

Lichtenstein's Hartebeest

Cookson's Wildebeest

Roan Antelope

Southern Greater Kudu

Australia
and the South Pacific

Chamois

Red Deer

Bull Tahr

Bull Buffalo SCI 123 2/8

GAME HUNTING
DOWN UNDER

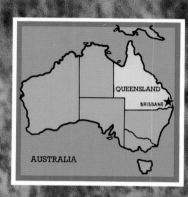

KINGHAM HUNTING PRESERVE

Kingham Hunting Preserve • P.O. Box 53 • KILCOY 4515 • Queensland, Australia • Tel: (071) 97 3115/84 5174

Buffalo

Buffalo

Banteng

Jarvan Rusa

G.P.O. BOX 472 DARWIN N.T 5794
AUSTRALIA
TELEPHONE: (089) 811599
TELEX: AA 10721050 FAX: 61-89-411016

NIMROD SAFARIS AUSTRALIA

BARRY LEES
Member International Professional Hunters Association
Official Measurer Safari Club International
Foundation for North American Wild Sheep
Game Conservation International.

Buffalo

Nimrod Safaris South Pacific Hunting Opportunities.

For clients wishing to hunt all the available South Pacific species. Nimrod Safaris are happy to provide the best of the species available from our hunting concessions. We are constantly searching for new concessions so we can offer, you the client, the best hunting opportunities. We will assist you to achieve your goals with our recommended hunting colleagues in New Zealand and other areas.

Guarantee of Success

Since 1978 we have achieved 100% success for the following big game species: Red Stag, Chamois, Tahr, Fallow, Sika, Wapiti and Goat. Each species has a single Trophy Fee and hunters may take the best trophy we can find at no additional cost. We want our clients to enjoy the hunt without the fear of "additional" or "unexpected" hidden charges.
Our clients know the "bottom line" before booking with us.

Transport

Ground transport is by Passenger Service Licenced vehicles of high quality. Where transport by air is required, in the interests of speed, schedule airlines are utilised. Often Helicopter transport is required for access to remote areas and when this is required only fully Licenced Helicopters are used. All costs of transport in New Zealand, land, sea or air are included in our trophy fees.

Best Times

Big Game March thru July, February and August also acceptable. The best trophies are taken early in the season. Stag "roar" in April.
Canada Geese February and March, May thru October.
Ducks May thru July.
Trout October thru April.
Salmon October thru April. Best fishing February, March and April.

Firearms and Fishing Tackle

There is no difficulty in bringing Firearms into New Zealand. A Firearms Licence will be issued by the N.Z. Police at your "Point of Entry" at a minimal cost. Scope-sighted rifles and shotguns are available. Fishing tackle at no charge. Ammunition, flies/lures expended, charged at local prices.

Climate and Clothing

New Zealand has a mild climate, but changes occur rapidly and a fine warm day may turn into rain or snow at any time. Clothing for all weather conditions should be brought along. For hunting warm clothes and good boots and for evenings, clothes suitable for dining (tidy casual) should be included. Wet weather gear is a prerequisite.

TERRY PIERSON
New Zealand Govt. Registered Hunting Guide.
Vice-President New Zealand Registered Hunting Guides Association.
Life Member and Vice-President International Professional Hunters Association.
Advisory Board GAME Coin.
Official Measurer Safari Club International.
Member F.N.A.W.S.

New Zealand Wildlife Safaris

New Zealand Wildlife Safaris

Since 1978 New Zealand Wildlife Safaris and Terry Pierson have been outfitting very successful hunts in New Zealand. In the past we have restricted our base of operations and hunting close to Christchurch, mainly Mt Hutt. We have broadened our hunting opportunities and now offer the finest hunting to clients over the whole of New Zealand.

The areas selected are chosen to suit the special and individual requirements of each client. It is conceivable that no two hunts may be on the same properties. These properties are in the main privately owned and usually provide sole access to this Company and its clients.

Our policy is to ensure that all our clients requirements are personally handled to the highest possible professional standard.

We welcome all wives and companions to join our unique experiences. They are invited to either join the hunts or enjoy the many alternative excursions available in this beautiful country.

For total individual attention only one hunter is booked at one time but where more than one hunter may wish to form a party, only experienced New Zealand Government Registered Guides are provided.

Telephone:
Terry and Gladys Pierson (64-3) 558-243
If no reply call:
Terry Jacobs   (64-3) 384-266
After hours   (64-3) 428-322

Or Write:
Wildlife Enterprises Ltd
P.O. Box 4058
Christchurch, New Zealand

Telex or Fax:
Attn Terry Pierson, Wildlife
Telex N.Z 4586 Cantcom
FAX (64-3) 789-658

**FELIX LALANNE
HUNTING SPAIN**

FELIX LALANNE

José Abascal, 55
28003 MADRID (SPAIN)
Phone 442 86 43
Telex 23829 GGEX E

SPANISH IBEX -- Truly the monarch of the mountains, the Spanish Ibex numbers 25,000 and is the number one trophy in Europe today. Its keen sight and sense of smell, combined with a wild and rocky habitat, make the ibex one of the finest and most challenging animals in the world to hunt. For the mountain hunter, the Spanish Ibex offers a unique hunting experience and a rare and beautiful trophy.

PYRENEAN & CANTABRIAN CHAMOIS -- Found in the mountainous regions of the north, the Pyrenean and Cantabrian chamois are two distinct and elusive big game species found in the beautiful mountainous regions of the North. The Pyrenean subspecies is physically larger than the Cantabrian. Both species give the hunter a sporty, mountain hunting experience. Again, these are two unique species, the Cantabrian chamois being exclusive only to Spain.

MOUFLON SHEEP -- The mouflon is not as mountain-oriented as his American and Asian wild sheep cousin, and is often found in dense forests. Ranging from 2,000 to 4,000 feet, the mouflon is a diurnal animal with keen senses and the only species of wild sheep indigenous to Europe. A prized and necessary trophy for the visiting sportsman.

WESTERN RED DEER -- The "stag", or Western Red Deer, is slightly smaller than its cousin, the Eastern Red Deer, and abounds in many mountainous regions of Spain. Its antlers are smaller, but usually have more points than the Eastern species. A wider crown makes this trophy the more elegant of the two.

FALLOW DEER -- Smaller than a red stag but larger than a roe buck, the fallow deer's horns palmate at the upper third, similar to moose. The fallow inhabits forest and open grassland alike. An impressive species which will test the skill of any hunter.

ROE DEER -- Smallest of the European deer family, the roebuck's likes are similar to the stag, often found in mountanous regions as well as dense forets. A beautiful species, it is one that will enhance the hunter's den as well as provide great sport in the field.

WILD BOAR -- Inhabiting most areas of the peninsula, the wild boar is a great trophy for hunters because of its difficulty to hunt. An electrifying "tusker" hunt is the favorite sport of many Europeans. The tusks of a good boar create a unique and decorative trophy, as well as a fascinating conversation piece.

HUNTING AREAS

1. SPANISH IBEX
2. PYRENEAN CHAMOIS
3. CANTABRIAN CHAMOIS
4. MOUFLON SHEEP
5. RED DEER
6. FALLOW DEER
7. ROE DEER

Trophy Hunt Ibérica

Javier Iñíguez

SPAIN -- The most southerly country in Europe enjoys an excellent climate all year round and is fast becoming one of the most attractive areas for the hunter. From high mountains to flat Castilian plains, its geography is largely responsible for the diverse climates and differing ecological systems found within an area of a few kilometres.

A large variety of species find ideal habitat here. Spanish ibex, Pyrenean and Cantabrian chamois, mouflon sheep, red deer, fallow deer, roe deer and wild boar roam this highly varied countryside. Spain is truly a hunter's paradise, with the added advantage of easy accessibility and excellent accommodations.

OFFERING OUR CLIENTS THE MAGNIFICENT OPPORTUNITY TO HUNT IN BEAUTIFUL SPAIN, GIVING THE BEST IN TROPHIES AND SERVICES.

**Maria de Molina, 66 - 28006
Madrid, Spain
262-5883/262-5710**

ELK
BIG HORN SHEEP
WHITETAIL
BEAR

Bonded and insured
Fully accomodated
deluxe hunts

ECHO CANYON OUTFITTERS LTD.

Box 831, Rocky Mountain House
Alberta, Canada T0M 1T0
Phone: (403) 845-6131

Seven-Foot Black Bears
Spring 1988
100% Success

ALBER

The province of Alberta is famous for its bull-shouldered, cow-nosed whitetails, with massive heavy antlers. Perhaps nowhere else in North America does the traveling whitetail hunter have opportunity for a better trophy...

150 points or better is as good as the outfitter or guide you hunt with.

It is sometimes confusing to assess a trophy by score alone. A high percentage of mature Alberta bucks grow some degree of irregular points in their racks. Even the mature typical bucks will commonly grow spurs and cheater points. What this means is that a buck which scores 150 on paper may actually have considerably more inches of antler before deductions. Many bucks which have been deducted out of the B&C running because of irregular points, are far more impressive than the cleaner, typical bucks with less total antler present, but which score better according to B&C. If there was ever a province full of deer that would challenge the fairness of the B&C scoring method for whitetails, it would certainly be Alberta.

Mass is what the non-resident hunter

should look for in an Alberta trophy. Mature trophy class bucks in Alberta typically sport inside spread credits of less than twenty inches. But bases of six inches and more are common, with fat tines and heavy main beams. Some hunters are so spread conscious that they might overlook a real monster in Alberta. While bucks with a twenty-four inch inside spread are cetainly not rare, it should be noted that bucks have been killed in Alberta scoring over 180 B&C typical, with an inside spread credit of only fourteen inches! In Alberta, mass and tine length are the keys to a great trophy.

Body size is of great concern to hunters coming to Alberta from other regions where body size is much smaller. Any mature Alberta whitetail buck is going to at least

crowd the 200 pound mark, field dressed. Large bucks will often dress 250 pounds while exceptional bucks will tip the scales at the 300 pound mark. Body length, from the front of the chest to the round of the rump will average near forty-eight inches. Such a buck will stand thirty-eight inches tall at the shoulder and his chest cavity will be from eighteen to twenty inches deep. While some B&C bucks are killed each year in Alberta which are not as large as described here, it must be remembered that many BOOK DEER are killed in Alberta which are only three and one half years old, still two years away from maturity!

Alberta's largest typical whitetail, scoring 204 6/8, was taken by Stephen Jansen in 1970 in the Dog Pound district, fifty miles northwest

of Calgary. It is interesting to note that this great buck had over twenty inches of deductions in its typical tines. Jansen's buck indisputably grew more typical inches of antler than any of its peers, including the world record Jordan buck. It can be said that this typical head acutally has more inches of antler present than any typical head ever killed. The second amazing fact about the Jansen Buck is that it was killed on the western side of the province, near the foothills fo the Rockies, instead of the central eastern region where most hunters expect to find the new world record.

The number one non-typical whitetail, scoring 277 5/8 was killed by Doug Klinger of Hardisty, Alberta in November of 1976. Klinger's great buck was taken along the famous Battle River in Alberta's

central eastern Parklands. This area is still producing many great trophies today.

The highest scoring typical whitetail bow kill for Alberta is Scott Simi's 171 5/8 buck killed near Calgary in September of 1979.

More recently, in September of 1984, Dean Dwernychuk, also of Calgary, bagged the number one bow and arrow non-typical buck scoring 241 2/8. Both Simi and Dwernychuk bagged their tremendous bucks near Calgary in the adjacent bow hunting only zone.

In recent years both typical and non-typical records have been challenged. In November of 1986 a typical whitetail was killed in the Swan Hills area. The huge buck had one main tine broken off which kept him from breaking the world record. It is con-servatively estimated that the Swan

Hills buck would have scored over 210 B&C had it not been for the broken tine.

In November of 1984, Jerry Froma killed a huge non-typical buck scoring 267 7/8. Froma's buck was taken near his home in Barrhead, Alberta. Neither Froma's non-typical or the Swan Hills typical buck were taken from areas usually thought of as prime trophy whitetail areas. The point is clear. A record book buck can pop up anywhere in Alberta.

Whitetail seasons for bow hunters are staggered in Alberta with some early seasons opening as early as the third week of August. The rifle season opens on the first Wednesday of November in most areas of the province and bow hunters are allowed to hunt during the rifle season. Sur-rounding Alberta's two major cities, Edmonton and Calgary, there are large zones open to bow hunting only. These bow only zones open in early September and continue through the month of November. There are many trophy deer in these bow zones since the harvest is relatively light and deer have little trouble maturing. However, the lands in these zones are all privately owned and sometimes present serious access problems. Located near cities with populations of over 500,000, there is certainly competition for access. Finding a productive hunting spot near Calgary or Edmonton is a matter of making the right connections before coming to hunt.

The rut occurs during the month of November and if weather is cold and there is snow on the ground, there will be evidence of the rut in progress during the entire month. As the November season opens, between the 2nd and 6th of November, depending on the calendar, the bucks will be making scrapes and looking for the first hot does which they will not generally find until around the middle of the month. During this very active pre-rut time rattling is very effective and bucks are on the move. The breeding usually begins by the 15th of November and peaks around the 24th. The last week of November finds the bucks coming off the peak, still following does until the season ends.

Typical hunting conditions in November are cold with temperatures ranging from slightly above freezing to -20 F. Hunters should be prepared for warmer as well as colder weather during the same time period. Hunting conditions are prime with temperatures well below freezing with a good layer of snow on the ground. In these conditions the bucks rut hard and give trophy hunters their best opportunity.

There are no specific color re-quirements for hunter clothing in Alberta. The hunter may wear what suits him. Tree bark and snow camo are both good selections for late fall.

At present there is no limit or sales deadline on non-resident whitetail licenses in Alberta. A non-resident license cost a total of $178.00 Canadian currency. Licenses can be purchased at the various Fish and Wildlife offices around the province or they may be purchased in advance, on the hunter's behalf, by his guide or outfitter. The bag limit for non-resident hunters is one male whitetail per season.

The non-resident hunter is required by law to hunt with a licensed guide when hunting any species of big game in Alberta. Alberta's trophy whitetail boom has, within the last several years, attracted untold numbers of guides and outfitters to the band wagon. Sadly, the majority of them are not qualified or experienced and their participation in professional hunting has resulted in many rip-off hunts. The guiding industry protested the lack of government control over such "Rip-Off" outfitters and subsequently the government spent three years designing a new policy for outfitters which was to be the beginning of intelligent regulation of wildlife resources and the outfitting industry. Sadly, after much deliberation, the government of Alberta decided not to regulate the outfitting industry, but rather let it operate with no control over where an outfitter may hunt or how many clients he can take into a given area. Severe overcrowding now makes quality hunting impossible in some prime areas of the province. Quality outfitters are in the minority and while there are still plenty of great trophies to be had, the non-resident hunter must really do his homework to ensure that he is not booking with a sub-standard operation.

Many long-time Alberta outfitters believe the government withheld regulating the outfitting industry so as to let it self-destruct and thereby eliminate the non-resident hunter in the future. This is now a very realistic possibility. Non-resident hunters who yearn for an Alberta wallhanger should be advised that their future opportunities are being further threatened with every passing deer season. Alberta law will not allow landowners to receive any compensation for hunting rights on their property. This antiquated concept has naturally created much ill will between landowners and outfitters. It is only natural for the landowner to resent the fact that an outfitter can prosper from the deer raised on his land, and he cannot. The result of the problem can be observed in more posted land and the continual decreasing habitat as landowners put it to the bulldozer. In short, Alberta is suffering severe growing pains as the demand on wildlife resources increase. New laws will have to be made and old ones changed if the great deer of Alberta are to survive the coming years.

For information on hunting seasons and regulations contact:

Alberta Fish and Wildlife Division
Main Floor, North Tower
Petroleum Plaza
9945 108 Street
Edmonton, Alberta
T5J 2G6

For information on reputable outfitters services contact:

Alberta Whitetail Outfitters Association
P. O. Box 1463
Rocky Mountain House, Alberta
TOM 1T0

Reprinted from their September 1988 issue with the compliments of BUCK-MASTERS WHITETAIL MAGAZINE, 3960 Brookridge Dr., Montgomery, AL., tel. 205-269-3337.

Hunting Journal
1989 Hunts

State/Province/Country _____

Hunting Companions _____

Outfitter _____

Address _____

Guide _____

Address _____

Hunting Areas/Camps _____

Rifle Used _____

Trophy Taken _____ Score _____

Date _____ Time _____

Trophy Taken _____ Score _____

Date _____ Time _____

Trophy Taken _____ Score _____

Date _____ Time _____

Trophy Taken _____ Score _____

Date _____ Time _____

Date Entered in Record Book _____

Comments _____

_____

_____

_____

Big Game Species in British Columbia

Caribou

Rocky Mountain Elk

Grizzly Bear

Black Bear

Moose

Mountain Goat

Dall Sheep

Stone Sheep

Wolf

NORTH BY NORTHWEST
TOURISM ASSOCIATION OF B.C.
3840 Alfred Avenue
Box 1030, Smithers, B.C. Canada V0J 2N0
Tel: (604) 847-5227 Fax: (604) 847-7585

NORTHWEST GUIDES
& OUTFITTERS ASSOC.
P.O. Box 2489
Smithers
British Columbia

NORTHWEST

BIG GAME HUNTING GUIDE

Super, Natural
North by Northwest
BRITISH COLUMBIA, CANADA

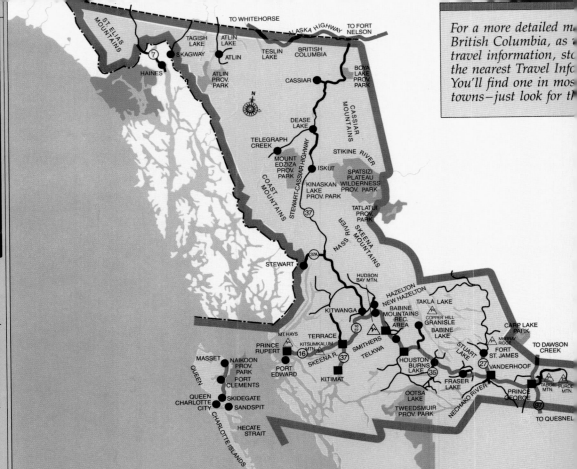

For a more detailed m...
British Columbia, as ...
travel information, sto...
the nearest Travel Info...
You'll find one in mos...
towns—just look for th...

Most of the North by Northwest region is accessible by major paved roads, commercial airlines or B.C. Ferries. A number of roads, including the Nass Road, are gravel.

When travelling the gravel roads, please be sure your vehicle is in good repair. Take spare tires, water and minor repair supplies with you, and fill up with gasoline whenever you reach a pump. It's a good idea to let a friend or the RCMP know where you're travelling and when you expect to return.

The Yellowhead Highway.

Tête Jaune Cache to Prince George. Both the Yellowhead Highway and Tête Jaune Cache were named after a blond French-Canadian trapper who guided early fur traders through the Rocky Mountains and who once concealed a fortune in furs in the area. To this day, the hiding place has been referred to as Tête Jaune Cache, although the town itself isn't the location; the exact spot is still not known.

McBride is a natural stopover for visitors travelling the Yellowhead. The surrounding views are magnificent, and for the height of beauty, the Teare Mountain forestry lookout, accessible by a narrow dirt road, is excellent. *Prince George*, the third largest city in British Columbia, is known as "The Hub of the North." Naturally, northern British Columbia's major entertainment, restaurants, shopping and nightlife revolve

around this large, centrally located city. But the town wasn't always so prominent–when Fort George, as it was originally called, was founded back in the early 1800s, the nearby Fort St. James was the undisputed capital of the northern fur trading empire. Today, the memory of Old Fort George lives on in Fort George Park.

If you're here in summer, visit the Folk Fest or head out of town to meet our wilder residents at the Tabor Mountain Moose Viewing Areas. In winter, be prepared for the time of your life at the 10-day Mardi Gras.

Prince George to Smithers.

The next stop, *Vanderhoof*, is the geographical centre of B.C. It's also the home of the Vanderhoof International Airshow, which takes place in early July and rates among the top five airshows in North America. For the remainder of the year, you can see other high flyers at the Nechako Bird Sanctuary, which shelters up to 50,000 Canada geese and other birds yearly.

Turn right at Vanderhoof and you'll travel back in time to the early fur trading days. *Fort St. James* National Park consists of five buildings, dating from 1884-89, which have been restored and refurbished. The town of Fort St. James has other historic sites, including the grave of a famous Carrier Indian chief, an original missionary church and a tribute to Russ Baker, one of the pioneer bush pilots involved in

the founding of Canadian Pacific Airlines.

The North Road from Fort St. James takes you into *Omenica Country*, famous for grayling, char, rainbow trout and Dolly Varden. Roads in the area are gravel, so travelling can be bumpy, but always rewarding. At Manson Creek, for example, you can visit an original Hudson's Bay Company building, still run as a store and post office.

Back on the main road, you'll pass *Fort Fraser*, one of the oldest communities in British Columbia. At *Fraser Lake*, catch the annual salmon run between Fraser and Francois Lakes. *Burns Lake*, the northern gateway to Tweedsmuir Park, also has excellent fishing for eastern brook trout, rainbow trout, cutthroat, lake char, kokanee, chinook, steelhead and many other species.

Granisle, located off the Yellowhead Highway on beautiful Babine Lake, has five fishing derbies a year. The lake is also popular for windsurfing, swimming and water

skiing. And no wonder–it's the largest natural freshwater lake in the province.

At *Houston*, the scenic splendour of the Bulkley River Valley suddenly surrounds you. The country around the community is dotted with lakes and rivers, many of which offer superb fishing, as well as a quiet serenity for nature lovers.

The town of *Telkwa* is just up the road, and offers the kind of folksy history that makes the North so fascinating. In the 1940s, for example, a land dispute between two neighbours resulted in a tussle over the cabin which stood on the controversial boundary. The argument was solved when the cabin was sawed in two and one half was hauled away. (The cabin, which had a long, colourful history, was later restored and still stands.)

Rugged Hudson Bay Mountain dominates the skyline of *Smithers*, a town renowned for its rustic Bavarian architecture. The mountain comes into its own in winter,

when skiers head down its 56km (33.5 miles) of runs, and kick up their boots at the winter festival. The rest of the year, anglers find plenty of action in neighbourhood streams and rivers–the local salmon and steelhead are rated among the best in the world. Another lure for visitors to the area is Driftwood Canyon–its fossil beds date back millions of years.

Hazelton to Prince Rupert.

The name "Hazelton" actually refers to three inter-related communities. *Old Hazelton*, first settled in 1866, was the original Mile Zero on the "Poor Man's Route" to the Yukon goldfields. *New Hazelton* and *South Hazelton*, along with the Old Town, are at the nucleus of eight surrounding Indian villages, all steeped in history and legends. (See "Native Culture" on reverse side.)

Heritage Park in *Terrace* gives a good portrait of early pioneer life in the region. And in the Kitselas Canyon on the Skeena River, you can

still see the winch mechanisms that helped sternwheelers struggle upstream. By the way, the world's record salmon was caught in the Skeena River–a whopping 43 kilos (95 pounds).

Outside Terrace, you'll come to Kitsumkalum Mountain, a popular skiing area. While you're driving, watch for our most colourful wildlife–kermode bears. This relatively uncommon species, although a member of the black bear family, is usually white, but can also be chestnut red, bright yellow, blue-grey or even orange.

A left-hand turn just before Terrace will take you to *Kitimat*. Named after "the people of the snow," you'll find the heritage of the Haisla Indians at the Kitimat Centennial Museum, as well as at nearby Kitimat Village. On a more modern-day note, the town is the home of the huge Alcan smelting complex; tours of the smelter are offered June through August.

You're now by the

ocean; Douglas Channel, on which Kitimat is located, is a prime fishing spot. As you turn back up the road, you'll be heading for the "Halibut Capital of the World," Prince Rupert.

Prince Rupert was founded by Charles Hays, the ambitious general manager of the Grand Trunk Pacific Railway. Determined to make it a rival to Vancouver as a transportation terminal, Hays never lived to see the city's growth; he went down on the *Titanic*. Today, the city is the major link between the services of the B.C. Ferry Corporation and the Alaska Ferry System. To get a better look at its majestic location on the Pacific Ocean, take the world's second steepest gondola lift up Mount Hays. A little further up the coast, you'll net all kinds of fascinating tidbits at the North Pacific Cannery, a historic restoration of the oldest standing fish cannery (built 1889) on the B.C. coast.

Speaking of fish, the Haw Yaw Haw Naw native salmon

of
d as
n at
tre.
rger
ign.

estival in June features tasty salmon, dancing and art exhibits—come sample it.

The Queen Charlotte Islands.

A ferry ride away from Prince Rupert, these mist-cloaked, evergreen islands reveal a world of timeless beauty.

For thousands of years, they were peopled only by the Haida Indians. Today, the descendants who survived the diseases white men brought to the Islands maintain their heritage. Slatechuck Mountain, for example, is the only known source of argilite, a soft black slate that is reserved for exclusive use by Haida artists.

Much of the Queen Charlottes remains in its original, natural state. Hike along a long, unspoiled beach trail in Naikoon Provincial Park. Watch for grey whales, Sitka deer and peregrine falcons. Then, in the Queen Charlotte Museum near Skidegate, marvel at the marvels of the old Haida ways.

For information, contact the Queen Charlotte Islands Chamber of Commerce, Box 357, Queen Charlotte City, B.C. V0T 1S0.

The Stewart-Cassiar Highway.

Although this highway was begun in 1926, the area has a long history of native culture, fur trading, telegraph construction and gold rushes.

The Hudson's Bay Company for example, had a trading post in Dease Lake in 1938. And in the mid-1860s, construction of the never-completed Collins Overland Telegraph was started and abandoned.

The Stewart-Cassiar branches off the Yellowhead Highway at Kitwanga; it may also be reached by taking the Nass Road, west of Terrace. This road, also dubbed the B.C. Timber Road, is an unrestricted logging route open for public use, so careful driving is advised. It passes through a number of interesting Nishga Indian communities.

On the way from Kitwanga to Stewart on the Stewart-Cassiar you'll pass the historic towns of Gitwangak and Kitwancool (described on the opposite side of this brochure under "Native Culture"), as well as the beautiful Bear Glacier, as delicately coloured as a robin's egg.

Stewart. To the public, Stewart is best known as the set location for a number of well-known movies, including "Bear Island," based on the Alistair McLean bestseller, and "Iceman," starring Timothy Hutton. A boom-and-bust town based on gold, silver and copper mining, it is set in spectacular countryside, with huge, glaciated mountains, salmon-laden streams and even a pretty little ghost town–Hyder, Alaska–nearby.

Mount Edziza and Spatsizi Plateau Parks. Heading through a forested landscape highlighted by dramatic mountain ranges, you'll arrive at Iskut, a Tahltan Reserve that is a good starting point for excursions into two of British Columbia's most spectacular protected wilderness areas. You can also camp in Kinaskan Lake Park.

Both Mount Edziza Provincial Park and Recreation Area, and Spatsizi Plateau Wilderness Provincial Park offer extraordinary terrains. In Mount Edziza, stark lava flows, basalt plateaus and cinder fields give the land exquisite watercolour tones. In Spatsizi Plateau, trail rides take you through wild valleys, uncut forests, rolling tablelands and rugged mountains.

Dease Lake. North of Iskut, has an airport for charter flights, and was the original entry point into the area for early Northwest and Hudson's Bay Company trappers who travelled in on the Liard and Dease Rivers. It's also the turning off point for *Telegraph Creek*, located on the magnificent Stikine River. The road is an experience itself. It follows the route of an original mountain trail that was hacked out by prospectors during the Cassiar gold rush, and passes through breathtaking scenery, with views of Mt. Edziza, the Grand Canyon of the Stikine, Tahltan Canyon and mountain ranges stretching to the horizon. In Telegraph Creek, the original Hudson's Bay Post is now a lodge/cafe.

Cassiar Country.

While millions of dollars of gold once came out of the creek beds during this region's gold rush, asbestos and tourism are the gold mines of today. The area around the small town of Cassiar is superb for fishing, with lake trout, Dolly Varden, pike, grayling and whitefish in abundance. Hunting for moose, caribou, mountain goat, mountain sheep, black bear, grizzly and wolf is also popular. There is no accommodation in the town of Cassiar itself, although private campgrounds are nearby.

Atlin.

Tucked away in the extreme northwestern corner of the province, this area was a sidebar of the Klondike, a bustling small town that enjoyed a rich cultural life at the turn of the century. Many of the original

My area in Northwestern British Columbia includes the headwaters of Skeena and Spatsizi Rivers and has its basecamp at Kluayaz Lake. The area is approximately 640,000 acres in size and borders the famous Spatsizi Park.

In that huge wilderness area of northwestern B.C. you find big moose, goats, caribou, grizzly, blackbears, some sheep, wolves, wolverines and small game. Due to the salmon in the rivers, there is a good grizzly population and the bears are big. Lots of dolly varden and the king of all fish - the steelhead - inhabit the waters of my exclusive guiding area.

In most cases you will fly 164 miles north from Smithers, B.C. and hunt out of basecamp or spikecamp. There is a cookhouse, showerhouse, cabins, meathouse and wooden sidewalks in the basecamp, but spikecamp is mostly a good tent. My wife Gertie has a reputation for being a good cook and cooks in basecamp, but our guide will cook in spikecamp.

For moose, caribou or grizzly hunts we sometimes use saddlehorses and packhorses to transport trophies, meat and gear. Mountain hunts are usually backpacking and demand that you be in good physical condition.

You will be on a fair chase hunt and the final responsibility wil be up to you. I have many years experience as a professional hunter and have successfully guided both rifle and bow hunters. Your trophies, of course, will be cared for in a professional manner.

There is daily jet service from Vancouver to Smithers and you can book your trip right through to Smithers from anywhere in the world. Upon arrival in Smithers, please contact Central Mountain Air Services at 847-4780. We have radio contact with Central Montain Air.

Goats, grizzly, caribou and sheep must be inspected before they can be exported. Please allow enough time in Smithers for inspection if you want to take your trophy with you.

I am looking forward to having you in camp, and my crew and i will do our utmost to make your hunt an unforgettable experience in our beautiful British Columbia.

Sincerely yours,

Karl Oysmueller, Guide-Outfitter

DIAMOND
M
OUTFITTERS

Howdy! I'd like to tell you about a great new hunting and fishing area in northwestern B.C. About 90% of this 5,000-square-mile area has never been hunted, and the rest only lightly. We encompass parts of the Skeena and Costal mountain ranges, where salmon, steelhead, dolly varden and rainbow trout are found in rivers and lakes. This area has one of the largest concentrations of grizzly bears in B.C., and due to abundant supplies of fish and berries, they are BIG! The mountain goats here are of the largest subspecies in North America, and a glance at the record books tells the rest. Stone sheep are hunted early in the season, followed later by hunts for goat, moose, caribou, grizzly, black bear and wolf. Where practical, we use horses to move camps and convey hunters. We fly to many small lakes where he have base camps established, and hunt on foot. We also make use of the rivers, using a jet boat for hunting and fishing. SInce so much of the area has had virtually no hunting pressure, we are always exploring new valleys for new adventures with game that is unaccustomed to man. Sound good? Come on along and see for yourself!

I am bonded and insured, and I give you my word that we try our hardest to see your hunt is enjoyable and successful.

LAMOUREUX OUTFITTERS LTD.

Martin and Sharon Lamoureux
Gen. Del., Ft. Ware, B.C., Canada V0J 3B0
Radio Mobile: 604-047-121, Ask the Ft. Nelson operator for 2M3827 on Fox Pass Channel.

- STONE SHEEP
- MOUNTAIN GOAT
- GRIZZLY BEAR
- MOOSE
- MOUNTAIN CARIBOU
- BLACK BEAR
- WOLVES AND WOLVERINE

HUNT IN NORTHERN BRITISH COLUMBIA

Trophy hunts in the Sifton/Kechika Range of mountains, management units 7-40 and 7-41. Hunts can be with horses, backstring, backpacking and riverboat, therefore we can arrange a trip to suit almost any person's needs.

We have clean, comfortable camps, with lodges, cabins and tents set in spectacular scenery. There is an abundance of wildlife in our remote wilderness area and each year we take some exceptional trophy animals.

This area is well known for its **Grizzly Bear** and trophy **Mountain Goat**.

SEASONS:

SPRING Grizzly Bear/Black Bear 12 days

SUMMER Fishing at its best! Excellent trout, rainbow, dolly varden, arctic char, grayling, northern pike.

River boat trips, camping, fishing, photography for the entire family.

FALL
15 day Stone Sheep/Goat
15 day Grizzly/Moose
15 day Moose/Mountain Goat/Mountain Caribou
8 or 7 day Trophy backpacking Goat hunts
10 day riverboat Moose/Black Bear

.. HUNTING .. FISHING .. PHOTOGRAPHY ..

Ed and Janice Smith
P.O. Box 161
Atlin, B.C., Canada
V0W 1A0 604-651-7515
Yukon Mobile Operator
White Mountain Channel 2M8424

SPATSIZI

STONE SHEEP
GRIZZLY BEAR
BLACK BEAR
MOUNTAIN GOAT
MOUNTAIN CARIBOU
MOOSE
WOLF

COLLINGWOOD BROS.
GUIDES & OUTFITTERS

P.O. Box 3070, SMITHERS, B.C. V0J 2N0

TEL: (604) 847-9692 · EVENINGS 846 9196 · TELEX 047-85610

FRED A. WEBB AND SONS

Fred Webb and Sons are professional guides and outfitters operating in New Brunswick, Newfoundland and the Northwest Territories, offering a wide range of hunting, fishing and photographic expeditions.

In New Brunswick, clients are met by staff members in either Fredericton, New Brunswick or Presque Isle, Maine and are flown by bush plane or driven into the main lodge in Nictau. This 4,000-square mile hunting area has such a large black bear population hunters are allowed to shoot two per year — from early May until the end of June. They also have a large, healthy herd of big northern whitetails, some with wide racks sporting 10, 12 or more points and field dressing occasionally to 250 pounds or more. Deer season begins the first three weeks of October for bowhunters, followed by four weeks of regular rifle hunting. Either sex deer is allowed on a regular license.

In mid-September the hunt begins in Newfoundland where Fred is in partnership with one of the finest outfitters in the province. Here they offer a superb opportunity to hunt two major trophies — eastern Canada moose and woodland caribou. Newfoundland enjoys the densest moose population per square mile of any place in the world and hunting pressure is carefully controlled.

Hunters are flown into mountain plateau camps by bush plane from mid-September through October.

The company now has a partnership with MIKE FREELAND, operating out of Yellowknife, Northwest Territories. Over the years Qaivvik has hosted hundreds of hunters from all over the world, working with a number of Inuit communities to hunt central Canada barren ground caribou, muskox, polar bear and Peary caribou.

Fred Webb and Sons have provided years of high quality service to clients from all over the world. They have earned the reputation for first-class hunts and a high percentage of successful kills. Clients are guaranteed an enjoyable and exciting sporting experience.

FRED A. WEBB and SONS
RR1, PLASTER ROCK
NEW BRUNSWICK, CANADA E0J 1W0 (506) 356-8312

A modern, secluded lodge on an eight-acre island providing a full line of services for trout and salmon fishing, and bird, bear and deer hunting.

Call or write for details: Don Breen
P.O. Box 402, Milton, Queens County, Nova Scotia, B0T 1P0 (902) 354-4354

Accommodation for 4-6 people overlooking the magnificent Lake Bras d'Or. One licensed guide for every two people.   Hunting for rabbit, waterfowl, upland birds and our specialty -- white tail deer. Great fishing for salmon, rainbow, speckled and brown trout.

Contact: Earl Rudderham
RR#2, Boisdale, Christmas Island, Cape Breton, Nova Scotia, B0A 1C0 (902) 871-2549

Comfortable accommodations and experienced guide service for brook and lake trout, bass fishing. Hunting guides for snowshoe hare, upland and big game including white tail deer and black bear.

Contact: Robert & Marie Gauthier
RR#2, Annapolis County, Nova Scotia, B0S 1A0
(902) 638-3509

Quality guiding, comfortable lodgings and hearty meals; some of the finest trout and salmon fishing and big game hunting anywhere.

Contact: Aubrey R. Beaver
P.O. Box 40, Sherbrooke, Nova Scotia, B0J 3C0
(902) 533-2235

Knowledgeable outfitting services for Atlantic salmon, brown trout, upland birds and big game in one of Nova Scotia's most outstanding lodges.

Contact: Tom & Marion Kennedy
Upper Stewiacke Valley, Nova Scotia, B0N 2P0
(902) 671-2749

Excellent hunting for white tail deer, black bear, black duck and upland game.

Contact: Bernie Amon
P.O. Box 85, Great Village, Colchester County, Nova Scotia, B0M 1L0
(902) 668-2062

Smallmouth bass fishing on wilderness lakes, brown trout on a pastoral stream, salmon fishing on the South Shore or the local river, hunting for upland birds and white tail deer, as well as historic and scenic attractions.

Contact: Perry and Judi Munro
RR#2, Wolfville, Nova Scotia, B0P 1X0
(902) 542-2658

Hunting Journal
1989 Hunts

State/Province/Country_____

Hunting Companions_____

Outfitter_____

Address_____

Guide_____

Address_____

Hunting Areas/Camps_____

Rifle Used_____

Trophy Taken_____ Score_____

Date _____ Time _____

Trophy Taken_____ Score_____

Date _____ Time _____

Trophy Taken_____ Score_____

Date _____ Time _____

Trophy Taken_____ Score _____

Date _____ Time _____

Date Entered in Record Book _____

Comments _____

_____

_____

_____

_____

90

Fred A. Webb and Sons • Professional Hunters
R.R. #1, Nictau, Plaster Rock
New Brunswick, Canada E0J 1W0 (506) 356-8312
U.S. ADDRESS: WEBB-QAIVVIK LTD., 441 CHURCH RD., LANDSDALE, PA. 19446 (215) 362-1510

Nictau, New Brunswick, Canada

Dear Sportsman,

Thank you for inquiring about our trips to the Canadian Northland. We have a long tradition in the hunting business. From the days of the month-long trip in the eastern wilderness for moose and caribou, until the present, when jet travel allows 10-day trips to the high arctic, members of our family have been guiding big game hunters.

It is a Canada-wide operation, working as we do at various seasons from Newfoundland to the Yukon. Fred Webb, of the present generation, began guiding bear and deer hunters in New Brunswick in the early fifties. In the late fifties he began working in the north, first as a guide and communications specialist on scientific exploration parties, and later in the development of big game hunts and fishing trips with the natives of the area. Two sons, Martin and Derek, are rapidly catching up as they expand their expertise in various aspects of the operation.

We term ourselves "Professional Hunters," rather than outfitters or booking agents, as our operation goes beyond the scope of either profession. In some cases we own the real estate and operate as outfitters. On other hunts we are partners, working primarily with the native Inuit (Eskimo), and Dene (Indian) peoples, developing, consulting, operating and booking the finest hunts available for all the northern species.

This is a year-round, full-time profession. With our years of experience and the cooperation of other top people in the business, we assure you a safe, enjoyable, and highly successful hunting experience.

Sincerely,

Fred

Fred A. Webb

Quebec

We are pleased to work with the Inuit (Eskimo) people of Ungava Bay in extreme northern Quebec, operating the only camps actually located on the bay itself. There we hunt the George River Quebec-Labrador caribou herd, currently about 650,000 animals. Caribou in the hunt area are semi-resident and not subject to dramatic population swings; they spend the entire

hunting season right on the coast. Since opening the first camp in 1981, trophy hunts have been 100% successful and resulted in a large number of record book entries.

Inuit guides are trained in proper field caping and in-camp taxidermists prepare the head for later shipment and mounting. Official scorers are in camp. Two animals per license; hunts are late August and September.

TRAVEL TO CANADA'S NORTHLAND

Northwest Territories and the Yukon

Fred Webb and Sons now have an interst in Qaivvik, Ltd., operating out of Yellowknife, Northwest Territories. Over the years Qaivvik (pronounced Kyevik) has hosted hundreds of hunters from all over the world, working with a number of Inuit communities to hunt central Canada barren ground caribou (now recognized as a separate Boone and Crockett big game trophy category), muskox, polar bear and Peary caribou.

To hunt central Canada barren ground caribou, hunters are flown to the main base camp at Courageous Lake, 150 miles north-east of Yellowknife. This camp, located above the tree-line, consists of guest tents, a cook/dining tent, staff tents and shower. In fall, the 350,000 strong Bathurst herd migrates south, spread out over many miles of the barrens. Usually they can be hunted successfully right from the lake, but flyouts are arranged to spike camps, as required. Wolf and wolverine may also be taken as animals of opportunity on this hunt; a small fee is charged.

In addition, grizzly bear and Dall sheep hunts can be arranged in Northwest Territories or the Yukon.

Webb-Qaivvik offers arctic hunts for polar bear, muskox and Peary caribou, singly or in combination, from various far northern communities. Inuit do all the guiding for polar bear by use of dogteam, and by snow machine for muskox and Peary caribou. These hunts are conducted during the months of October and November, and February through April. All equipment and the hunter are transported by machine- or dog-pulled sled. For these hunts, caribou or down clothing and arctic sleeping bags are supplied by Webb-Qaivvik, and a detailed information kit is sent to all booked hunters.

The traditional polar bear hunt lasts up to 15 days, and is affected most by climatic conditions and the abundance of seal, the bear's primary food source. Trophies to 10½ feet have been taken by several hunters. The small, white Peary caribou is found only on certain arctic islands and is now included in Safari Club's North American big game records book. Hunts are from mid-October to mid-November. Muskox make a unique and impressive trophy; we have virtually 100% success and have placed numerous animals in the record book. Hunts take place both spring and fall.

Muskox

Of over 200 muskox trophy hunters the past 6 years, all but 2 have been successful. Many muskox taken are over 100 points, while the #1 in the Safari Club International book comes in at over 120 points. Look at the record book to see the number of trophies in the top 10 taken by our clients!

Hunts take place in October and early November as well as late February, March and April.

Polar Bear

One of the most exciting and traditional hunts in the world, the Polar Bear hunt, covers 15 days. Although the Polar Bear cannot be exported to the U.S.A., there are now upwards of 50 Polar Bear trophy hunts annually in the Northwest Territories — the only area in the world to hunt Polar Bear.

Peary Caribou

''Peary Caribou'' have only been sports hunted since 1983, and although smaller than our ''Canadian Central Barren-Ground Caribou,'' are a unique species and listed in the ''Safari Club'' record book. Season for trophies is between October 10th and November 10th.

Peary Caribou are a unique Canadian sub-species, found only on the Arctic Islands. Inuit (Eskimo) hunters have primarily left large adult male caribou alone if favour of the more tender meat of females and the young.

Arctic Hunts

Since 1977 Qaivvik has offered Polar Bear, Muskox and, more recently, Peary Caribou and combination trophy hunts to the discerning sportsman.

These have been offered in a number of Arctic communities now including Holman, Melville Island, Eskimo Point, Repulse Bay, Sachs Harbour, Paulatuk and Cambridge Bay.

The Inuit (Eskimo) do all of the guiding by dogteam for

Caribou. All Arctic hunts are in the winter months; October and November, and February through April. All gear, including tents, food and sleeping bags, as well as the trophy hunter, are transported by Komotik (or sled) pulled by the dog team or snow machine.

Caribou or down clothing and Arctic sleeping bags are provided by Qaivvik, while a detailed information kit is forwarded to all confirmed hunters.

The exceptional warmth of the winter coat is the result of individual hairs which are hollow. The air cells in the hair act as an insulating layer to conserve body heat. Fur covers the entire animal. The large blunt muzzle is well-furred, and the short broad ears are also furry. Thus caribou are well able to withstand the most extreme temperatures of their habitat in winter.

Both male and female caribou have antlers which are shed and re-grown every year. Adult males begin to shed their antlers in early November after the rut, while females usually lose them after calving in June. Calves develop their first antlers in fall when they are about three months old, and carry them until May or June of the following year.

Caribou are generally silent animals except after calving and during the rut. After calving, cows communicate with their young in short grunts. Males vocalize during the rut with a snorting, bellowing sound. Sometimes a startled caribou will emit a breathless snort as it leaps on its hind legs before running off. Another sound which caribou make, though not vocal, is the sharp clicking noise which emanates from the movement of the tendons and bones just above the hooves. This noise is heard most clearly on calm cold days as large groups of animals journey across the tundra.

Caribou have several gaits. When migrating, they move with a leisurely, but determined walk, covering as much as 20 to 65 km. a day. Under easy travelling conditions over hard-packed snow or ice they can walk at about seven km/hr. When startled, a caribou runs in a loose, even trot. The head is held high and the tail erect. If the animal becomes extremely alarmed such as when pursued by wolves or dogs, or harassed by low-flying aircraft, it will break into a gallop. The hind legs are set far apart, swinging in front of the forelegs, and the head is extended forward.

Caribou are excellent swimmers. The hollow hairs of the pelage enable them to float high in the water, and their broad hooves propel them along at speeds of about three km/hr. In short spurts they have been clocked at ten km/hr. At water crossing, caribou normally select narrow, if not always easy, stretches, but they can swim for long distances and have been observed crossing parts of Bathurst Inlet which are up to ten km wide.

Life History

In early spring, when long hours of daylight return to the Northwest Territories,

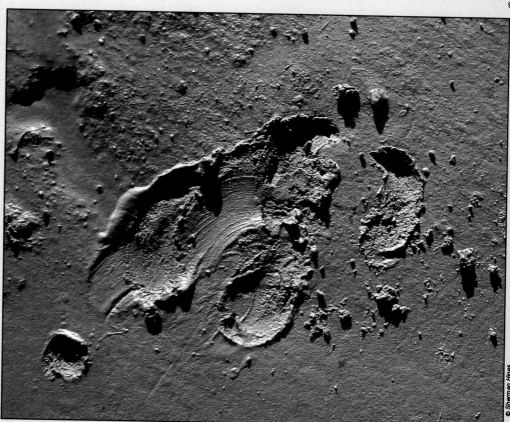

© Sherman Hines

barren-ground caribou begin to move in a great northward migration. Individuals band together, and each small group joins another and another until long lines of caribou are moving steadily to their calving grounds, which may be as far as 700 km away.

By the time the herds pass the last stunted trees of the northern forests and spread out over the still-frozen barrenlands, they may number in the thousands. Cows and yearlings lead the way, while bulls lag behind. Even in mid-May, when temperatures soar and small lakes are breaking up, groups of bulls still linger not far from treeline, grazing their leisurely way northward to the barrens.

Meanwhile, the cows have forged ahead. Their urgency to reach the traditional calving ground is so great that nothing can hold them back. Even if calves are born along the way, they may be left behind as cows continue on with the herd. When the animals reach the calving grounds, they divide into smaller groups, and spread out over an area which may be as much as 10,000 square km. for the larger herds.

The calving grounds are often located in high, rocky, windy areas which seem to be most unlikely spots for the birth of new calves. It is not known exactly why such inhospitable places are chosen, but several advantages have been suggested. The area may be far from predators such as wolves, many of which remain near treeline to den. Mosquitoes and blackflies

hatch there later than in areas closer to treeline. A high, exposed spot may be drier than surrounding lowlands. Finally, all calving grounds seem to have a common factor in that they offer the lichens, sedges, grasses and herbs necessary for caribou to forage on during the spring and early summer.

Most calves in the Northwest Territories are born during the first two weeks of June. On individual calving grounds births usually occur in the same time period of about five days, with all calving finished in three weeks. When the females are close to calving, they band together in groups. A cow about to give birth lies down on a dry patch of ground and goes into labour. Within minutes, the calf is born. Caribou produce only one calf at a time and the famale devotes all her attention to it, licking it, sniffing it and learning its characteristics. At the same time, the calf learns to recognize its mother from all the other cows.

Caribou calves are precocious and can stand and suckle within a few mintues of birth. In an hour, a calf can follow its mother, and in a few days it can outrun a man. As soon as the calf can keep up with its mother, it begins to associate with other cows and calves. Is it most important now that a strong cow-calf bond has been established, for the calf must be able to distinguish its mother in a herd of milling animals. Cows usually search diligently for calves lost along the trail, and in most cases are able to find them. Life ends

quickly for calves which are not found, for they cannot survive without their mothers and the safety of the herd.

As more and more cows, calves and yearlings group together in "post-calving aggregations", the herd begins to approach the sizes that seemed to early explorers to be "numbers beyond counting". By early July, huge herds of thousands of caribou are moving across the tundra. Tales were told of caribou herds in the millions, and it must have seemed that the animals stretched as far as the eye could see and were indeed limitless, but it is likely that early estimates were greatly exaggerated.

The formation of large post-calving aggregations usually coincides with the arrival of blackflies and mosquitoes on the tundra. It is thought that caribou behaviour at the time of year is governed largely by the need to seek relief from insects. The herds often travel into the prevailing winds and stop for temporary respite on windswept ridges and patches of ice and snow. Near the sea, caribou travel to the shore for the cold wind which blows off the ice, and some may even wade into the water. During the days which are too hot for mosquitos, the caribou rest and food, moving on in the evenings when insects reappear.

During the summer, the caribou suffer much stress. Hordes of blackflies and mosquitos torment the animals, preventing them from feeding in peace and taking a great toll on energy reserves. Calves especially suffer at a time when they require energy for growth and development. Insects also may drive the animals to frenzied stampeding in which many are injured and calves become separated from their mothers.

Other problems arise from predators. On the calving ground, very young calves are susceptible to grizzly bear attack. Wolves are also present on the calving grounds and when the herds begin to move, follow along with them. One reason for the formation of large herds may be for protection against wolves. Many animals are better able to sense the approach of danger than a lone caribou. If a wolf appears within the herd, one animal in an alert posture informs others of the danger and the herd flees as a group.

Wolves attack caribou in several ways. A pack may cut off an animal from the herd and then close in with a sudden rush. Two or more wolves may run relays after a herd to weaken a selected animal, or the wolves may set up ambushes, with one or two animals chasing the caribou and others lying wait further along the direction of the

chase. A healthy, alert caribou can ea outrun a wolf and its chances of escape usually excellent. But a caribou which I been singled out by wolves, possibly I cause it lagged a few seconds behind because it showed some weakness, often fall victim.

Water crossings are another dan for the caribou herds. Rivers and lal which were frozen during the spring mig tion are open in midsummer, becom swift and treacherous torrents. The he are wary at water crossings and ma caribou amass at the edge waiting u some determined animal takes the plur and strikes out for the far shore. The en group then follows behind until the lake river is a mass of swimming caribou.

By mid-August, summer on the b renlands is nearly over and the carit begin to move leisurely back southwa The large herds have become numerc small bands, constantly moving, join together and splitting apart. The carit drift about near the treeline, spread over thousands of square kilometres u mid-October and early November wh the rut occurs.

The rut is spectacular in its intens The bulls are in their prime with glossy r coats and antlers polished and smo from being scraped against young tre

easily obtaining food. A secondary result of poor nutrition in cows may be a reduced calf crop the following spring.

Poor weather on the calving grounds can severely affect a new calf crop. Newborn calves may die directly from exposure to the cold, wet conditions. They may become separated from their mothers in blizzards or be trapped in deep snow. In strong winds, a newborn calf may simply be unable to stand up and feed, and therefore die from weakness.

Wolf predation is responsible for many losses, both on the calving ground and later on. It is estimated that is some instances wolves may kill 20-30% of calves and 5% of adult caribou per year.

Accidents resulting in crippling injuries are common among caribou and account for a number of deaths in each herd. The main cause of accidental death is drowning, particularly during migrations across dangerous ice and treacherous rivers.

Finally, hunting must be considered in relation to caribou numbers. Barren-ground caribou have always been important to the inhabitants of the Northwest Territories. Both Inuit and Dene relied on caribou not only as a main source of food, but for all the necessities of life. Hides provided clothing, sleeping robes, dog harnesses and tents; bones were fashioned into needles and utensils; antlers became tools, and clothes and moccasins were sewn with the sinew from the back of the caribou. All parts of the animal were used, and those who lived by hunting the caribou were truly "people of the deer".

When the caribou followed age-old routes and arrived in expected places at the right time, life was good for the caribou eaters. But if caribou unpredictably changed their path, death followed. When they did come, in seemingly endless numbers, they were killed with the abandon of people who have known starvation. And if in those days caribou were wasted, the consolation exists that the overall effect on the health of the herd was probably insignificant. Today, when the stresses on caribou are much greater, there is no latitude for wastage.

While there are few restrictions on hunting by native people, resident sport hunters are allowed only two barren-ground caribou yearly (in some cases three). Non-resident hunters are also allowed two animals, but they must be hunted in different locations and the services of a licenced outfitter must be obtained. Residency status for sport hunters is obtained after two years — the strictest such requirement in Canada.

eir flowing white manes swing back and h as they threaten and challenge each er.

The battles rage for two or three eks, until about mid-November. By the e they are over, winter has settled on the th and the migration continues into the est.

Winter is spent foraging for food in the est. Lichens are the mainstay of the ter diet, supplemented by dried horse-s, sedges, willows and birch twigs. rbou use their excellent sense of smell ead them to lichens under the snow, and ir broad hooves to clear feeding craters.

Not all caribou winter in the forests. me, such as those found in the Wager d the Melville areas, remain year-round the tundra; and much further to the th, the small Peary caribou spend all ir lives on the arctic islands. Generally, dra wintering caribou travel to snow-e areas of hilly country where they feed lichens, sedges and purple saxifrage. winters of light snowfall, they remain in valleys and lower slopes where food is re abundant.

e Future of Caribou

To the original inhabitants of the land d to the first explorers, the caribou herds seemed limitless. Stories of endless flowing rivers of animals were common, and even as alte as 1912, E.T. Seton, travelling across the arctic by canoe, worte of 30,000,000 caribou. Later, more accurate studies, based on usable range size, show such numbers to be impossible. Regardless, however, of the extend of exaggeration of early figures, there is no doubt that the great herds have declined and have withdrawn from many traditional ranges.

Several factors contribute to caribou mortality and have varying degrees of importance in the overall decline. Some authors have suggested that the herds may be cyclic, with regular ong-term fluctuations in umbers. Others have discussed overgrazing and subsequent abandonment of ranges during years of a population high. Destruction of winter range by fire may also deflect caribou from traditional wintering areas. Winter starvation may also occur if caribou are unable to obtain sufficient forage on burned-over ranges.

Adverse weather conditions may cause starvation. In most winters of cold, dry and loosely packed snow, caribou forage without much difficulty. But if the winter is unusually mild, or if freezing weather follows rain early in the winter, an icy crust may prevent the animals from

HUNT CANADA'S
YUKON

Dall, Stone and Fannin Sheep • Moose • Mountain Caribou • Barren Ground Caribou
Goat • Grizzly • Black Bear • Wolf • Wolverine

The Yukon Outfitters' Association

Melvin Spohn shot this huge **world record** Alaska-Yukon moose in Canada's Yukon Territory. Its antlers measured 73 1/8 inches across the widest spread. The current edition of the **SCI Record Book of Trophy Animals** scores it at 297 5/8 points, the new record for the species.

The Yukon Outfitters' Association is a group of dedicated registered big game outfitters. Together, their hunting areas cover roughly 185,000 square miles of rugged unspoiled wilderness. The area has some of the finest hunting and fishing, as well as scenic beauty, left in the world today.

All of us are dedicated to the conservation and management of our wildlife resources. The Yukon Outfitters' Association works very closely with the Yukon Game Branch. Our objective is better quality service for the **non** resident hunter and sportsman. Yukon Outfitters' Association members are substantial contributors to the Foundation for North American Wild Sheep, Safari Club International and Wildlife Management Projects of the Yukon Government, and the Department of Tourism, Yukon.

YUKON OUTFITTERS ASSOCIATION

RICK FURNISS
Yukon Outfitting
Hunt Consultant & Professional Hunter
Box 5364, Whitehorse, Yukon, Canada Y1A 4Z2
403-667-2712

INTRODUCTION: The Yukon Territory is a 207,000 square mile huge undeveloped mountain country with only 22,000 residents, 16,000 of which live in the capital of Whitehorse. This territory is literally the last frontier, especially for hunting. My hunting area is over 10,000 square miles making it one of the largest hunting concessions in the world. By comparison, my hunting area is much larger than Switzerland and is over three times the size of Yellowstone park, the largest game sanctuary in the continental USA. I have the exclusive rights to outfit hunters in this vast area, much of which has never been hunted.

I offer hunts by horse packtrain, rubber raft river float and fly-in backpacking for all ages and physical abilities. I hunt the area lightly and usually hunt new country with each party by moving base camps. To do this we hunt primarily from mobile tent camps in the manner traditional to the North. My hunts are an adventure and an experience, as well as hunting expeditions I provide comfortable camps and good food but there is no luxury. I take a limited number of clients to assure a high quality personalized service.

I've hunted all 27 North American big game. I'm an archer and official scorer for Pope & Young archery records. I have experience flying the bush. Outfitting has been my full time profession since 1975. Licenced as guide since 1967. I am an active member of Yukon Outfitters Association, Int'l. Professional Hunters Association (currently vice-president) and Safari Club Int'l. I am a Canadian and a permanent Yukon resident.

NANCY and RICK FURNISS

HUNT THE CANADIAN YUKON
RICK FURNISS
Yukon Outfitting
Hunt Consultant & Professional Hunter
Box 5364, Whitehorse, Yukon, Canada Y1A 4Z2
403-667-2712

INTERNATIONAL
PROFESSIONAL HUNTERS' ASSOCIATION

BOX 17444   SAN ANTONIO   TEXAS   78217   U S A

TELEPHONE 512/824–7509

PRESIDENT
Don Lindsay

VICE PRESIDENTS
WESTERN SECTOR
Lynn Castle

Rick Furniss

Mike Branham

Dooley Gilchrist

VICE PRESIDENTS
EASTERN/AFRICAN SECTOR
Tony Sanchez Arino

Robin Hurt

Coenraad Vermaak

Terry Pierson

The I.P.H.A. has stringent entry requirements for its members.

They are subject to the scrutiny of a disciplinary enquiry in the case of complaint.

Each member pledges:

- TO PROMOTE WORLDWIDE, THE GOOD MANAGEMENT OF WILDLIFE
- TO COLLABORATE WITH GOVERNMENTS IN THE CONSERVATION OF FLORA AND FAUNA
- TO MAINTAIN A SPORTSMANLIKE CONCEPT OF HUNTING
- TO PREVENT ILLEGAL AND UNSPORTSMANLIKE PRACTICES
- TO SAFEGUARD WORLDWIDE, THE INTERESTS OF CLIENTS.

This is a worldwide brotherhood of professionals, with an international clientele.

THE CREAM OF THE PROFESSIONALS

I P H A is at your service. For further information or assistance please write to IPHA, P.O. Box 1317, Parklands, 2121, South Africa.

NOUVEAU • QUEBEC
Land of Arctic Adventures

COME LIVE YOUR DREAM

The Land of Arctic Adventures

Arctic Quebec is a different world from the one we know. It's a world of treeless tundra ridges, of brawling rivers where trout and salmon abound, a world diamond studded with literally thousands of lakes many of which have yet to feel the dip of a paddle or the splash of a lure.

For eight months of the year this world is locked under ice and snow, but when summer comes the pace of life is intense. On the calving grounds young caribou test their legs, somehow sensing that every second counts before the October snows again sweep the land. On the tundra ponds Canada geese guard over goslings which within months will embark on an epic journey to the southern wintering grounds. And among the tag alders in sheltered gulleys, ptarmigan call raucously to each other.

For sportsman and nature lover, outdoor enthusiast and photographer, Arctic Quebec is a new world to discover. It's a sportsman's paradise.

IN THE LAND OF THE INUIT

. . . and you'll find a lifetime of memories in the land of the Inuit.

Quebec's tundra region is a vast land of rolling tundra ridges and brawling rivers, a land still young and unfettered, where you can find clear horizons and solitude. Its southern boundary is the taiga located some 600 miles north of New York City, to the west are the steely waters of Hudson Bay, to the east the cold waters of the Labrador Sea which stretches north like a giant horseshoe around Ungava Bay. In all, this land of the Inuit covers some 300,000 square miles.

This is the land of the Inuit. A total of 6,000 Inuit and a smattering of whites from the south call Arctic Quebec home. While many reside in Kuujjuaq (Fort Chimo, population 1,150), most live in scattered settlements along the shores of Ungava and Hudson Bay, clinging to the ways of their forefathers and at the same time adapting to the innovations from the south.

Their culture dates back some 4,000 years and they've adapted well to the rigors of their environment. It's a way of life basically dependant on fishing and hunting for subsistence and, while the Inuit have adopted many of white man's inventions, they retain an inbred ability to understand the ways of the animals with which they share this vastness; an ability to comprehend the migration habits of the fish, the animals and birds and predict their patterns.

For this also is the land of the caribou. Numbering some 600,000 head, they roam free and wild across the tundra ridges, forever following the restless winds — great herds that wander through the seasons.

Here, in this land of the Inuit, is where memories are made, where adventure lingers.

BIG GAME OUTFITTERS
MEXICO

CARLOS GONZALEZ HERMOSILLO

SAUZALES 44 MEXICO, D.F. 14330, MEXICO CITY, MEXICO
905-671-1177 10am - 2pm / 905-671-2064 5pm - 8pm
TELEX: 017-77-472 ESPCME / FAX: 905-671-2207

"More than 25 years Alaskan Outfitting Experience"

LYNN CASTLE Master Guide
Alaskan Guide and Outfitter

An up to 25-foot tide twice daily allows tidal grass flats to be hunted in spring, and the salmon creeks in the fall. We hunt the calm inside waters, so don't worry about motion sickness. Our success ratio approaches 100% for both Brown and Black Bear, with only extremely adverse weather or a client's shooting ability causing problems. Brown Bear average over 8 1/2 feet, with several much larger taken each year. Nearly every Black Bear makes the SCI Record Book. Most clients bring non-hunting companions, with the private quarters and nature of the hunt allowing participation. Non-hunting companions will enjoy the almost endless abundance of wildlife, including whale, seal, sea lion, sea and shore birds, deer, bear, Alaskan solitude and fishing. Only three hunters will be booked, although a larger single group can also be given exclusive use of the "Alaskan Solitude".

WILDMAN LAKE LODGE
ALASKA

129

Mark's Guide Service

Mark Sandland
Registered Guide & Pilot
3942 Cosmos Drive
Anchorage, Alaska 99503
907-248-1452

WE SPECIALIZE IN RECORD CLASS
GRIZZLY BEAR & MOOSE

THE TRAILIN HOUND OUTFIT

LION HUNT
SUNNY SOUTHERN ARIZONA

LOYD SMITH

11000 OLD SPANISH TRAIL
TUCSON, ARIZONA 85748

(602) 886-0645

Licensed Guide

Multiple Use Managers guides are well experienced, most of them are wildlife biologists as well. Wayne Long, owner / biologist / guide has over 25 years experience in managing wildlife and hunting operations.

MULTIPLE USE MANAGERS, INC.

P.O. Box L
West Point, CA   95255
(209) 293-7087

Specialists in:
Planning
Developing
and Managing
of Recreation
and Wildlife
Resources

MULTIPLE USE MANAGERS INC.
QUALITY HUNTING AT QUALITY LOCATIONS

At our 54,000 acre SANTA ROSA ISLAND off the coast of Southern California, we have the world's best trophy Roosevelt Elk hunting as well as excellent mule deer hunting. In Northern California on our 63,000 acre DYE CREEK PRESERVE we offer outstanding hunting for black-tailed deer, wild boar, upland game and waterfowl; also fishing for bass, trout and steelhead. Trophy class Columbian Black-tailed Deer are available at our north coast PILOT ROCK DEER CLUB. We also provide exceptionally good HONKER and DUCK hunting on two different properties in Southern Oregon.

HUNT TEXAS!

777 RANCH
HONDO, TEXAS

Fallow Deer

Corsican Rams

Scimitar-Horned Oryx

Aoudad Rams

"We Are the Best"

Take home rewarding memories and friendships along with your exceptional trophies. Enjoy our comfortable ranch style lodging and home cooked meals.

Experience the Hunt of a Lifetime . . .
Experience the Triple Seven Ranch!

All photographs taken on 777 Ranch by wildlife photographer Mark Mayfield

Gemsbok

Sika Deer

Main Lodge

Four Wheel Drive Jeeps

Pure Nubian Ibex

Elk Herd

Nilgai Antelope

TRIPLE SEVEN RANCH
P.O. Box 458297 • San Antonio, Texas 78280-8297
Ph. 512/675-1408   Fax: 512/675-2949

North American
Hunting Laws & Customs

by Jerome Knapp

Game in North America has always been publicly owned. This does not mean that one can hunt on private land without the owner's permission; to do so is an act of trespass punishable by law. What it does mean is that the privilege of hunting is granted to all.

There is plenty of publicly owned land in which to hunt — many tracts especially managed for game. There is also much privately owned land where one can obtain permission to hunt, either as a courtesy or for a fee. In recent years, unfortunately, more and more private property has been "posted" — closed to hunting and so marked with warning posters. Nevertheless, there is still a good amount of unposted private land. There are also some tracts of private land that are posted only to prevent overcrowding and to deter unwanted visitors. Permission to hunt there can be obtained from the owners. In some areas, such lands are frequently patrolled by conservation officers, law officers, or security guards, who may demand to see written permission. The North American continent is vast, and attitudes to hunters and hunting differ from place to place.

In the United States and Canada, both the federal government and the state or provincial government undertake specific wildlife-management duties. The federal governments derive their authority for certain wildlife laws from the right they have to negotiate foreign treaties with other nations, to regulate interstate or interprovincial commerce, and to control federal lands.

Non-migratory game is, however, the responsibility of the state or province. Each state and province has its own hunting seasons, bag limits, and other regulations. For instance, a state with a large turkey population may have a spring and a fall season, and may permit the shooting of hen turkeys in the fall, whereas a neighboring state with a less abundant turkey population may allow only a spring season, or may not allow turkeys to be shot at all.

In the United States, the major federal game-management laws are the Lacey Act, the Migratory Game Bird Treaty Act, the Migratory Bird Hunting Act, the Pittman-Robertson Act, the Marine Mammals Protection Act, and the Endangered Species Act. The Lacey Act was passed in 1900 and prohibits the interstate transportation of illegally killed game. The law was an important weapon in fighting illegal market shooting.

Migratory birds are afforded protection by the Migratory Game Bird Treaty Act of 1918. This was passed to give the United States Government authority to enter into a treaty with Canada, and it has since been used to authorize treaties with Mexico, Japan, and Russia. These treaties prohibit the killing, transportation, or importation of migratory birds for commercial reasons. They also limit the open season to 3 1/2 months in the United States and Canada, and to four months in Mexico. Furthermore, the treaties give total protection to many species of shore birds, provide guidelines for legal shooting hours and daily bag limits, regulate the use of baits, and prohibit the use of live decoy ducks or geese, shotguns holding more than three shots, calibers exceeding 10 gauge, the use of powerboats for taking wildfowl, and electronic calling devices.

The Migratory Bird Hunting Act, passed in 1934, requires all duck hunters in the United States over the age of sixteen to buy what is known as a "duck stamp" before they may legally shoot migratory wildfowl. The stamp costs $5 and must be signed by the hunter and kept with his state hunting license. The purpose of the stamp is to raise revenue for the establishment and management of wildlife refuges for migratory birds. The duck stamp is one of the highlights of United States conservation legislation. Canada has similar provisions, which make possession of a Federal Migratory Bird Permit a prerequisite of hunting any migratory game bird.

Until 1937, when the Pittman-Robertson Federal Aid in Wildlife Restoration Act was passed, state legislatures were known sometimes to divert revenues from the sale of hunting licenses to purposes unconnected with hunting. The P-R Act, as it is known, generates federal funds from taxes on the sale of sporting arms and ammunition, and permits their disbursement to the individual states through a formula based on land area and the number of licensed hunters in each state. P-R funds are not disbursed, however, if hunting-license revenues are diverted. As the funds generated are considerable, exceeding $86m in 1978, diversions have been avoided by state legislatures, and the budgets of their fish and game departments have consequently benefited. The act was one which hunters pressed for in order to provide sound funding for wildlife management, and it has proved to be one of the most effective ever devised in the United States.

All marine mammals, including the polar bear and the walrus, are protected in the United States by the Marine Mammals Protection Act of 1972. This placed a moratorium on the hunting of polar bears.

The act came into being largely as a reponse to an unsporting use of aircraft in the hunting of the bears, so there is hope that the ban will one day be lifted to allow hunting by traditional methods. Other endangered species, most of which are not game, are protected to some extent by other acts, some of which affect the import of trophies.

Endangered or threatened animal and plant species, and products derived from them, may not be imported into the United States. The act that forbids this, the Endangered Species Conservation Act of 1969, lists the species in question, and this listing sometimes causes controversy, especially when an animal listed is known to be thriving — as are, for instance, the leopard and the lechwe antelope in many parts of Africa — and may legally be hunted in many of the countries where it thrives. Such listings are often the result of pressures brought to bear upon the legislators by the anti-hunting lobby.

Obtaining a hunting license in the United States or Canada is relatively straightforward, although a majority of the states and provinces require novices to pass a safety course before they may be issued with licenses. State and provincial game laws otherwise lay down rulings on such points as seasons, bag limits, hunting methods, and possession and transportation of game. The seasons and limits on the various species of game are established by the game commission of each state after reference to data provided by biologists and game managers. Unfortunately, legislatures in some states override the commissions and pass laws based on emotional and political evaluations rather than on facts. For example, in some states, the legislature prohibits the hunting of antlerless deer, even when there are too many deer and, therefore, a sound ecological basis for decreasing the herds' numbers. This is usually because the voters, for sentimental reasons, are against the hunting of antlerless deer, and the politicians, being more concerned with votes than with sound game management, give way to the voters. In many other states, however, the game commissions enjoy a wide degree of independence and are free to pursue sound management programs.

It is difficult to give a summary of the hunting seasons, as they vary so much from state to state, or province to province. By and large, the seasons are open during the fall and winter months, from September until December, and for some game in some states, even later. (The rabbit-hunting season is generally long; in fact, there is no closed season on rabbits in some western states.)

Deer seasons are mostly open in October and November. In some southern states, the deer season extends into December. In the western states, the season can start as early as September (in some parts of California, even in August.) The prime deer-hunting time in the Great Lakes states and provinces and in New England is November.

Seasons for upland game birds are more or less the same as those for deer, but in the northern and western states and Canadian provinces, the season may open as early as mid-September. The end of the season for some species in the South may not come until December or January. Dove seasons in the northern states traditionally

open early in the fall, as do waterfowl seasons in Alaska and Canada, because the birds there migrate early.

Planning a Hunting Trip

A hunting trip should be an enjoyable and rewarding experience, and one of the secrets of a successful trip lies in the planning. When planning a hunting trip, the wise hunter will write in advance to the game department of the state or province where he wants to hunt. In this way, he will get information about the seasons, the regulations, and the outfitters and licensed guides. This step should be taken about six months in advance of the trip; indeed, for a big-game hunt in the mountains of Alaska or British Columbia, a year's planning and preparation is barely adequate. The top outfitters there are usually booked a year in advance. Six months ahead will do for small-game trips, particularly if a guide is to be hired or an outfitter booked. The better goose and duck camps on James Bay, in Canada, are booked six months ahead, and the top waterfowl guides in Louisiana and the best woodcock and grouse guides in New Brunswick are usually booked fairly early on for the peak of the season.

Say that you are planning a moose-hunting trip. You should then write the states or provinces that have moose hunting (Montana, Wyoming, Alaska, all of the Canadian provinces, and the Yukon and Northwest Territories — the addresses are given at the end of this article.) If your vacation is restricted to certain times of the year, you must plan accordingly. If you are a teacher, for example, you should plan a trip to Alaska, the Yukon, or the Northwest Territories, for the moose season there opens in mid-August before school opens.

As a substantial part of the outlay on a hunting trip is the cost of obtaining the services of a guide, it is good to know, for example, that nonresident hunters in the state of Alaska and the provinces of Ontario and Quebec are not required to be accompanied by a guide when hunting moose.

The game departments you write to will be able to give information about areas with good moose-hunting prospects and high rates of success, but obtaining this sort of information will take time.

No matter where you hunt, good topographical maps are of value, but they are essential in the wilderness areas of Canada and Alaska. Once you have pinpointed the best hunting areas, you should buy topographical maps of them. Canadian topographical maps may be obtained from the Map Distribution Office, Department of Mines and Technical Services, Ottawa, Canada. If your hunting area is in any state east of the Mississippi River, the appropriate maps can be obtained from the Map Information Office, U.S. Geological Survey, Washington, D.C. 20244. For states west of the Mississippi, write to the Map Information Office, U.S. Geological Survey, Federal Center, Denver, Colorado 80225. When writing to any of these offices, name the region or state where you plan to hunt. You will then be sent a master sheet showing by number areas covered by the topographical maps. Order the desired maps by number. There will be a small fee, but any experienced outdoorsman knows that such maps are

other method used is to have a lottery of all the applications received by a certain previously announced deadline.

Each state or province has a different method of handling applications. Some insist that payment be sent along with the application, the cash being refunded if an application is unsuccessful. In some cases, payment has to be made in a specified way — certified check, money order, or some other way. The important thing is read the instructions carefully and to follow them to the letter. One of the commonest causes of failure to get a license is that the hunter failed to note the deadline for applications.

Here are some important points to remember when filling in an application:
1. Be sure that your full name, address, and zip or postal code appear on both your application and the back of your check or

5. Do not make the mistake of applying more than once for the same permit. As computers are often used to take applications, a computer may very well be programmed to throw out both applications if it detects a duplicate. In some cases, the duplicating of applications is a serious enough offense to cause the authorities to refuse to consider your application at all.
6. Above all, be sure that your application gets in on time. Check to see if the deadline is a postmark date or if the application must be in the hands of the proper authority by a specific date.

If you are not making the arrangements by yourself, you will probably be relying on a guide or an outfitter. Of course, your chances of a successful hunting trip will be much higher if you have a guide, but your trip will be more expensive. The money spent is a good investment, however, especially if you are travelling a long way and want to have a good chance of obtaining a trophy. In addition, you may not have the equipment necessary for hunting alone, and you will certainly not have the guide's experience of hunting in the area.

In most big-game hunts, you should hire the services of an outfitter instead of a guide. The outfitter has all the necessary equipment — saddle horses, pack horses, tents, boats, canoes, and even airplanes, his own or chartered, to fly you in. He will also have a crew of guides — and they will be competent, if he wants to build up and retain a good reputation.

Visiting Canada

If you are planning to hunt in Canada, the following is important. Hunting licenses are issued by each province, but if you are intending to hunt migratory birds, you will also need a Federal Migratory Bird Permit, which may be purchased at any post office. The nonresident hunter will have little trouble in bringing rifles and shotguns into the country. As a visitor, he will not require a permit in order to possess a rifle or a shotgun. He must, however, furnish the customs authorities with a full description, including the serial number, of each of the guns he brings in. This enables the customs to clear the guns quickly upon the hunter's return. For the sportman coming into Canada from the United States, one additional requirement is that he first register his firearms at a United States Customs office, so that he will have no difficulty in bringing them back to the United States. A visitor may bring two hundred rounds of ammunition into Canada duty-free, but he may not bring in

worth far more than their price.

Getting a hunting license for big game in Canada, Alaska, and many of the other states is no problem, as you can buy one on arrival, together with the necessary tags. Some states are not so easy: Wyoming, for example, has a limit on the number of permits issued for hunting antelope, and to get a permit, a hunter must enter a lottery and hope for the best. More and more states are adopting a quota system that limits the number of licenses or permits issued. This system is often refined to the point where, at a local level, each wildlife-management area or zone is allocated a specific number of permits; this allows for more control over the numbers of game shot and for more intensive management of game. Permits are sometimes available on a first-come, first-served basis. An-

money order.
2. Make sure that you have the proper application form (some states have different forms for different game) and that you have stated the proper unit, area, or hunt number on the form. Be sure to fill in a second or third choice, if offered.
3. If there is to be a lottery, there may be a priority system for previously unsuccessful applications. Check any negative replies you have previously received from the authority in question to see if you qualify for such a priority.
4. "Party permits" are available in some states. If you are applying for one, check the rulings on priorities, as priority applications often cannot be made when applying for party permits. Remember that members of the same party must always apply for the same area.

© Sherman Hines

pistols and revolvers.

Dogs from the United States must be accompanied by a certificate, signed by a licensed veterinarian, that the dog has been vaccinated against rabies during the preceeding twelve months and not less than two weeks before the date of entry. The certificate must give the date of vaccination and must have a legible and accurate description of the dog. The customs official at the port of entry will initial the certificate and return it to the owner.

If they are planning to stay for only a limited period, hunters visiting Canada from countries other than the United States are well advised to leave their dogs at home, as dogs from other countries are subject to a sixty-day quarantine. This is no problem for most overseas hunters,

since big game is usually their primary interest. It should be no deterrent to those who want to hunt upland birds or waterfowl, either, because most outfitters and guides can provide the necessary dogs. (Always verify this well in advance of your hunting trip.)

Nonresident hunters can bring boats, motors, camping vehicles, and tent trailers into Canada without any problem. However, these may need to be registered with the customs office to facilitate matters when leaving the country. Detailed information about visiting Canada may be obtained from any Canadian embassy, consulate, or tourist office, or from the Canadian Office of Tourism, 150 Kent Street, Ottawa, Canada K1A 0H6.

United States customs regulations differ slightly from Canadian when it comes to dogs and firearms. Visitors to the United States, whether from Canada or from any other country, may bring in a dog for which they have a valid vaccination certificate. The dog must have been vaccinated not less than thirty days and not more than twelve months before the date of entry. If an attenuated-virus vaccine thas been used, the certificate is good for thirty-six rather than twelve months.

Nonautomatic firearms and up to 1,000 rounds of ammunition may be brought into the United States for lawful sporting purposes, provided that the firearms and any unused ammunition are taken home when the visitor departs. As in the case of entry into Canada, the firearms must be registered with customs at the port of entry. There is usually no difficulty with formalities at ports of entry where the officials are used to hunters and their firearms coming and going. However, at other ports, where hunters are seldom

checked through, uncertain or inexperienced officials can sometimes cause delay. To avoid problems of this kind, you should acquire all the information you need beforehand by applying to a United States embassy or consulate, or direct from the Customs Service, P.O. Box 7118, Washington, D.C. 20044, or from the Bureau of Alcohol, Tobacco, and Firearms, U.S. Treasury Department, Washington, D.C. 20026. When writing to the Bureau, state

the length and purpose of your visit and request information about any recent changes in the regulations. Letters and printed regulations so obtained should be kept so that they can be shown to customs officers, who are uncertain of the rules.

In the United States

When planning a trip in the United States, remember that the use of handguns for hunting purposes is allowed only in some states. In others, the possession and carrying of firearms require special permission. So if you want to hunt with a handgun, then remember to check the laws in the state you are going to visit.

Both the international and the national transport of firearms is problematic. Regulations vary from country to country, from

province to province, and from state to state. Most authorities ban the carrying of loaded weapons on any kind of public transport, but this is not the problem, as there is no reason to have firearms loaded when you are travelling. In most places, however, it is illegal to carry any kind of firearm, even unloaded, onto a commercial aircraft or to the baggage-screening point at an airport. Although they do not apply internationally, the United States

Department of Transportation's guidelines are a helpful indication to what you should do when transporting guns and ammunition by air. Safety regulations require passengers to declare guns in baggage being checked in for flights. At the time you make your ticket reservation, inform the airline that you will have unloaded guns and ammunition with you. Make sure that each gun is unloaded. Some airlines insist that you remove bolts and detachable magazines and pack them with the ammunition, separately from the guns. On arrival at the airport, go straight to the ticket counter — never directly to the security and baggage-screening point — and inform the ticket agent that you have arms and ammunition. Be prepared to permit the agent to inspect the

Upland Game and Waterfowl Outfitters 2

GEORGE RIVER
PTARMIGAN SHOOT

The George River Valley provides some of the world's best ptarmigan hunting, but until now it has been largely inaccessible. However, we have organized hunts to take place this Spring. The guides are Sandy and Stanley Annanack, managers of the Kannig and Akuliak camps, both top-notch hunters and guides. This is a limited-opportunity hunt by special permit. The capacity for each hunt is eight hunters, with limited space available.

DYMOND LAKE HUNTING LODGE

Dymond Lake Hunting Lodge

Imagine a crisp morning out on the marsh. Overhead you sight in on the Giant Honkers, Lesser Canadas, all flying inland from Hudson Bay; Snow and Blue, smattered with Rosses and Brants flying low; arriving in waves. You bag your limit of choice birds in no time in a "hunter's paradise." Sound like every hunter's dream? Well, this experience can be yours at Dymond Lake Lodge. Located just 15 miles west of Churchill, we offer our parties the thrill and excitement of hunting on some of the best marshes in Northern Manitoba. The area around Dymond Lake is a staging and feeding ground for ducks and geese flying down from northern nesting areas. Together with the many varieties of geese come the ducks: Green-Wing Teal, Shoveler, Pintail, Scaup, and Black- and Green-Head Mallards. On the tundra and eskers of the Dymond Lake area Ptarmigan are abundant. Dymond Lake Lodge offers its hunting parties the chance to limit out with a full selection of birds.

At the Lodge we offer first-class Northern accomodations for up to 16 guests. There are two separate three-bedroom cabins, each heated with wood or gas and equipped with propane lights. The cabins are roomy, containing indoor washrooms and central shower areas. The larger cabin has an attractive lounge.

After an exciting day's hunt, our guests are treated to hearty home-style cooking in our dining room. At Dymond Lake Lodge, "all you can eat" is our policy.

So if you're looking for a first-class hunting package, book with Dymond Lake Lodge. Excellent accomodation, fine food and a unique shooting experience all add up to a memorable trip in "hunter's paradise" -- Dymond Lake Lodge.

The Hunting: At Dymond Lake Lodge, we offer you the hunter's choice. Whether you prefer pass shooting on the eskers, shooting over decoys on the ponds and saltgrass flats, jumpshooting ducks on the ponds or jumping ptarmigan on the tundra and eskers, we offer first-class hunts.

For goose hunters, we set natural willow, spruce and tamarack blinds positioned near popular feeding grounds. Decoys are expertly set; then it's up to you. Just sit tight and prepare for the experience of a lifetime.

Hudson Bay Goose Shooting: We are the first lodge situated on the west side of Hudson Bay, so the birds have not been shot at when they arrive at the feeding grounds around Dymond. It's Hudson Bay Goose shooting at its finest.

Ducks abound in the dozens of ponds around Dymond Lake, so after you limit out on geese enjoy excellent jump shooting. Or take a walk on the eskers and enjoy the challenge and excitement of a Ptarmigan shoot. It's very different from ducks and geese.

Items to Bring: To ensure a pleasant hunt, we encourage our guests to bring warm clothing of a layering type, including gloves and cap. Waterproof boots are essential, and hip

waders are optional. We suggest each hunter bring shotgun shells with a maximum of 200 rounds. Extra ammo is available at the camp. Other personal items should include raingear, camera and film, and your own shotguns.

Package Plan: When you book your hunting trip through Dymond Lake lodge, every package includes pickup at Churchill airport and round-trip transportation from Churchill to Dymond Lake. You will receive clean, modern accomodations and delicious home-cooked meals. After the shoot, your birds are processed and packaged by our staff! Guides are provided for your party, as well as radio communications with Churchill.

Dymond Lake Lodge lies in the Central Flyway of North America. That means quality hunting with the best selection of prime ducks

Let Dymond Lake Hunting Lodge introduce you to a hunter's paradise -- your choice of hunting -- your choice of bird: geese, ducks, ptarmigan -- shoot with friends on the busy North American Flyway -- it's hunting at its best.

and geese. Dymond Lake Lodge offers a unique hunting experience, giving you a choice of hunting locations complemented by a choice of popular outpost trips.

Our most northerly outcamp is located on Hubbard Point, offering the best in Barrens shooting 40 miles north of Dymond Lake on the shore of Hudson Bay. Guests have the option of booking a complete week's stay.

Button Bay outpost cabin, located just southeast of Dymond Lake, has accomodations for six guests and is designed for a small private hunting party.

If you limit out early or just wish a change of hunting for a day or so, our Nowell Lake camp located 20 miles west of Dymond Lake on the North Knife River offers a one- or two-day fly-in service from the hunting lodge. Fall fishing is excellent. Choose from Brook Trout, Arctic Grayling or Northern Pike for action and excitement. All outpost cabins are fully equipped and modern.

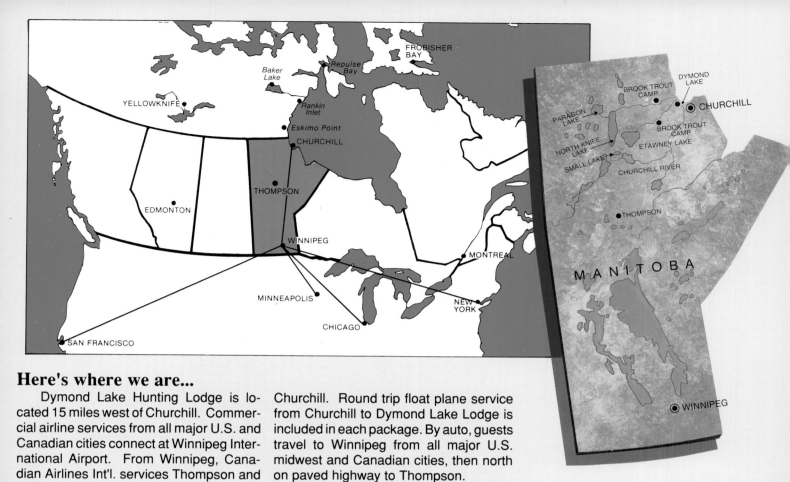

Here's where we are...

Dymond Lake Hunting Lodge is located 15 miles west of Churchill. Commercial airline services from all major U.S. and Canadian cities connect at Winnipeg International Airport. From Winnipeg, Canadian Airlines Int'l. services Thompson and Churchill. Round trip float plane service from Churchill to Dymond Lake Lodge is included in each package. By auto, guests travel to Winnipeg from all major U.S. midwest and Canadian cities, then north on paved highway to Thompson.

Our Guides and Staff

Our experienced guides are anxious to ensure your hunting is the best it can be. Most have been in the Churchill area most of their lives and know well the habits of the various geese that will end up as part of your bag. Our customers have only the highest praise for these hard-working men. Our guides, and all our staff, are friendly, courteous and anxious to make your trip a successful and memorable one. Side trips are available for those interested in fishing. Northerns, Brook Trout and Arctic Grayling are within 25 miles. Fly out in the morning and return in the afternoon, an enjoyable diversion from the demands of bird hunting.

To ensure any reservation we require a $500 deposit along with your reservation form. Reservations in writing should be mailed to: Doug & Helen Webber, Dymond Lake Lodge, Box 304, Churchill, Manitoba. Reservations by phone can be made by calling collect: (204) 675-___5

Shotshell Game Guide

GAME	SHELL		SHOT SIZE	CHOKE	GAUGE
GEESE	LEAD:	Super-X	2, 4	Full, Mod.	12, 16, 20
	STEEL:	Double X	BB, 2, 4	Full, Mod.	10, 12, 16, 20
	STEEL:	Super Steel	T, BBB, BB,	Mod.	10, 12
			1, 2, 3	Full, Mod.	
DUCKS	LEAD:	Super-X	4, 5, 6	Mod., Imp. Mod., Full	12, 16, 20
		Double X	4, 5, 6	Mod., Imp. Mod., Full	10, 12, 16, 20
		Super Pigeon	6	Mod., Imp. Mod., Full	12
TURKEY	LEAD:	Super-X	2, 4, 5, 6	Full	12, 16, 20
		Double X	BB, 2, 4, 5, 6	Full	10, 12, 16, 20
PHEASANT	LEAD:	Super-X	4, 5, 6, 7 1/2	Imp. Cyl., Mod., Imp. Mod.	12, 16, 20
		Double X	4, 6	Imp. Cyl., Mod., Imp. Mod.	12, 16, 20
		Xpert	6	Imp. Cyl., Mod., Imp. Mod.	12, 20
		Super Pigeon	6	Full, Mod., Imp. Mod.	12
	STEEL:	Super Steel	4, 6	Full, Mod., Imp. Mod.	12, 20
GROUSE	LEAD:	Super-X	5, 6, 7 1/2	Imp. Cyl., Mod.	12, 16, 20
PARTRIDGE		Xpert	6, 7 1/2, 8	Imp. Cyl., Mod.	12, 16, 20
WOODCOCK	LEAD:	Xpert	7 1/2, 8, 9	Imp. Cyl., Mod.	12, 16, 20
SNIPE	STEEL:	Super Steel	6	Imp. Cyl, Mod.	12, 20
RAIL					
QUAIL	LEAD:	Super-X	7 1/2, 8, 9	Imp. Cyl, Mod.	12, 16, 20, 28
		Xpert	7 1/2, 8, 9	Imp. Cyl, Mod.	12, 16, 20
DOVE	LEAD:	Super-X	7 1/2, 8, 9	Imp. Cyl., Mod., Imp. Mod.	12, 16, 20, 28
		Xpert	7 1/2, 8	Imp. Cyl., Mod., Imp. Mod.	12, 16, 20
	STEEL:	Super Steel	6	Imp. Cyl., Mod., Imp. Mod.	12, 20
RABBIT	LEAD:	Super-X	4, 5, 6, 7 1/2	Imp. Cyl., Mod.	12, 16, 20, 28, 410
		Xpert	6, 7 1/2	Imp. Cyl., Mod.	12, 16, 20
SQUIRREL	LEAD:	Super-X	4, 5, 6	Mod., Imp. Mod., Full	12, 16, 20, 28, 410
		Xpert	6	Mod., Imp. Mod., Full	12, 16, 20

British Columbia Salmon Species

Sockeye (Red-landlocked form-kokanee) North American sockeye originate in fresh water habitats from the Columbia River in the south to the coast of Alaska. In B.C., major spawning runs of sockeye are found in the watersheds draining into the Fraser, Skeena and Mass Rivers, and those of Smith and Rivers Inlets. Young sockeye may wait till their third year to migrate seaward. Once in salt water, B.C. sockeye seem to move north along the coast until returning to home streams to spawn as four- or five-year-olds. Adult sockeye average six to seven pounds. Sportsmen catch them with spoons or bait.

Coho (Silver) In B.C., this mainstay of salt water sport fishing spawns in over half of the 1,500 streams for which records are available. Coho enter the sea between April and July each year, moving both north and south within 40 kilometres (25 miles) of the coast. In late fall and winter, they move south. Coho return to their home stream in early spring, maturing as young as two years old. Adult coho vary from 2.7 to 5.4 kilograms (four to 12 pounds). They are most readily taken in salt water on sport fishing gear that includes fly, spoon, spinner or bait.

Pink (Humpy) Pink salmon is the most numerous of the five species of Pacific salmon. Spawning mainly in rivers and streams near the coast, they are found from California to the mouth of the Mackenzie River. Major spawning grounds are between Puget Sound, Washington and Bristol Bay, Alaska. With a fixed, two-year life span, there is no overlapping betwen pink "stocks" of one year and those of the next. The abundance of yearly stock varies in some areas; for instance, the Fraser River has a predominantly odd-year cycle of pinks, while the Queen Charlotte Islands have an even-year cycle.

Chinook (King) Chinook come mainly from river systems in B.C., the most important being the Fraser River. Chinook are known to migrate vast distances in salt water, and are found sparsely distributed throughout the Pacific Ocean from California to the Gulf of Alaska. Since the age of chinook adults returning to spawn varies from two to seven years, many river systems have more than one stock; some rivers have spring, fall and winter runs. At full growth, chinook salmon vary between five and 30 pounds. The world record chinook is 57.27 kilograms (126 pounds). Sportsmen find spoon, fly or bait effective.

Steelhead Steelhead, a sea-going rainbow trout, have major spawning grounds centred between northern Oregon and northern British Columbia, in coastal rivers and streams as well as tributaries to major river systems. Steelhead are prized as game fish by sport fishermen because of their fighting qualities. They can be caught by bait, spinner or fly when they come back to fresh water for spawning at the age of four or five years. Mature steelhead usually weight 3.5 to 4.1 kilograms (eight to nine pounds), but sometimes reach 16 kilograms (36 pounds).

NORTH BY NORTHWEST
TOURISM ASSOCIATION OF B.C.
3840 Alfred Avenue
Box 1030, Smithers, B.C.
Canada V0J 2N0
Telephone: (604) 847-5227
Fax: (604) 847-7585

NORTHWEST

NORTHWEST GUIDES
& OUTFITTERS ASSOC.
P.O. Box 2489
Smithers
British Columbia

SPORT FISHING GUIDE

Super, Natural
North by Northwest
BRITISH COLUMBIA, CANADA

For a more detailed m
British Columbia, as
travel information, st
the nearest Travel Info
You'll find one in mos
towns—just look for t

Map labels: ST. ELIAS MOUNTAINS, TO WHITEHORSE, ALASKA HIGHWAY, TO FORT NELSON, TAGISH LAKE, ATLIN LAKE, ATLIN, TESLIN LAKE, BRITISH COLUMBIA, SKAGWAY, ATLIN PROV. PARK, BOYA LAKE PROV. PARK, HAINES, CASSIAR, CASSIAR MOUNTAINS, DEASE LAKE, TELEGRAPH CREEK, STEWART-CASSIAR HIGHWAY, STIKINE RIVER, MOUNT EDZIZA PROV. PARK, ISKUT, SPATSIZI PLATEAU WILDERNESS PROV. PARK, KINASKAN LAKE PROV. PARK, COAST MOUNTAINS, TATLATUI PROV. PARK, NASS RIVER, SKEENA MOUNTAINS, STEWART, HUDSON BAY MTN., HAZELTON, NEW HAZELTON, TAKLA LAKE, BABINE MOUNTAINS REC. AREA, COPPER HILL GRANISLE, CARP LAKE PARK, KITWANGA, BABINE LAKE, MURRAY RIDGE, FORT ST. JAMES, TO DAWSON CREEK, MT. HAYS, TERRACE, KITSUMKALUM MTN., SMITHERS, TELKWA, STUART LAKE, PRINCE RUPERT, SKEENA R., HOUSTON BURNS LAKE, MASSET, NAIKOON PROV. PARK, PORT EDWARD, KITIMAT, OOTSA LAKE, FRASER LAKE, NECHAKO RIVER, TABOR MTN., PURDI MTN., PRINCE GEORGE, FORT CLEMENTS, QUEEN CHARLOTTE CITY, SKIDEGATE, SANDSPIT, TWEEDSMUIR PROV. PARK, HECATE STRAIT, QUEEN CHARLOTTE ISLANDS, TO QUESNEL

Most of the North by Northwest region is accessible by major paved roads, commercial airlines or B.C. Ferries. A number of roads, including the Nass Road, are gravel.

When travelling the gravel roads, please be sure your vehicle is in good repair. Take spare tires, water and minor repair supplies with you, and fill up with gasoline whenever you reach a pump. It's a good idea to let a friend or the RCMP know where you're travelling and when you expect to return.

The Yellowhead Highway.

Tête Jaune Cache to Prince George. Both the Yellowhead Highway and Tête Jaune Cache were named after a blond French-Canadian trapper who guided early fur traders through the Rocky Mountains and who once concealed a fortune in furs in the area. To this day, the hiding place has been referred to as Tête Jaune Cache, although the town itself isn't the location; the exact spot is still not known.

McBride is a natural stopover for visitors travelling the Yellowhead. The surrounding views are magnificent, and for the height of beauty, the Teare Mountain forestry lookout, accessible by a narrow dirt road, is excellent. *Prince George,* the third largest city in British Columbia, is known as "The Hub of the North." Naturally, northern British Columbia's major entertainment, restaurants, shopping and nightlife revolve around this large, centrally located city. But the town wasn't always so prominent—when Fort George, as it was originally called, was founded back in the early 1800s, the nearby Fort St. James was the undisputed capital of the northern fur trading empire. Today, the memory of Old Fort George lives on in Fort George Park.

If you're here in summer, visit the Folk Fest or head out of town to meet our wilder residents at the Tabor Mountain Moose Viewing Areas. In winter, be prepared for the time of your life at the 10-day Mardi Gras.

Prince George to Smithers.

The next stop, *Vanderhoof*, is the geographical centre of B.C. It's also the home of the Vanderhoof International Airshow, which takes place in early July and rates among the top five airshows in North America. For the remainder of the year, you can see other high flyers at the Nechako Bird Sanctuary, which shelters up to 50,000 Canada geese and other birds yearly.

Turn right at Vanderhoof and you'll travel back in time to the early fur trading days. *Fort St. James* National Park consists of five buildings, dating from 1884-89, which have been restored and refurbished. The town of Fort St. James has other historic sites, including the grave of a famous Carrier Indian chief, an original missionary church and a tribute to Russ Baker, one of the pioneer bush pilots involved in the founding of Canadian Pacific Airlines.

The North Road from Fort St. James takes you into *Omenica Country*, famous for grayling, char, rainbow trout and Dolly Varden. Roads in the area are gravel, so travelling can be bumpy, but always rewarding. At Manson Creek, for example, you can visit an original Hudson's Bay Company building, still run as a store and post office.

Back on the main road, you'll pass *Fort Fraser*, one of the oldest communities in British Columbia. At *Fraser Lake*, catch the annual salmon run between Fraser and Francois Lakes. *Burns Lake*, the northern gateway to Tweedsmuir Park, also has excellent fishing for eastern brook trout, rainbow trout, cutthroat, lake char, kokanee, chinook, steelhead and many other species.

Granisle, located off the Yellowhead Highway on beautiful Babine Lake, has five fishing derbies a year. The lake is also popular for windsurfing, swimming and water skiing. And no wonder—it's the largest natural freshwater lake in the province.

At *Houston*, the scenic splendour of the Bulkley River Valley suddenly surrounds you. The country around the community is dotted with lakes and rivers, many of which offer superb fishing, as well as a quiet serenity for nature lovers.

The town of *Telkwa* is just up the road, and offers the kind of folksy history that makes the North so fascinating. In the 1940s, for example, a land dispute between two neighbours resulted in a tussle over the cabin which stood on the controversial boundary. The argument was solved when the cabin was sawed in two and one half was hauled away. (The cabin, which had a long, colourful history, was later restored and still stands.)

Rugged Hudson Bay Mountain dominates the skyline of *Smithers*, a town renowned for its rustic Bavarian architecture. The mountain comes into its own in winter, when skiers head down its 56km (33.5 miles) of runs, and kick up their boots at the winter festival. The rest of the year, anglers find plenty of action in neighbourhood streams and rivers—the local salmon and steelhead are rated among the best in the world. Another lure for visitors to the area is Driftwood Canyon—its fossil beds date back millions of years.

Hazelton to Prince Rupert.

The name "Hazelton" actually refers to three inter-related communities. *Old Hazelton*, first settled in 1866, was the original Mile Zero on the "Poor Man's Route" to the Yukon goldfields. *New Hazelton* and *South Hazelton*, along with the Old Town, are at the nucleus of eight surrounding Indian villages, all steeped in history and legends. (See "Native Culture" on reverse side.)

Heritage Park in *Terrace* gives a good portrait of early pioneer life in the region. And in the Kitselas Canyon on the Skeena River, you can still see the winch mechanisms that helped sternwheelers struggle upstream. By the way, the world's record salmon was caught in the Skeena River—a whopping 43 kilos (95 pounds).

Outside Terrace, you'll come to Kitsumkalum Mountain, a popular skiing area. While you're driving, watch for our most colourful wildlife—kermode bears. This relatively uncommon species, although a member of the black bear family, is usually white, but can also be chestnut red, bright yellow, blue-grey or even orange.

A left-hand turn just before Terrace will take you to *Kitimat*. Named after "the people of the snow," you'll find the heritage of the Haisla Indians at the Kitimat Centennial Museum, as well as at nearby Kitimat Village. On a more modern-day note, the town is the home of the huge Alcan smelting complex; tours of the smelter are offered June through August.

You're now by the ocean; Douglas Channel, on which Kitimat is located, is a prime fishing spot. As you turn back up the road, you'll be heading to the "Halibut Capital of the World" Prince Rupert.

Prince Rupert was founded by Charles Hays, the ambitious general manager of the Grand Trunk Pacific Railway. Determined to make it a rival to Vancouver as a transportation terminal, Hays never lived to see the city's growth; he went down on the *Titanic*. Today, the city is the major link between the services of the B.C. Ferry Corporation and the Alaska Ferry System. To get a better look at its majestic location on the Pacific Ocean, take the world's second steepest gondola lift up Mount Hays. A little further up the coast, you'll net all kinds of fascinating tidbits at the North Pacific Cannery, a historic restoration of the oldest standing fish cannery (built 1889) on the B.C. coast.

Speaking of fish, the Haw Yaw Haw Naw native salmon

...of
... as
... at
...tre.
...rger
...ign.

...estival ın June fea-
...ures tasty salmon,
...lancing and art ex-
...ibits–come sample it.

The Queen Charlotte Islands.

A ferry ride away
...rom Prince Rupert,
...ese mist-cloaked,
...vergreen islands re-
...eal a world of time-
...ss beauty.

For thousands of
...ears, they were
...eopled only by the
...laida Indians. Today,
...e descendants who
...urvived the diseases
...hite men brought to
...e Islands maintain
...eir heritage. Slate-
...nuck Mountain, for
...xample, is the only
...nown source of argil-
...e, a soft black slate
...at is reserved for
...xclusive use by
...aida artists.

Much of the Queen
...harlottes remains in
...s original, natural
...ate. Hike along a
...ng, unspoiled
...each trail in Naikoon
...rovincial Park.
...atch for grey
...hales, Sitka deer
...d peregrine fal-
...ns. Then, in the
...ueen Charlotte
...useum near Skide-
...ate, marvel at the
...arvels of the old
...aida ways.

For information,
contact the Queen
Charlotte Islands
Chamber of Com-
merce, Box 357,
Queen Charlotte
City, B.C. V0T 1S0.

The Stewart-Cassiar Highway.

Although this high-
way was begun in
1926, the area has a
long history of native
culture, fur trading,
telegraph construc-
tion and gold rushes.
The Hudson's Bay
Company for ex-
ample, had a trading
post in Dease Lake in
1938. And in the mid-
1860s, construction of
the never-completed
Collins Overland
Telegraph was started
and abandoned.

The Stewart-Cas-
siar branches off the
Yellowhead Highway
at Kitwanga; it may
also be reached by
taking the Nass Road,
west of Terrace. This
road, also dubbed the
B.C. Timber Road, is
an unrestricted log-
ging route open for
public use, so careful
driving is advised. It
passes through a
number of interesting
Nishga Indian com-
munities.

On the way from
Kitwanga to Stewart
on the Stewart-
Cassiar you'll pass
the historic towns of
Gitwangak and Kit-
wancool (described
on the opposite side
of this brochure
under "Native Cul-
ture"), as well as the
beautiful Bear Glacier,
as delicately coloured
as a robin's egg.

Stewart. To the pub-
lic, Stewart is best
known as the set loca-
tion for a number of
well-known movies,
including "Bear
Island," based on the
Alistair McLean
bestseller, and "Ice-
man," starring
Timothy Hutton. A
boom-and-bust town
based on gold, silver
and copper mining,
it is set in spectacular
countryside, with
huge, glaciated
mountains, salmon-
laden streams and
even a pretty little
ghost town–Hyder,
Alaska–nearby.

*Mount Edziza and
Spatsizi Plateau Parks.*
Heading through a
forested landscape
highlighted by
dramatic mountain
ranges, you'll arrive
at Iskut, a Tahltan Re-
serve that is a good
starting point for ex-
cursions into two of
British Columbia's
most spectacular pro-
tected wilderness

areas. You can also
camp in Kinaskan
Lake Park.
Both Mount Edziza
Provincial Park and
Recreation Area, and
Spatsizi Plateau Wil-
derness Provincial
Park offer extraordin-
ary terrains. In
Mount Edziza, stark
lava flows, basalt
plateaus and cinder
fields give the land ex-
quisite watercolour
tones. In Spatsizi
Plateau, trail rides
take you through wild
valleys, uncut forests,
rolling tablelands and
rugged mountains.

Dease Lake. North of
Iskut, has an airport
for charter flights,
and was the original
entry point into the
area for early North-
west and Hudson's
Bay Company trap-
pers who travelled in
on the Liard and
Dease Rivers. It's also
the turning off point
for *Telegraph Creek,*
located on the magni-
ficent Stikine River.
The road is an experi-
ence itself. It follows
the route of an origi-
nal mountain trail
that was hacked out
by prospectors dur-
ing the Cassiar gold
rush, and passes
through breathtaking
scenery, with views
of Mt. Edziza, the
Grand Canyon of the
Stikine, Tahltan Can-
yon and mountain
ranges stretching to
the horizon. In Tele-
graph Creek, the origi-
nal Hudson's Bay Post
is now a lodge/cafe.

Cassiar Country.

While millions of
dollars of gold once
came out of the creek
beds during this re-
gion's gold rush, as-
bestos and tourism
are the gold mines of
today. The area
around the small
town of Cassiar is
superb for fishing,
with lake trout, Dolly
Varden, pike, gray-
ling and whitefish in
abundance. Hunting
for moose, caribou,
mountain goat, moun-
tain sheep, black bear,
grizzly and wolf is
also popular. There is
no accommodation in
the town of Cassiar it-
self, although private
campgrounds are
nearby.

Atlin.

Tucked away in the
extreme northwest-
ern corner of the pro-
vince, this area was a
sidebar of the Klon-
dike, a bustling small
town that enjoyed a
rich cultural life at the
turn of the century.
Many of the original

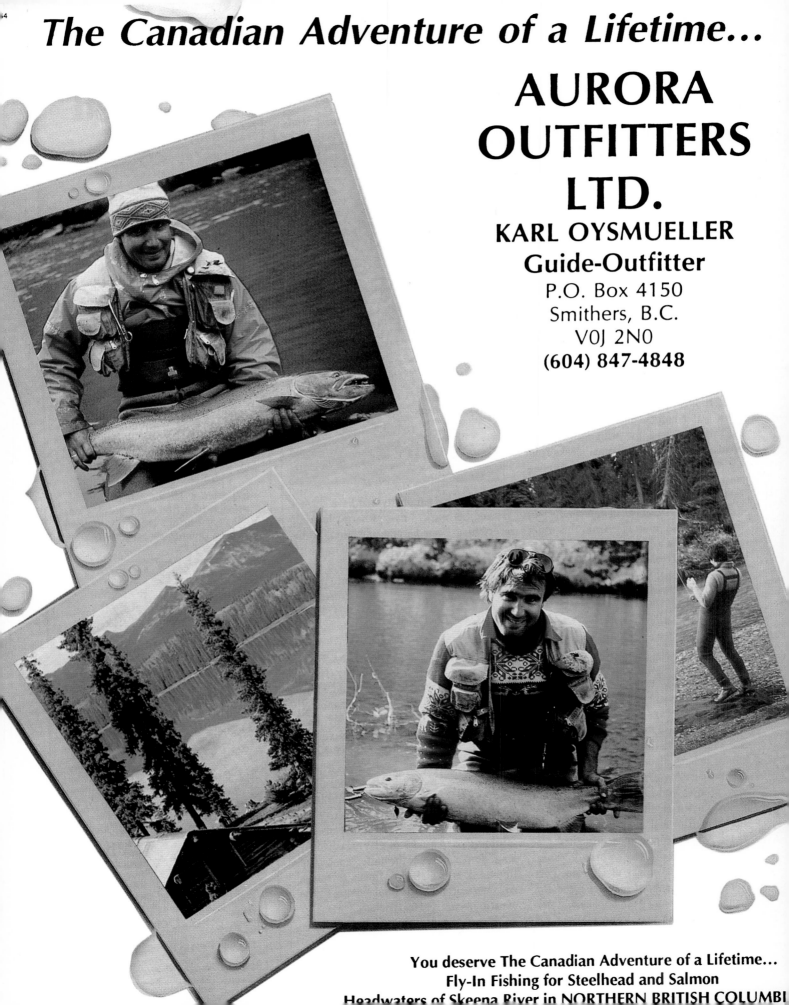

166

Edelweiss Ventures
Saltwater Chartering

3930 McNeil Street
Terrace, B.C.
CANADA V8G 3L2

Lou Haselmeyer
(604) 635-7378

MINI CRUISING · SALT WATER CHARTERS
EXTENDED CRUISING
COME ABOARD THE 35' M. V. MONTEGO BAY
FOR THE FUN AND FISHING TIME OF YOUR LIFE!
Range: 350 miles Sleeps Four
Food & Fishing Gear Supplied

30-Minute
Video Presentation
$15.00
Deductible when booking

1000 SQUARE MILES OF TERRITORY, LOCATED IN WEST CENTRAL BRITISH COLUMBIA

At **NANIKA GUIDING**, the hunter can choose from seven different pre-packaged hunts or book combination hunts tailored to preferred species. The hunts vary from road access areas to the fly-in pristine areas, for an unforgettable wilderness hunting experience.

We offer top quality hunts for the serious hunter. Moose, Mountain Goat and Grizzly are the main trophy animals, along with Black Bear and Wolf. Your trophy and meat will be prepared for transport. Spring hunts include Grizzly, Black Bear and Wolf. Fall hunts include Moose, Mountain Goat, Black Bear, Grizzly and Game birds.

During the summer months Nanika Guiding offers guided wilderness camping, hiking, sightseeing and fishing trips into the coastal mountains to experience the natural, unspoiled glacial lakes, subalpine valleys, and mountain beauty. A guided canoe trip to four lakes and the beautiful Nanika Falls can be arranged upon request. Write or phone for more information.

Fishing	Cutthroat
	Rainbow
•Fly Fishing	Lake trout
•Light tackle	Kokanee
•Fly-in	Dolly Varden

Hunting	Moose
	Mountain Goat
•Fly-in	Black Bear
•Boat	Grizzly
•Hiking	Grouse
•Backpacking	Ptarmigan

FROM JANUARY TO DECEMBER
CONTACT B. PEDEN OR J. TOUROND
NANIKA GUIDING
R.R. #2
BURNS LAKE
BRITISH COLUMBIA
CANADA V0J 1E0
(604) 695-6351
(604) 695-6542

Old Remo Fishing Lodge

OLD REMO FISHING & GUIDING LTD., 66 RALEY ST., KITIMAT, BRITISH COLUMBIA V8C 1H1 604-632-3326/6443

OLD REMO FISHING LODGE is located on the banks of the majestic Skeena River, a few miles west of Terrace, near the settlement of Old Remo. The accommodations are simple but comfortable, consisting of eight twin-bed rooms and two washrooms with showers. Meals are served in the dining room in the main lodge (European and Canadian cuisine) by our friendly staff. In the evenings, the fishermen gather together in the warm atmosphere of the main lodge to exchange stories of the day.

Transportation to and from the Terrace Airport is provided. All meals, transportation, accommodation and guiding services are included in the price. We also have a smokehouse, and will smoke your fish if desired.

Our fishing is done mainly in the Skeena, a mere two-minute walk down a wilderness trail, or in other hot spots to which our experienced guides will drive you. We also have a 21' jet boat to get to those remote, otherwise inaccessible locations.

April/May is an excellent time for steelhead fishing in the Kitimat River (about an hour's drive away), as well as for chinook fishing in the Skeena and Kalum. This is also a great time for fly-fishing, as is the fall. From the last week of June until about the 10th of July, we specialize in chinook fishing on the Kitimat River, which has been producing fantastic runs in the last few years; then for the rest of July there is superb chinook fishing in the Skeena, right by the lodge. Many trophy-sized fish are landed here every year. As well, there are also steelhead in the Skeena from about mid-July on. The latter part of August until mid-September is good for coho fishing in the Kitimat River and for coho and steelhead in the Skeena.

Most of our staff is fluent n English and German. For those of you who speak other languages, we'll surely find some way to communicate! Warmth and hospitality are abundant, and we'll do our best to make you feel at home.

SPATSIZI --

is a wilderness park, British Columbia's second largest park in the Province. Some 3,000 square miles of crystal clear lakes, streams and rivers, towering mountains, vast snowfields and virtually one of the last great wilderness areas in British Columbia. This immense park is made up of the mountain reaches known as the Eaglenest Range and the Spatsizi Plateau. The river drainages include Spatsizi River and Upper Stikine; between mid-June and late September this Spatsizi Wilderness offers some of the finest sports fishing available in northern British Columbia. Angling that can satisfy the most demanding purist or the beginner learning the art of angling or fly fishing on virtually untouched waters. All against a backdrop of some of the most magnificent scenery and wildlife country in North America. The area is accessible only by air with virtually no people and 200 air miles from the nearest incorporated town and roads no closer than 60 miles from its border.

The main sports fish are Rainbow Trout, Arctic Grayling, Dally Varden Char, Lake Trout (Char) and Whitefish.

The size of the fish will vary according to the water being fished. Rainbow averaging 1 1/2 lbs. are available on several of the lakes and the Spatsizi and Upper Stikine Rivers. Larger Rainbows up to 4 lbs. can be caught in smaller numbers in some of the lakes.

Arctic Grayling run up to 2 lbs., Dolly Varden up to 15 lbs. in the Stikine drainage and Spatsizi Rivers and Lakes, Lake Trout up to 20 lbs. in the larger lake known as Cold Fish Lake.

Apart from having base camps on Laslui Lake and Cold Fish Lake, within Spatsizi Park we have our sister camp on the Firesteel River, which is the virtual headwaters of the Finlay River system situated within Tatlatui Park. The Firesteel River -- a Trout Fisherman's Paradise -- has always been the favourite for the dry fly fisherman.

We are offering this fishing experience to you as the exclusive guide-outfitter within the Spatsizi reches as our guests. You are not competing -- those hot spots are yours to fish.

SPATSIZI

WILDERNESS FISHING
SPATSIZI WILDERNESS VACATIONS
P.O. Box 3070
Smithers, British Columbia, Canada

V0J 2N0
(604) 847-9692
(604) 847-9790

NORTH KNIFE LAKE LODGE, situated deep in the heart of Manitoba's Northland, caters to the serious sportsfisherman. A short, one-hour plane ride from Churchill or Thompson puts you down in the finest Lake Trout country in Canada. Just 130 miles southwest of Churchill, North Knife Lake stretches out for 30 miles with sections up to six miles wide. Linked with the waters of the North Knife River, the lake is home for the scrappy Northern Pike, magnificent trophy Lake Trout and the elusive Arctic Grayling. North Knife Lake Lodge offers the discriminating fisherman a chance to experience the thrill and excitement of hooking the big ones -- for many it's a dream come true. Our guests consider North Knife Lake Lodge a "very special place to fish." We have to agree, there's nothing like it!

Our new Five Star Lodge was completed in 1987. Combined with our existing modern cabins, we can now accomodate 28 guests at North Knife Lake. The new lodge consists of kitchen, licensed dining room and lounge, games area, conference facilities and four guest rooms. A separate building houses the sauna. Our kitchen offers a variety of delicious, home-cooked meals for breakfast and dinner. They're guaranteed to please every fisherman's appetite! Meals are served family-style in our dining room. Out on the lake, a mouth-watering shore lunch of fresh fish is prepared for you over an open fire by one of our experienced guides.

Fishing Package: Our North Knife Lake Lodge fishing package includes round-trip transportation from Churchill or Thompson to our lodge via Twin Otter plane, five-star accomodations, delicious meals and shore lunch daily. Your party will be outfitted with new 30hp Yamaha motors, Lund boats and gas. We also process and package all your catch and carefully handle your trophy fish. Of course, we also offer an exciting and memorable fishing vacation you're sure to enjoy.

Special Features: Our lodge is the only lodge on North Knife Lake, and we maintain radio contact with the town of Churchill. Our skilled guides are courteous and helpful. North Knife Lake Lodge is owned and operated by your hosts Doug and Helen Webber, offering friendly service and Northern hospitality. Our trips are 3, 4 and 7 days.

When you've limited out fishing, take a break and enjoy the Churchill area. We are known as "the polar bear capitol of the world", and encourage our guests to book aerial sightseeing tours to observe the "great white bear", the famed Beluga whale and the rare Siberian Ross Gull in their natural habitats. Other events popular with our guests include nature tours, canoe trips, moose hunts and winter adventure outings.

We have two float planes based at North Knife Lake Lodge available for sightseeing tours and for daily fly-out service to our outpost lakes.

Tackle: For Lake Trout and Northern Pike, we recommend a medium to heavy action casting rod and a heavy-duty bait casting or spinning reel. Ten to 20-pound test line is adequate for Lake Trout and Northern Pike, while Grayling provides lots of action on light spinning tackle or a fly rod. We have a good supply of popular lures at the lodge and we encourage you to bring some of your favourites as well.

Trophy Policy: At North Knife Lake we are dedicated to preserving quality sportfishing for future generations. With this in mind, we have instituted a trophy management policy. Our policy allows one Lake Trout and one Northern Pike over 10 pounds, one Arctic Grayling over two pounds, and one Brook Trout or Whitefish over four pounds per guest for the purpose of mounting. If you're not after trophy fish for mounting, you are allowed one Lake Trout and three Northern Pike under eight pounds, plus one each of the other species. We do not include your shore lunch catch in this count, though we do ask that shore lunch fish be under six pounds -- so eat your fill! All fishing is on barbless hooks. Barbless lures are available at the lodge, as well as barbless hooks for your favourite lures.

Items to Bring: To ensure a pleasant fishing trip, we encourage our guests to bring warm clothing. Your clothing should be of a layering type, including a warm hat and gloves. Waterproof boots and rain gear are important, as well as a complete change of clothes. Other personal gear should include tackle, camera, film and sunglasses. Baggage is limited to a maximum of 40 pounds per person, so plan carefully.

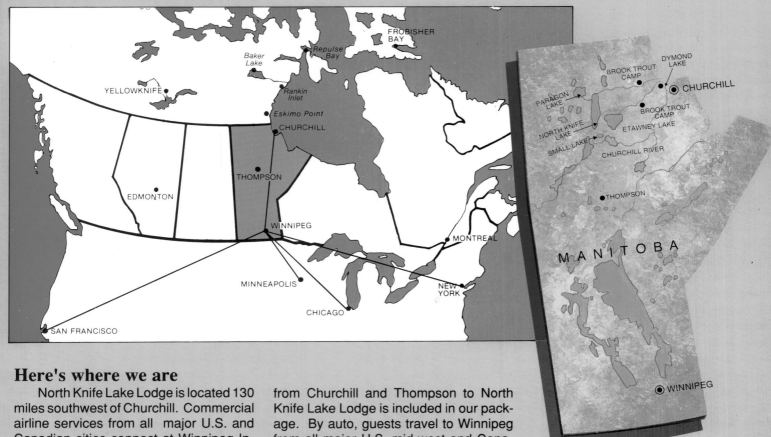

Here's where we are

North Knife Lake Lodge is located 130 miles southwest of Churchill. Commercial airline services from all major U.S. and Canadian cities connect at Winnipeg International Airport. From Winnipeg, Canadian Airlines Int'l services Thompson and Churchill. Round trip plane service from Churchill and Thompson to North Knife Lake Lodge is included in our package. By auto, guests travel to Winnipeg from all major U.S. mid-west and Canadian cities, then north on paved highway to Thompson.

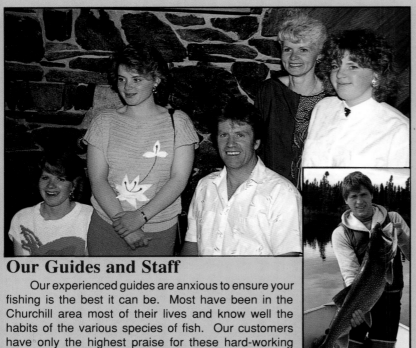

Our Guides and Staff

Our experienced guides are anxious to ensure your fishing is the best it can be. Most have been in the Churchill area most of their lives and know well the habits of the various species of fish. Our customers have only the highest praise for these hard-working men. The guides, and all our staff, are friendly, courteous and anxious to make your trip a memorable one.

Conference Facilities

For those of you who are interested in combining business and pleasure, we have conference facilities available at the Lodge.

Welcome to North Knife Lake Lodge

Among serious fishermen, Northern Manitoba has a long-standing reputation for fine sportsfishing, and North Knife Lake Lodge prides itself in allowing our guests the opportunity to experience the area's fishing at its best. Our outcamp service gives you a choice. Whether you're fishing for Walleye, Lake Trout, Northern Pike, Whitefish or Grayling, we've got the spot. Our outcamps are complete housekeeping cabins located on prime fishing lakes and rivers. Each cabin contains propane cooking facilities, propane fridge, gas lights and a woodstove. All cooking and eating utensils are supplied and comfortable bunks ensure a good night's sleep.

Etawney Lake outcamp is a six-guest housekeeping cabin situated at the headwaters of South Knife River. This camp is highly recommended for Lake Trout and Northern Pike. Anglers have been known to catch up to 40 Lake Trout and 60 Northern Pike per day -- per boat!

Small Lake outcamp is a six-guest housekeeping cabin located at Small Lake on the Churchill River System. Walleye and Northern Pike fishing is excellent here, although Trout and Whitefish are also abundant.

Our outpost tent camps are located on five excellent fishing lakes: Wishart, Stinson, Paragon, Hibbert and Knifehead. Our outpost tent camps are the only camps on these lakes and are designed for one-day fly-out trips from the Lodge. Wishart, Stinson and Hibbert offer Walleye, Lake Trout, Northern Pike, and Whitefish. Knifehead offers Lake Trout and Northern; Paragon, Arctic Grayling and Northern.

NOVAS

Sleek silver Nova Scotia salmon glide in from the sea to join four species of resident spotted trout in the lakes and streams. Then, shimmering American shad join the migration and, behind them, come the seatrout back from rich feeding in the estuaries. By summer, smallmouth bass will be active in the warm water lakes and, by fall, giant stripers will have entered fresh water . . .

Be ready for them. Book early with one of the outfitters listed below.

North Mountain OUTFITTERS	Single party bookings in each of our two lodges and one guide for every two hunters ensure privacy for hunting upland birds, white tail deer and black bear. Contact: Roger & Anna Ehrenfeld P.O. Box 149, Middleton, Nova Scotia, B0S 1P0 (902) 825-4030 (days) or (902) 825-6629 (evenings)
River View LODGE	Salmon and trout fishing in two famous streams, hunting for upland birds, waterfowl and big game from a comfortable secluded lodge on the Medway River. Contact: Moyal Conrad Greenfield, Queens County, Nova Scotia, B0T 1E0 (902) 685-2423 (lodge) or (902) 685-2378/2376
Meisner's Meadow Recreational Lodge	Outfitting services for fishing and hunting -- smallmouth & striped bass, salmon, ducks, geese and white tail deer in the Annapolis Valley and the South Shore of Nova Scotia. Contact: Ron Seney Meisner's Section, RR#3, New Germany, Nova Scotia, B0R 1E0 (902) 644-3015 (lodge) or (902) 644-2818 (South Shore Depot)
TURNER'S West Branch Lodge	Two secluded cabins on the St. Mary's River providing guides for trout and salmon fishing and white tail deer hunting. Contact: Phillip Turner RR#1, Aspen, Guysborough County, Nova Scotia, B0H 1E0 (902) 833-2303
STEWIACKE VALLEY OUTFITTERS	Experienced guides, home-cooked meals and private hunting land for snowshoe hare, white tail deer, black bear and fishing for Atlantic salmon and brown trout. Contact: David & Linda Kennedy RR#3, Brookfield, Colchester County, Nova Scotia, B0N 1C0 (902) 673-2023
Rattling Buck Outfitters	Hunting, upland birds, fishing and recreational activities. Bow/rifle hunting with master guides. Contact: Bruce Wheaton Carl Cameron, Box 555, Partridge Is., N. S., B0M 1S0 Parsboro, N.S. B0M 1S0 (902) 254-2071/(B) 443-7627 (902) 254-3208/ (B) 254-2500
CHETICAMP OUTFITTERS	A sporting package designed for every need. Hunting black bear and white tail deer; river and deep sea fishing. P.O. Box 448, Cheticamp, Nova Scotia, B0E 1H0 Contact: Rene Aucoin (902) 224-3701, Gilles (902) 224-2776, Pat (902) 224-2254
KEJI LODGE	Come to their new lodge for black bear, white tail deer, Atlantic salmon; bowhunting too. Contact: Ralph Shaw Box 99, Caledonia, Queens Co., Nova Scotia B0T 1B0 (902) 859-2930

COTIA

 The NORMAWAY Inn

We offer some of the best salmon fishing and accommodations in North America on the famous, spectacular Margaree River, acknowledged as perhaps the most beautiful salmon stream on the continent.

Please contact: David MacDonald, Owner, P.O. Box 178, Margaree Valley, Nova Scotia, B0E 2C0 (902) 248-2987

A modern, secluded lodge on an eight-acre island providing a full line of services for trout and salmon fishing, and bird, bear and deer hunting.

Call or write for details: Don Breen P.O. Box 402, Milton, Queens County, Nova Scotia, B0T 1P0 (902) 354-4354

Accommodation for 4-6 people overlooking the magnificent Lake Bras d'Or. One licensed guide for every two people. Hunting for rabbit, waterfowl, upland birds and our specialty -- white tail deer. Great fishing for salmon, rainbow, speckled and brown trout.

Contact: Earl Rudderham RR#2, Boisdale, Christmas Island, Cape Breton, Nova Scotia, B0A 1C0 (902) 871-2549

Comfortable accommodations and experienced guide service for brook and lake trout, bass fishing. Hunting guides for snowshoe hare, upland and big game including white tail deer and black bear.

Contact: Robert & Marie Gauthier RR#2, Annapolis County, Nova Scotia, B0S 1A0 (902) 638-3509

Quality guiding, comfortable lodgings and hearty meals; some of the finest trout and salmon fishing and big game hunting anywhere.

Contact: Aubrey R. Beaver P.O. Box 40, Sherbrooke, Nova Scotia, B0J 3C0 (902) 533-2235

Knowledgeable outfitting services for Atlantic salmon, brown trout, upland birds and big game in one of Nova Scotia's most outstanding lodges.

Contact: Tom & Marion Kennedy Upper Stewiacke Valley, Nova Scotia, B0N 2P0 (902) 671-2749

Excellent hunting for white tail deer, black bear, black duck and upland game.

Contact: Bernie Amon P.O. Box 85, Great Village, Colchester County, Nova Scotia, B0M 1L0 (902) 668-2062

Smallmouth bass fishing on wilderness lakes, brown trout on a pastoral stream, salmon fishing on the South Shore or the local river, hunting for upland birds and white tail deer, as well as historic and scenic attractions.

Contact: Perry and Judi Munro RR#2, Wolfville, Nova Scotia, B0P 1X0 (902) 542-2658

 NOVA SCOTIA so much to sea

Jack MacIsaac
Minister of Tourism

Fishing and Hunting New Brunswick Canada

FISH STORIES AND TALL TALES COME TRUE IN NEW BRUNSWICK

Forests and wilderness...lakes and streams...and some of the finest fishing rivers in the world make New Brunswick, Canada the place to be if you want your dreams to come true.

Fish for challenging smallmouth bass or the king of gamefish...the world renowned atlantic salmon.

Hunt for black bear, trophy whitetail and a variety of birds such as ruffed grouse and woodcock.

Relax and enjoy your stay in superb outfitting establishments where you become king of the New Brunswick outdoors.

Want to learn more...call toll free 1-800-561-0123.

Lynn Castle's
UNALAKLEET RIVER LODGE
NORTHWEST ALASKA BERING SEA

King of the Salmon - June

Another great trip! Aug.

Four hundred air miles northwest of Anchorage, across the Yukon River to the shores of the fabled Bering Sea, lies a remote Eskimo village named Unalakleet (pronounced U-NA-LA-KLEET). Unlike most trophy fish areas in Alaska, there is no fishing competition from other lodges on the Unalakleet watershed. Nor must you fly out to enjoy really top Alaskan fishing, as we enjoy a wide variety of Alaska's finest sportfish right at our front door. The UNALAKLEET RIVER LODGE, is located a short 20-minute boat ride upriver from tidewater, making our fresh sea-run salmon some of the strongest and hardest fighting fish you will ever encounter. They are guaranteed to test your angling skill.

We kick off the season mid-June with one of the strongest King Salmon runs in the State, which normally extends through mid-July. These powerful and spirited ocean fresh monsters will average 25-30 pounds, with fish in the 50-60 pound class caught every season. That's a lot of fish in anyone's book!

As Winston Moore writes of the Unalakleet River in *The Pan Angler:* "It's the best I've been able to find for big fish."

In July, over one million Pink (Humpback) Salmon enter the Unalakleet River. Pinks aggressively take both lures and flies, earning them the reputation for striking "anything that hits the water." You can catch these fiesty fighters one after another "unti

your arms fall off." Can you think of a better way to spend a family vacation?

Beginning late June through mid-September, the hardiest and most colorful of the Pacific salmon family has made its way to our doorstep. The northern Chum (Calico) Salmon is unquestionably the most underrated of all of Alaska's game fish. While the average Calico weighs between 8-12 pounds, fish of 16 to 20 pounds are occasionally hooked. Pound for pound, this multicolored member of the salmon family will outfight any fish in Alaska, including the legendary Sheefish.

We enjoy one of the most intense Silver (Coho) Salmon runs in all Alaska. These famous hard-hitting, jumping fish enter the river late July and remain throughout September. Known for their aggressive striking characteristics, these 8-20 pound hunks of TNT readily take both lures and flies. Many experienced anglers feel that Silvers are the most exciting of all the Pacific salmon.

Very likely, the largest Arctic Grayling found in Alaska are Native to the clearwater streams and rivers entering the Bering Sea. And the Unalakleet drainages are literally loaded with these lovely "sailfish of the North." Averaging 2 to 2-½ pounds, guests have landed several monsters weighing in excess of 4 pounds, and 24 inches in length! It is just a matter of time before a UNALAKLEET RIVER LODGE guest catches the new Alaskan World Record Grayling . . . . And it could be you!

Throughout the summer months, schools of brilliantly colored Arctic Char, and their silvery cousins, the Dolly Varden, move in and out of the river following the various runs of salmon. Average size of these excellent eating beauties runs 3-6 pounds. During the last week of July and the first week of August, Char and Dollies swarm by the tens of thousands into jthe Unalakleet's salmon spawning beds. At this time fishing is literally "a fish a cast" on both flies and lures.

Fishing on the Unalakleet is conducted from river boats equipped with either prop and/or jet driven Mercury outboards. Normally each boat is limited to two guests and their personal guide. Catch and release, while not a hardfast rule, is practiced on most species, particularly in the upper tributaries when fishing for trophy grayling.

The Unalakleet River boasts the heaviest salmon runs in the Bering Sea fishery, and is spawning home to literally millions of fish: mighty Kings, fiesty Pink Salmon, the explosive Calico or Chum Salmon, and fighting Silvers, in addition to trophy-sized Arctic Grayling, Dolly Varden and Arctic Char. In addition, our optional fly-out program offers trophy Northern Pike and Sheefish.

Originally the showcase lodge of the Silvertip group, UNALAKLEET RIVER LODGE now operates under the very capable leadership of Master Guide and pilot Lynn and Penny Castle, who for more than twenty-four years, have built a reputation unequaled in Alaskan wilderness circles. Their goal is to offer guests unequalled hospitality and fishing adventure in Northwestern Alaskan waters.

Arctic Char • July - Sept.

Silver Salmon • Aug. - Sept.

Included as part of the regular lodge program is the opportunity to visit a comfortable wilderness tent camp accessibly only by jet-boat and/or aircraft. Typically these camps include your guide(s), private sleeping tents with cots and mattresses, dining tent, cook and radio communications.

Rates INCLUDE lodging based on shared accommodations, guide services, meals, one over-night excursion to wilderness tent camp, and transportation between Unalakleet and the lodge. Unalakleet is serviced daily by major airlines from Anchorage and Nome. Group rates apply throughout season on space available basis. Special family discounts available during late July. Whether with family or friends, or your next business meeting, we invite you to come with us and experience Northwestern Alaskan fishing at its best!

For Reservations (Oct.-May):
Lynn and Penny Castle
UNALAKLEET RIVER LODGE
P.O. Box 536
Bandera, Texas 78003
Phone: (512) 796-4909

Seasonal Address (June-Sept.):
Attn: Manager
UNALAKLEET RIVER LODGE
P.O. Box 99
Unalakleet, Alaska 99684
Phone: (907) 624-3030

GLACIER BAY AND SOUTHEAST ALASKA

Glacier Bay National Park's 16 glaciers calving into the sea is one of Nature's major spectacles. Less than 200 years ago, Glacier Bay was a great icefield. Today, ice has receded nearly 100 miles, leaving a magnificent bay full of all manner of wildlife, including three species of whale, seal, sea lion, nearly 200 species of sea and shore birds including Bald Eagle, Brown and Black Bear, moose, deer, wolf, mountain goat and innumerable species of fresh- and salt-water fish.

Entry into Glacier Bay is strictly limited by concession permit, insuring a truly remarkable wilderness experience. As Alaska Licensed Master Guide No. 61, I have conducted fishing and exploration cruises throughout Southeast Alaska and Glacier Bay for more than two decades.

You'll cruise aboard our new 72' yacht "Alaskan Solitude." One double and three triple cabins, three full baths, spacious salon (with three more double cabins if necessary) and lots of covered deck space make for a very comfortable voyage.

You'll fish a different lake or creek each day for Pink, Chum, Sockeye or Silver Salmon, Arctic Char, Cutthroat or Rainbow Trout. Many areas are literally "a fish a cast." Giant Pacific Halibut are fished directly off the "Alaskan Solitude"; several over 200 lbs. are landed each year. We also watch whale at close range and cruise up-bay to the glaciers to watch icefalls. An up to 25-foot tide twice daily allows crab to be picked up off the beach or from our traps. Your non-fishing companion would enjoy beach combing, an abundance of wildlife, incredible scenery, glaciers and pristine wilderness.

We cruise the calm inside waters, so don't worry about motion sickness. Our six-day fishing/exploration trips assure sufficient time to catch several different species of fish, have a crab feed or two, see spectacular icefalls and enjoy unique Alaskan solitude in complete comfort. Your group will have exclusive use of the vessel.

Booking
Agents 4

SPECIALITY HUNTS AND CONSULTING SERVICES

I provide a consulting service for anyone interested in arranging a hunt for any species of game in North America. This service is only provided on a very personal basis over the phone. Like my Yukon Outfitting business, I offer this service to a small number of very special clients.

I personally escort a few select clients on very special hunts all over North America, Africa, Mexico & Europe.

I am one of only 11 people who has successfully hunted **all** 27 North American Big Game Animals. I am recognized as a world authority for North America Big Game Hunting. I have been the special North American Technical Consultant to the Record Committee for Safari Club International.

If you wish to arrange a hunt through me you must send a deposit to me. Upon receipt of a deposit I finalize a reservation for you with an outfitter I know is reputable. I will thoroughly discuss the details with you prior to committing your deposit to any outfitter. If you are considering a hunt soon, anywhere, for any species, then let my knowledge and experience work for you to get the best hunt available.

Rick Furniss
Professional Hunt Consultant

Global Expeditions

P.O. Box 1230, Waterdown, Ontario L0R 2H0, Canada (416) 689-7925 Fax (416) 689-3206 Telex 061 8996 CNO WTDN
A Division of Canada North Outfitting Inc.

Red Stag

We offer classic hunts for red deer stags in six different countries. Our most attractively priced hunt for these magnificent trophy animals is $3675 US for a six day 2×1 hunt in the Scottish Highlands — and this price includes three red stags per hunter, and the roundtrip airfare from New York.

The pursuit of the red stag in the Scottish Highlands is the classical stalking experience. Here there is no shooting from the seat of a 4×4, or from the comfort of a blind: the red stag must be stalked in the true sense of the word, by a physically fit, and competent, rifleman. And the stalk takes place amid the scenic grandeur of the Highlands and in the company of the friendly people who live there.

The only extras you have to pay for on this hunt are liquor and phone calls, tips to staff, and the packing and shipping home of trophies.

Trophy Kudu and Leopard

Hunt leopard and trophy kudu in South West Africa. This safari of 14 days, one on one, is the best value we know of in Africa today at $4485 US, which is inclusive of roundtrip airfare from New York to Windhoek. We can also arrange a ten day 1×1 antelope only hunt, with the same outfitter, for $3985 US.

The safari takes place in the rugged thornbush country some 200 miles north of Windhoek. The chances of taking a kudu in the 55 inch class or bigger are excellent, as are the chances of killing a leopard. The trophy fees are: Leopard under 80 inches $1000. Leopard over 80 inches with prime coat $2000. Southern greater kudu $400. Gemsbuck $400. Mountain zebra $350. Red hartebeest $350. Damara dikdik $100. Cheetah $500. Steinbuck $100. Springbuck $130. Warthog $100. Baboon $100. Ostrich $150.

We have other southern African budget-priced hunting programmes, plus classical safaris in Botswana, Zambia, Zimbabwe, Tanzania, and South Africa.

Tahr and Chamois

Climb the steep slopes of New Zealand's southern alps in pursuit of two of the world's most sought after trophies: the chamois and the tahr. The cost, for an eight day 2×1 hunt, inclusive of roundtrip airfare from Los Angeles is $3945 US. For a 1×1 eight day hunt the cost is $4745 US. There are no trophy fees for free-ranging chamois and tahr.

The Himalayan tahr is regarded as the No 1 trophy of the South Pacific, and hunting him is not easy, especially as his preferred habitat lies at around 6000 feet, near the permanent snow line. The chamois shares the tahr's liking for the mountains, and lives among the rocky outcrops and alpine meadows at somewhat lower altitude. Only those in good physical shape should consider undertaking this hunt.

For more information write, or call, Tudor Howard-Davies at Global Expeditions. Tudor joined us recently after spending 18 years in Africa, all but six of them as a professional hunter in four different countries. His last job there was as editor of MAGNUM, South Africa's only hunting and shooting magazine.

We can take you hunting ibex in Egypt or sitatunga in Botswana; stalking roe deer in England or wild sheep in British Columbia; shooting ducks in Mexico or geese in Canada; fishing for char in the Arctic or salmon in Scotland. In short we can take you wherever you want to go in pursuit of whatever you want to hunt.

WE BOOK QUALITY HUNTS AROUND THE WORLD

Global Expeditions Inc.
Safaris and Adventure Travel

African Safaris, priced for the budget-conscious hunter, are our specialty. For example, we have a ten-day, 1 x 1 plains game hunt in South West Africa for less than $4,000, airfare included — with similar hunts in Botswana, Zimbabwe, South Africa, Zambia and Tanzania. We offer classic big game safaris in these countries too — plus deer stalking in Scotland, hunting in New Zealand, bass fishing and bird shooting in Cuba, and more.

For more information contact Global Expeditions Inc., P.O. Box 1230, Waterdown, Ontario, Canada L0R 2H0   Tel.: (416) 689-7925   Telex 061 8996 CNO WTDN   Fax: (416) 689-3206

Printed in Hong Kong

North-Western Safaris offer hunting in all four Provinces of South Africa for the complete range of Southern African species. No effort is spared in securing the best possible trophies for clients.

North-Western
Safaris
South Africa

North Western Safaris
Private Bag X2626, Potgieterus 0600
Transvaal, Republic of South Africa
IN U.S. CONTACT: North-Western Safaris
Box 5909, San Jose, Ca 95150
408-866-4672

Leopard
Eland
Kudu
Waterbuck
Blue Wildebeest
Zebra
Bushbuck
Gemsbuck
Cape Hartebeest
Klipspringer
Blesbok
Impala
Grey Duiker
Steenbuck
Crocodile
Bushpig
Warthog
Mountain Reedbuck
Buffalo
Lion
Sable Antelope
Nyala
Common Reedbuck
Suni
Red Duiker
White Rhino
Springbuck
Black Springbuck
White Springbuck
White Blesbuck
Bontebok
Red Lechwe
Vaal Rhebuck
Fallow Deer
Cape Grysbuck
White-tailed Gnu
Caracal
Serval
Baboon
Jackal

**NORTH WESTERN
TRANSVAAL**

**NORTH EASTERN
TRANSVAAL**

CAPE PROVINCE

ZULULAND

Rifles and Accessories 5

IT'S A STEEL

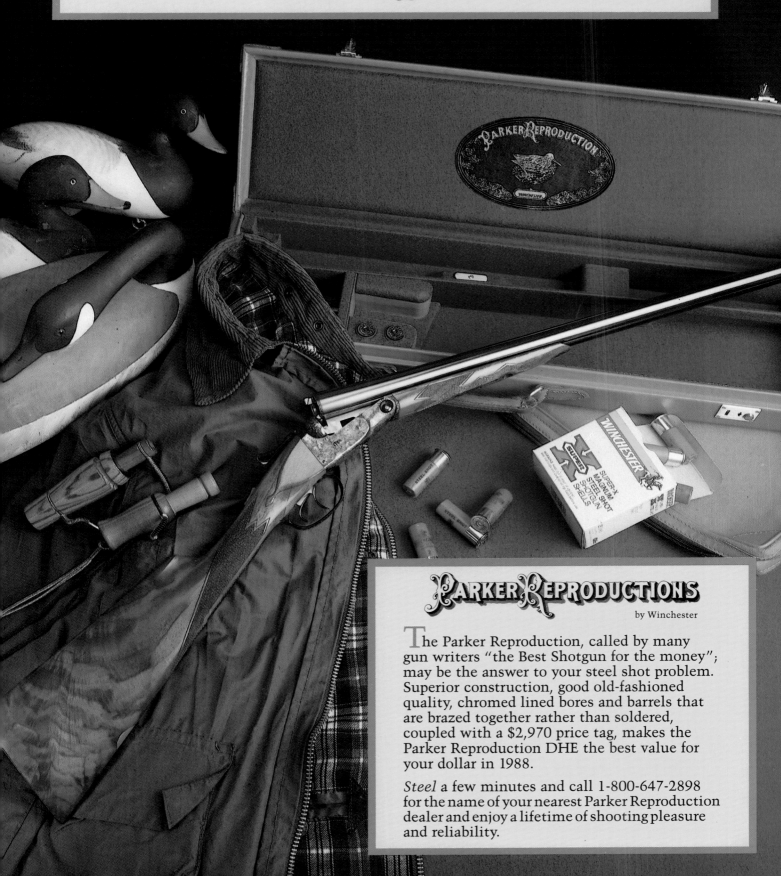

Blaser Hunting Rifles

BLASER Model R 84 Bolt Action Rifle

The new BLASER R 84 system is a new concept in the bolt action rifle world. It has been escpecially designed for the serious hunter and shooter who appreciates fine quality firearms. Two piece take down for ease of portability and quick change of barrels.

AUTUMN SALES INC., 1320 LAKE STREET, FORT WORTH, TX 76102 TEL 817-335-1634

BLASER JAGDWAFFEN GBMH, BOX 1149, 7972 ISNY, WEST GERMANY TEL 0 75 62/70 20Y

The fast operating gliding bolt on two long rails is extremely quiet and smooth.

Scopes and interchangeable barrels are optional.

PETER HOFER: HUNTING RIFLES

Ferlach, Austria

Weapons made to meet your wishes -- because there is more to exquisite hand-crafted precision weapons than just perfect technique.

Ferlach's fine, reliable hunting weapons have enjoyed notable renown throughout the hunting world for more than 400 years.

Peter Hofer of Ferlach is proud to produce hunting weapons which, in these fast-moving and transitory times, last for generations.

Since all our weapons are exclusively handmade, you yourself can stipulate all the technical and artistic features of your own weapon. For the hunting of various game, you can choose between twenty-five different break joint gun

systems and over 100 calibres.

Designs range from simple but accurate utility guns to works of art, decorated with silver, gold, platinum and precious stones. Whether it be a hunting weapon with several exchangeable barrels or a combination of two, three, four or five barrels, absolute firing precision is a foregone conclusion.

You will therefore own a unique hunting gun that is the only one of its kind in the world.

We would be delighted to demonstrate our artistic abilities and craftsmanship in the production of your own individual weapon.

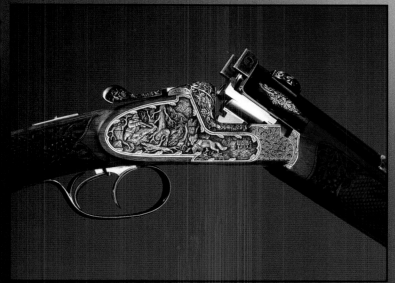

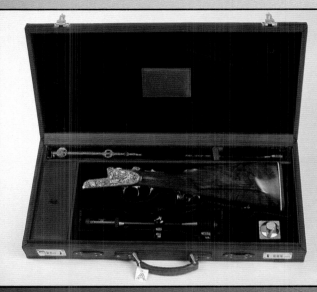

Peter Hofer - Jagdwaffen
hunting rifles
Büchsenmachermeister - Craftsman Gunsmith

Exquisitely hand- crafted precision hunting rifles based on the expirience of 400 years gunsmith tradition in Ferlach.
Erlesene handgearbeitete Präzisionswaffen basierend auf 400-jähriger Erfahrung der Büchsenmachertradition in Ferlach.
A-9170 FERLACH - F. Lang Str. 13 - ✆ (0 42 27) 36 83 AUSTRIA

HOLLAND & HOLLAND ARE NOW KNOWN FOR MORE THAN THEIR GUNS AND RIFLES

For over one hundred and fifty years Holland & Holland big game and stalking rifles have been used all over the world — from the Highlands of Scotland and the Himalayas to the jungles of India, Africa and South America and in the frozen wastes of the North American continent. Today, in addition to their world renowned guns and rifles, Holland & Holland offer a complete range of shooting clothing and accessories. The instructors from the Holland & Holland Shooting School, who make frequent instructional visits to America, have a deservedly high reputation. A visit to Holland & Holland will help you to prepare for every kind of hunting expedition. Please write for our new Gun and Rifle Price Lists, our Shooting and Clothing and Accessories Catalogue and the Holland & Holland Shooting School folder.

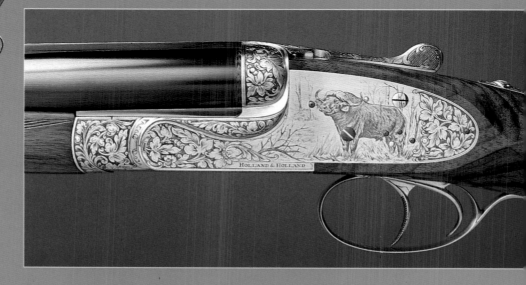

HOLLAND & HOLLAND
LIMITED

33 Bruton Street, London W1X 8JS

Telephone 01-499 4411   *Telex* 269021 GUNNER G

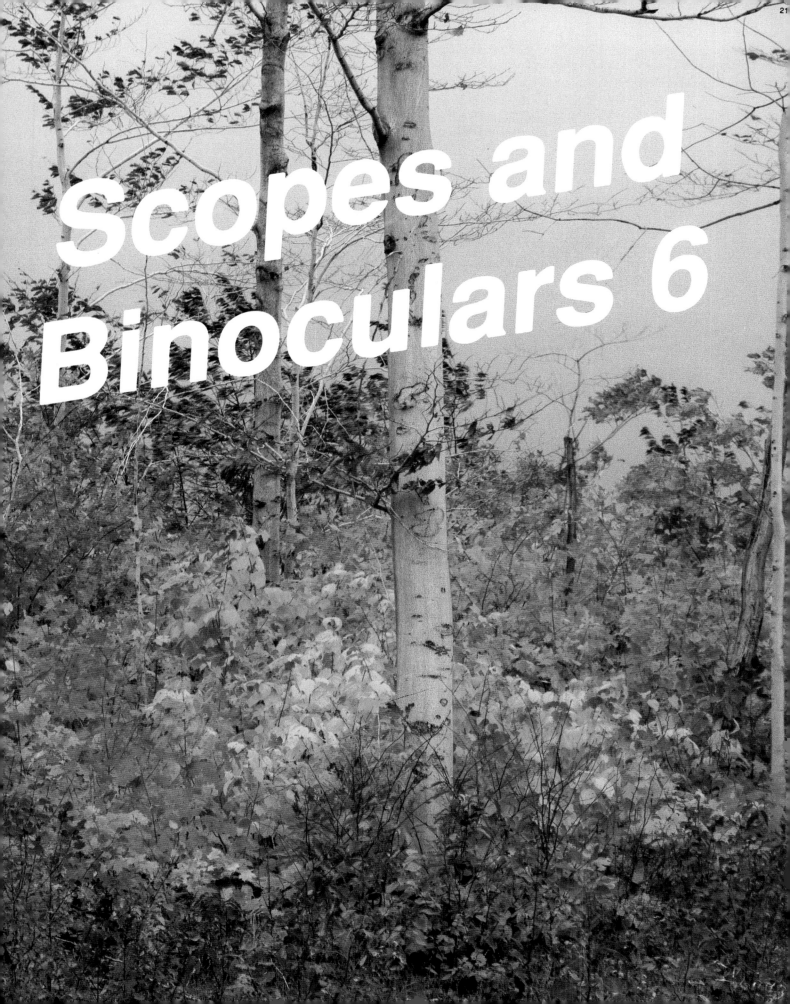

Scopes and Binoculars 6

Ammunition & Accessories 7

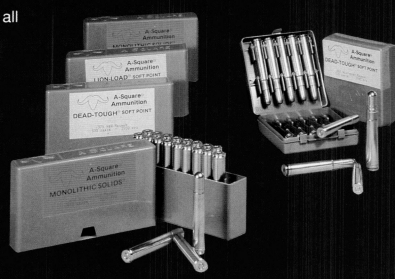

200% expansion drops game on the double.

For bull-stopping power, it's tough to beat Federal rifle cartridges loaded with Hi-Shok® bullets. All Hi-Shok bullets feature a precisely tapered jacket that ensures excellent initial penetration, plus mushroom expansion up to 200% of the original bullet diameter. So a 30 caliber Hi-Shok bullet expands through its target to a 60 caliber mushroom. And if that doesn't drop your game, nothing will.

This season, try a box of Federal ammunition with Hi-Shok bullets. In the red box with the diagonal stripes.

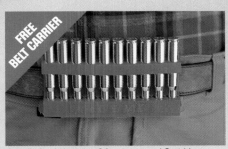

FREE BELT CARRIER

Only Federal gives you 2 free ten-round Cartridge Carriers™ in every box. Wear on your belt or slip in a pocket to keep ammo handy, quiet and secure.

FEDERAL®
THE DRIVING FORCE IN AMMUNITION.

Federal Cartridge Company
Anoka, MN 55303

MADE IN THE U.S.A.

© F.C.C. 1988

Shock power

Choosing the right cartridge for African game hunting

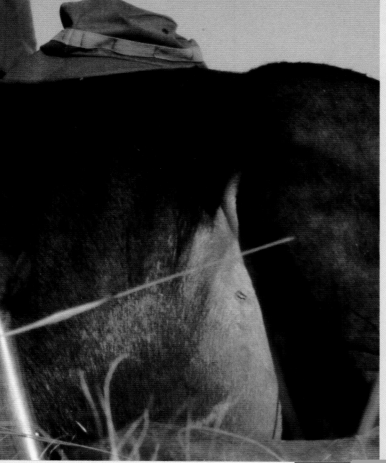

by Art Alphin

Cartridge Choices

The conventional wisdom for unlimited hunting in Africa recommends three rifles: a light, a medium and a heavy. Thus equipped, it is hard to go far wrong. However, some countries now limit a hunter to two rifles. Even where not so limited, a two-rifle battery is cheaper and more convenient. Certain considerations must be kept in mind when selecting a two-rifle battery.

African game is, as a rule, tougher and more tenacious than game anywhere else on earth. Further, the days of Karamajo Bell are *over*. The game is wary of man, and far more alert. The trophy hunter may not get second and third chances. He may well travel 15,000 miles for a kudu and have his *one* trophy kudu for three seconds through the brush on a raking shot. These conditions — the wary and tenacious game and the possibly difficult shots — place a premium on good bullets and powerful cartridges.

A complicating factor in the choice of cartridges and bullets is the terrain involved. In Southwest Africa, South Africa, and certain parts of other countries, the range on light and medium game can easily exceed 300 yards. Yet in other areas, such as Zimbabwe and Zambia, the bush is quite thick and range may be limited to 150 yards or less. In all probability, *you will have more close range shots than you expect.* Trouble can result if poor bullets are coupled with a high-velocity cartridge. At close range, bullets may break up and not penetrate to the vitals.

Of all factors in anchoring African game, penetration is *key*. The bullet may have to penetrate one or two feet into the animal before even reaching the vitals. In such cases, high velocity and rapid expansion can frequently fail miserably. It is better to penetrate clean through than not far enough. While entrance wounds close over, exit wounds let blood out and air in. Consequently, use tough

expanding bullets, or if in doubt use solids.

Those hunters taking elephant, rhino, hippo and buffalo must have a heavy rifle in .416 or larger. The choice here is determined by the trade-off between recoil and proficiency in placing the first shot. For those who are recoil shy, either the .416, the .450 Ackley, the .458 Lott, or the .460 Short A-Square are good

Two-Gun Combinations

Conditions	Rifle #1	Rifle #2
Long range acceptable, dangerous game not a factor	7mm Magnum or .300 Magnum	.375 H&H
Long range probable, dangerous game to be taken	.300 Magnum	.416 Hoffman or .416 Rigby
Average terrain, dangerous game not a factor	.30-06	.375 H&H
Average terrain, dangerous game to be taken	.338 Win or .340 Wby	.416 bore or .450 bore
Safari primarily for dangerous game	.338 bore or .375 H&H	.450 bore or .500

cartridges. For seasoned riflemen *only,* the .460 Weatherby and .500 A-Square are good. If versatility is required, then a .416 must be chosen. It has enough bullet to transmit the shock necessary on dangerous game, yet has flat enough trajectory and low enough recoil for use on other game. Rifles in .450 bore and larger are best for dangerous game, but they lack versatility for reasonable use on medium and non-dangerous game. In all cases, practice before the hunt is essential.

The shooter must also remember that his professional hunter would like to live to a ripe old age. He does not want to follow wounded, dangerous game that someone else has stuffed up. Those who take an inadequate rifle for use on dangerous game are placing an undue burden on their professional hunter. They are forcing him into back-up shots and increasing the probability of follow-ups on wounded animals. In short, they are playing russian roulette with their professional hunter's life.

Given all these considerations, a two-gun battery must be carefully chosen. Some good combinations are listed above.

In all cases, back-up sighting systems are essential and an extra scope, already set up in mounting range, is an excellent idea.

In the final analysis, shooters must make decisions based on their marksmanship, the terrain, and the game to be taken. If you put a good bullet with the most power practical in the right place on the first shot, you will come home a happy hunter.

Ballistics

A hunter going to Africa is required to choose his cartridges but is only given the scantest of data. The only commonly available measure of effectiveness is kinetic energy. In and of

Supplies 8

When I need my photo taken . . .
I give my guide my CONTAX camera

Sherman Hines

CONTAX 167MT

Vario-Sonnar 3.4/35-70 · Carl Zeiss

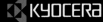

FROM THE ROCKIES...

SHERMAN HINES INSISTS
ON USING FUJICHROME FOR SUPERB COLOR AND CLARITY

 **FUJICOLOR** *SUPER HR*

IT'S LIKE CARRYING
YOUR SLR AND 3 DIFFERENT LENSES.
INTRODUCING THE FUJI DL-400 TELE.

35mm
To shoot a scene.

70mm
For a portrait.

Macro
For ultra-close creative shots.

The camera you see above is the ultimate in tele-wide cameras.

The new Fuji DL-400 Tele has a 35mm wide angle lens which you can automatically switch over to a second lens, a 70mm telephoto. That's a full 2x magnification difference.

And that's just the beginning.

The DL-400 Tele offers automatic "macro" focusing in the tele-mode to 19.5 inches. So you can shoot those artistic ultra-close shots without changing lenses.

Plus the DL-400 Tele has a built-in self-activating flash with our exclusive built-in diffuser in the wide-mode and a pop-up automatic flash in the tele-mode.

In addition, with the DL-400's "Landscape" feature, you can override the autofocus and shoot breathtaking scenery right through your car's glass.

What's more, the DL-400 Tele has Fuji's exclusive Drop-In Loading.

Our ingenius "Prewind" that rewinds the film back into the cassette for safe keeping. An 8-function LCD display panel. A lithium battery. And a free roll of quality Fuji Super HR Film.

So keep a DL-400 Tele in your camera bag right next to your SLR. Only don't be surprised if you use the 400 a lot more often.

DROP-IN

FUJI CAMERAS

How to improve your

Hunt Photographs

by Sherman Hines, master photographer

In my short association with the big game hunting industry, I have become quite aware that the industry lacks good quality photography, both from the outfitters and the hunters.

I will cover most major questions and problems having to do with photographing your trophy animal.

First things first:

CAMERA

Any camera will do, but one that has interchangeable lenses is ideal. 35 mm, full frame, is best; any make is fine. Even the Fuji 35 mm throwaway camera is excellent value at $9.95 (Cdn.). It's not the camera, but how you use it!

FILM

Negative film: For prints only. Never use ISO film speed more than 200, no matter what the salesman at the camera shop tells you. You DON'T NEED IT. Also, it's so grainy it makes miserable

The big question is: negative or slide film? What you need for your personal use will provide the answer. If you want only prints, then buy negative film. If it's for brochures, then use positive slide film.

The reason? Quality, plus the least expensive way to do it in each case.

Slides reproduce much better in brochures and books than do photograph prints. If you want enlargements from slides, have an inter-negative made and print from that. The prints may even be better quality than if you used original negative film. Again, 200 ISO film speed is as fast as you will need. I personally use Fuji film because I get excellent results. A quality inter-neg costs $10.00 to $20.00 from a professional lab, and the prints will be superb. If you have slides and need a top quality print, I recommend Rivercrest Photography, 402 King St., Bridgewater, Nova Scotia B4V 1A9, tel. 902-543-0262. They guarantee quality results; they make inter-negs from slides at $15.00 US, and beautiful 20" x 30"

(Left) Bright sunlight gives high contrast and dark shadows. Use your flash or reflector to throw light back into the shadows to get detail. Or, when a cloud moves in front of the sun and lessens the contrast (right), you get much better detail everywhere. You may still use a flash set on a weak power.

prints.

Positive or slide film: For quality reproduction in magazine articles and brochures. Also good for audio-visual shows in Outfitter's booths at conventions.

enlargements for only $20.00 US.

The mistake most people make is that they try to get quality prints *directly* from slides, and that's just not possible. They gain contrast, and lose detail and colour.

FLASH

Outdoors, especially on sunny days, use your small flash. It's very important to use on <u>every</u> kill photo. Fill-in flash gets rid of dark eye sockets, high contrast, dull days and underexposure.

REFLECTOR

If you carry a fold-up reflector (you can buy it at any camera store) you'll get a more natural fill light, and you can see what you're doing, especially when the subject is backlit. You can use natural reflected light from buildings, clouds, sky or snow.

Notice first the effect of the POLARIZER FILTER. It darkens the sky and gives greater overall colour saturation (left). Right photo is without polarizer. Now look at the two different angles I took only seconds apart and two steps forward and to the right. Remember to take different angles <u>every</u> time.

EXPOSURE

Make several exposures of each setup. After thousands of dollars spent on getting the animal, don't begrudge the few dollars it costs to photograph it thoroughly. As a professional, *every* photo I take is bracketed (one exposure at the meter reading, then an f-stop under, then another photo an f-stop over) at different exposures, because I can't afford to <u>screw up!</u>

If you have a manual camera, take at least five photos, using different exposures each time. For example, in daylight (bright sun), using 100 ISO film speed, use 125th of a second f-16. Also do one at f-22 and one in between f-16 and f-22, then between 11 and 16, and finally a fifth exposure at f-11. Now, you're covered! You're bound to have one good exposure; in fact, you'll probably have three usable slides. Keep one, and use the others for printers or magazines.

LENS CHOICE

If only one lens is possible, a 28 mm or 35 mm wide-angle lens is your best choice. This is a kill photo lens, not for wildlife. As a second lens, a 200 mm is long enough.

POLARIZER FILTER

It protects your lens, and works simply by rotating it. You get maximum effect from the filter when the sun is 90° to the subject. The blue sky will darken, and you'll get greater colour saturation to your slides or prints. I use my polarizer on about 80% of my photographs. Get rid of the U/V and skylight filters, they're excellent little items sold by the camera stores.

Backlighting and using a gold-coloured reflector (a 36" circle that folds up to a 12" circle that's easy to carry in your pack) is one of my favourite, but among the most difficult, kinds of lighting. A reflector, held off to the side of the camera, is more controllable than a flash on the camera. Note the expressions; you don't have to make everyone look angry.

Now, down to business:

PREPARING THE KILL

Cut away bushes and brush with your knife to show the antlers.

Move the animal into a life-like position.

Pull the animal around until it faces the sun or light source (for example, an opening in a forest) if you don't have a flash.

Clean up blood, tuck in the tongue and close the mouth. Neat and tidy is nicer.

Position animals without antlers, such as bear, leopard or lion, to best show its size.

Prop up or hold up the head to show the trophy.

YOU HAVE FOUR CHOICES FOR A PHOTOGRAPH:
1) Hunter with animal;
2) Animal with hunter;
3) Animal and hunter share importance;
4) A product with animal and hunter, most likely a rifle or scope.

In #1, the hunter is in front and is equal to, or more important than, the kill. In shot #2, the animal is most important and the hunter is secondary. In shot #3, the two are equally important; in #4, the emphasis is on the product. This, of course, is a special case.

Let's face it, you know what the hunter looks like; each time in each photo he or she is the same, but the kill is different each time.

FEATURE THE ANIMAL!

POSITIONING THE HUNTER WITH TROPHY

<u>STEP ONE</u>: Get behind your trophy. Have it between you and

These are both photographs of people using the animal as a prop.

It is not always necessary to do the "look-into-the-camera" mug shot. Try a few with the subject, in this photo Holly Smith, looking away from the camera. Make sure it's a good angle for the animal.

These two photos were taken at about the same time. The left photo was taken into the light without fill light; it produced a poor photo. I made the photo

on the right by reversing the position 180° to the other side, thus putting the sun behind me. It's brighter and has much better colour.

the camera. Control your rifle; keep it with you (unless you are endorsing it: then it must be more prominent).

<u>STEP TWO</u>: SMILE! Don't blow the photo at this point. Look pleasant and relaxed. Hunters often look mean and nasty, and you can improve your image as a hunter by looking happy about acquiring your trophy.

<u>STEP THREE</u>: Check the background for sticks, trees, or anything objectionable protruding from the hunter's or guide's head. Hunters don't need antlers.

POSITIONING THE PHOTOGRAPHER

Take several different angles to make sure you have the best one. Try high, low, normal, side and frontal. That's five angles, each one at five exposures, for a total of 25 photos. What the hell! Spend 15 minutes and $15.00 on film. You won't be sorry.

Nothing takes the fun out of showing off your trophies faster than lousy, out-of-focus photos.

TAKING THE PHOTO

Frame the viewer <u>carefully</u> on the subject, making sure the f-stop (depth of focus) is sufficient for the animal *and* the hunter to be sharply in focus. Use f-16 or f-22 if there is enough light. <u>DO NOT</u> try to hand-hold your camera at a shutter-speed lower than 1/30th of a second. Use your sporting scope tripod for your camera.

SQUEEZE the button on your camera <u>exactly</u> the same way you squeeze your trigger; you don't want to move your camera any more than your rifle. After you've done all this, you'll be rewarded with sharper, more interesting, better quality photos that will really feature your hunt.

Cont'd on page 240

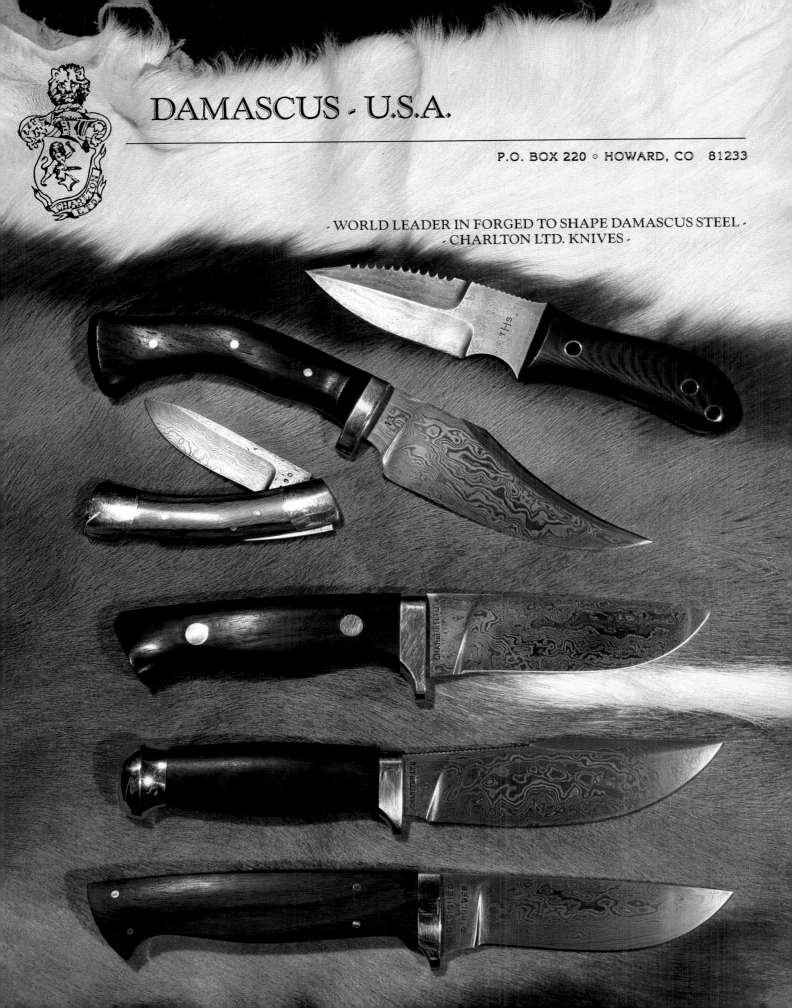

DAMASCUS - U.S.A.

P.O. BOX 220 ○ HOWARD, CO   81233

- WORLD LEADER IN FORGED TO SHAPE DAMASCUS STEEL -
- CHARLTON LTD. KNIVES -

Kustom Krafted Knives

Alex J. Collins has for many years designed many of the most creative and innovative custom knives in the industry. Respected by his contemporaries, Alex has consistently won awards for his knives. For a personal design, write or call Alex and he will produce a knife that will give you excellent value and lasting pleasure.

Alex J. Collins

K.K.K. Co.
1834 W. Burbank Blvd.
Burbank, Calif. 91506
(818) 840-8400

(Improve your photos continued from p. 236)

(Above and right) Use a telephoto lens for a change of pace. Above I did a self-portrait using a 210 mm lens, wide open at f-3.5; that makes the background out of focus. Above, I used a tripod; at right, I got the low angle by simply sitting my camera on the snow.

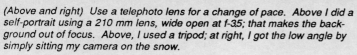

(Left and above) Environmental kill photos are always a nice departure from just filling the frame with hunter and animal. Show <u>where</u> you took the animal; show the land and how you got there.

The importance of ANGLES cannot be overemphasized. Going low, as in bottom left, features the animal; going high, as in bottom right, shows that spread. At top left, we have a medium angle, which is about what we normally do. At top right, by going in close we use the wide angle lens (28 mm) to slightly distort the rack of horns. Going in close also serves to make the animal appear larger relative to the hunter.

Art Alphin sells rifles, and this kill shot is perfect to that end. This photo says to the viewer, "Here is a photo of the rifle I used to kill this animal." That's fine: the emphasis is on the rifle because it's the subject. The animal is secondary, and the hunter is third in line for attention.

242

ACTION-PACKED
VIDEO CASSETTES
Brilliantly photographed and narrated by Sportsman/Photographer George Klucky

As the man behind the camera, George Klucky narrates each adventure as it unfolds . . . the triumphs, the disappointments, the touches of humor. These videos are unique . . . the **real thing** . . . no faked sequences. George Klucky captures the "moment of truth" between the hunter and his quarry.

VIDEO TAPES NOW AVAILABLE
African Safari with Irvin Barnhart
Where the Salmon and Trout are King
Spring Black Bear in NB Canada with Al King
The Challenge of the Eastern Wild Turkey
Ruger Presents Alaska
Utah Mountain Lion
Trophy Caribou Hunting
Johny Johnson's Big 4 Safari
Lord of the Tundra
Thomas & Thomas Presents Labrador
Alaskan Rainbow Trout and Silver Salmon
Riley's Alaskan Brown Bear
Lynn Castles, Unalakeet River Lodge, Alaska
Hunting with Larry Rivers, Alaska
Grizzly and Moose Hunting in the Talkeetna Mtns., Alaska

GEORGE KLUCKY

Throughout his life George pursued his interest in nature and the sport of hunting and fishing. His travels through North America, Canada and Africa expanded his awareness of others who shared his enthusiasm. In 1969 George started filming his adventures and those of his colleagues. Klucky's footage has appeared on television in the United States and Canada. His films are backed by narration with music highlighting the sound track of the events and catches he captures on film. George is a renowned guest speaker, presenting his films and experiences to sports clubs and fund raisers. He's a regular on national television wildlife programs and is a reoccuring guest on *Call of the Outdoors, Cabin Fever,* and *Woods and Waters.* His films are currently on tour throughout Canada and the Northeastern United States.

ORDER FROM: Wilderness Adventures
311 North Street, Room #11
Pittsfield, MA 01201
(413) 443-1510

GEORGE
KLUCKY
WILDERNESS ADVENTURES

ACTION PACKED HUNTING AND FISHING FILMS . . .

"Klucky never misses the shot."
Ted Williams
Renown Fly Fisherman

Dear Sportsman,

The North American Outdoorsman is proud to present, to you, the most exciting and highest production-quality videos in the marketplace today. N.A.O.'s cameras will go afield, each year, to bring home the beauty and excitement we all seek and share in the great outdoors. Our programs are committed to portraying sound conservation practices and good sportsmanship, as well.

At last, affordable, high adventure, high quality outdoor videos within reach of all who love the land and water, and all it has to offer. Comments from our viewers will continue to serve as a guideline for the subject matter of our future shows. The North American Outdoorsman's pledge is to provide the type and quality videos you deserve.

Arnold Alward
President

Rocky Mountain Rainbows and Arctic Goose Hunt

High in Alberta's Canadian Rockies for Rainbow Trout provides action so fast above and below the surface you will be reaching for a net.

We then head north to James Bay to hunt Blue Geese. The Cree Indian guides will share with you proven hunting methods that have stood the test of time.

Three Trout to Dream About and Minipi's Discovery

On a single cast with three flies on his leader, Lee Wulff hooks and then lands three great Brook Trout totalling seventeen pounds in weight.

In Minipi's Discovery, you will fly into that great fishing area with Lee in his seaplane when he alone had cast a fly in those magnificent trout waters.

Flashing Silver

The Queen Charlotte Islands off British Columbia lie in the path of the annual Coho migration. These great bays and inlets provide fly fishermen with the type of action that separate fish tales from fantasies. You'll witness a majestic Bald Eagle that competes with the anglers for these silvery beauties. Unbelievable jumping action and spectacular underwater photography.

San Juan River Tarpon and A World Record Marlin

Fly fish for Tarpon with Jack Nicklaus, Curt Gowdy and Lee Wulff and watch two young native lads take one in their own inimitable style.

Lee Wulff takes a world's record Striped Marlin, on a fly, in Ecuador and lands a 148 pounder on a twelve pound test leader tippet. Narrated by Curt Gowdy.

Dead River Rough Cut

Two Maine woodsmen in a remote wilderness area...living in the last tarpaper remains of a former German prisoner of war camp, hunting, trapping, and logging with a team of oxen. Running counterpoint to the sync-action of the movie are their reflections on women, politics, death and taxes. Red Ribbon, American Film Festival. (some profanity).

Leaping Silver and Atlantic Salmon Angling Techniques

Joan Wulff demonstrates the fine art of fly casting for Atlantic Salmon on a Labrador river. Lee Wulff shows his techniques for playing, landing and releasing a 24 lb. salmon taken on a #16 fly.

Autumn Silver

In Autumn Silver, Joan and Lee Wulff fish for Atlantic Salmon on a Nova Scotia river, the Stewiake, in October when the fall foliage is at its peak, as brilliant as the leaps of the salmon. You'll see good casting, high leaping fish, and a beautiful sequence of fishing in a silvery fog that drifts in from the sea. This film won the "Teddy" award as Best Fishing Film of 1980.

Moose and Caribou in Newfoundland

Lee Wulff hunts the wild interior of the island of Newfoundland for the native Caribou and the lordly Moose. Go out to hunt each day from a lonely tent camp and thrill to the sight of the great game animals in their unspoiled terrain. A beautiful hunting film with great shots of magnificent animals.

With Camera and Gun in Newfoundland

Camera and Gun in Newfoundland lets the viewer judge whether Lee Wulff, the hunter, or his wife, the photographer, has the best of the sport. They end up with both steaks and photographs...among them one of the only known pictures of white Bull Moose. Magnificent shots of Moose and Caribou to be enjoyed by hunter and non-hunter alike.

The Way it Was: Angling in Newfoundland, 1938-1940

You'll see wild trout in schools, sea-run Brook Trout and the magnificent spectacle of the once fabulous run of salmon leaping Humber Falls. This is a film to make old-timers remember what it was like "back then" and newer generations wish they could, somehow, have been there to enjoy it.

Big Northern Pike

Northern Ontario when seen from the air seems to have more water than land. Lee and Joan Wulff fly into this great wilderness with big Walleye and Northern Pike on their mind. Sinclair Cheechew will host our visiting anglers on Kesagami Lake where the water is always cool and fishing hot!

Where the Biggest Bluefins Swim

The present World's record tuna was caught in the Strait of Canso in the Province of Nova Scotia. Lee Wulff, then in his 77th year, will show you that catching big tuna is not just a young man's game, but one of skill and endurance rather than great strength. Lee lands a 960 pounder on a 130 lb. test line. This film won the "Teddy" as best fishing film for 1983.

To order: North American Video, Box 102, Hardour Road, Kittery Point, Maine 03905   207-439-3739

THE NORTH AMERICAN OUTDOORSMAN®

THE NORTH AMERICAN OUTDOORSMAN® Video Selections

Whitetail
In Whitetail we join Lee Wulff on a deer hunt in the fall splendor of the New England woods. Share in the lore of hunting with Lee and then the drama and excitement as he stalks a rare and elusive White Buck, while his companion experiences the frustrations and final triumph of his first hunt. Some of the finest Whitetail footage ever filmed.

Soliloquy to a Salmon and The Atlantic Salmon
Soliloquy to a Salmon reflects Lee Wulff's thoughts as he plays and releases an eighteen pound Atlantic Salmon on Quebec's St. Jean River. Many consider this 1965 "Teddy" award winning film to be Lee's finest. Lee also brings in a seventeen pound fish using only the three foot tip of his fly rod to accomplish it. This takes place in beautiful Newfoundland.

Courageous Lake Caribou
The barren grounds in Canada's N.W.T. liven when the Bathurst herd migrates south. Leonard Clarke harvests a fine trophy and Albert Fish dresses it in a manner seldom seen in the outside world. You'll see virgin fishing for Lake Trout, Pike and Arctic Grayling. The action above and below the surface will have you wiping the smell of fish from your hands.

Giant Tuna, Small Boat
Travel with Lee Wulff to the coastal waters of Newfoundland's Notre Dame Bay. You'll see Lee troll for these great sea rovers from a sixteen foot Boston Whaler and hook and land a 650 pound Bluefin on an 80 lb. test line. Follow their small boat far offshore into a storm as they finally capture and release another great Bluefin out where the icebergs drift down from Labrador.

Big 3 in Newfoundland
It's the peak of the rut and the moose are on the move! Woodland Caribou are getting herding tendencies, and Black Bear are at their peak weight. Arnold Alward is in pursuit of a trophy Bull Moose. Bob Costas is licensed for all three big game animals. Their hardy trek over the Long Range Mountains will etch exciting memories, not only for themselves, but for all those who view this exciting video.

Ungava Char
Ungava Bay is an inland sea in northern Quebec's sub-Arctic. The Payne and Tunilik Rivers feed this great bay and provide a watery highway for Arctic Char returning to spawn. Russ Carpenter and Sammy Cantafio take you above and below the surface to witness the evasive action that Char are famous for.

To Ecuador for Marlin
Joan and Lee Wulff probe the Humbolt Current for Striped Marlin and Pacific Sailfish. Joan plays a Striped Marlin that makes fifteen consecutive jumps in a single run of the camera. Share the excitement when Lee casts to surfacing marlin with a light outfit, his thrill when he hooks a big Black Marlin on his light tackle.

Upland Gunner
Go afield in the grouse and woodcock coverts of Maine's colorful autumn, to a Georgia plantation to see coveys of quail roar into flight over a fine pointing dog, hunt ringneck pheasants in Oregon where that great game bird was introduced to America. See excellent dog work and shotgunning at a snow-covered game farm in Missouri.

Atlantic Salmon at Helen's Falls
The George River in Quebec's sub-Arctic draws one of the largest migrations of salmon in North America plus a migration of outdoor notables like Gene Hill, Jim Rikhoff and Tom Hennessey who cast their flies in pursuit of this silvery treasure. Arctic Char will thrill the viewer with the fastest surface and underwater action ever filmed.

The Fly Fisherman's World
Travel with Lee Wulff to Montana to fish for trout with a delicate six foot fly rod, and to Labrador where he challenges a great Atlantic Salmon on the same featherweight rod. Join him in the Florida Keys to land a hundred and thirty pound Tarpon and continue on to Pinas Bay, Panama, to share the thrill of playing and subduing a high leaping, deep diving, Pacific Sailfish.

Mistassini for Me
Art and Kris Lee share the happiness and heartbreaks when fishing for trophy Northern Pike. Charley Jolly takes you below the surface to show you what kind of spunk big Lake Trout have. Joe Loon goes off the beaten path where 4 and 5 lb. Brook Trout are caught with consistency. A fishing tale that fell prey to our cameras for all to enjoy.

Minipi Trout
Fly along in Lee Wulff's supercub as he and Curt Gowdy go in to fish untouched waters in the great Minipi Basin of Labrador. Lee discovered that most fabulous Brook Trout area of the Canadian north and took Curt in with him to share that miraculous fishing before it became known. You'll see big wild Brook Trout in flashing action.

Hit the High Trail to Adventure with: Curt Gowdy, Lee Wullf, Gene Hill, Jim Rikhoff and others.

SAFARI PRESS

LUDO J. WURFBAIN

QUALITY BOOKS only from SAFARI PRESS

A small selection from our fine books...

J. Mellon AFRICAN HUNTER This classic is now in its THIRD EDITION! 522 pp, 382 illus. Regarded as the most comprehensive title ever on African hunting. There are fifty-two chapters on twenty countries and over 200 animals included in this large-format book. This is THE STANDARD reference work on Africa -- don't be left without! $105.00 post paid.

E. Foa AFTER BIG GAME IN CENTRAL AFRICA 330 pp, 29 plates, numerous text illus, limited to 1,000 copies. Edouard Foa was the premier collector for the Paris National Museum. He pursued his game in the area of what is today Tanzania and Zambia. Much on the elephant and the other members of the big five, as well as the plains game. REDUCED to $45.00 (was $75.00).

R. Ruark HORN OF THE HUNTER The story of an African hunt. 315 pp, 50 photos. Ruark's most sought-after book is back in print. No other book gives you the "feel" of Africa like this book can. Ruark will take you to the land that every hunter longs to see. Here in the jungles and the plains, the reader comes to know the ferocity of the wounded buffalo, the acid sweat of fear. $35.00.

T. Bulpin THE HUNTER IS DEATH 348 pp, illus. The life story of George Rushby, professional ivory hunter, adventurer and the hunter who killed the man-eating lions of the Njombe district in Northern Rhodesia (today Zambia). This is the only book on the life of this famous ivory hunter, prospector, adventurer and poacher who killed as many elephants as Neumann, Sutherland, Bell and Taylor. $30.00.

C. Boddington FROM MT. KENYA TO THE CAPE -- Ten Years of African Hunting 288pp, over 100 pictures. Spanning a single decade, this book takes you from Kenya to Southwest Africa, Zimbabwe, Zambia, South Africa and Botswana. Boddington tells us about the Africa of today in 19 different hunting areas. Covered are the big five, and plains game such as kudu, sable and sitatunga. The appendices will also give you tips on rifles, cartirdges, equipment and how to plan a safari. $32.50.

To order, send price of the book plus $2.25 P&H to Safari Press, P.O. Box 3095, Long Beach, CA 90803, USA. Or call in your order toll free: 1-800-451-4788 (in CA 213-430-3693, in Canada 1-800-848-5649). 8am to 5pm Pacific Time. VISA & MC accepted.

ALL OUR BOOKS 100% SATISFACTION GUARANTEED OR YOUR MONEY BACK!

Send $2.00 for our large 1989 catalogue of books and videos. Free with purchase.

WE DISTRIBUTE THE HUNTERS GUIDE TO PROFESSIONAL OUTFITTERS IN THE US, AFRICA AND EUROPE.

By appointment to H.R.H. The Duke of Edinburgh, Rifle Makers

HOLLAND & HOLLAND
LIMITED
Incorporating Rowland Ward of Knightsbridge Ltd.

33 BRUTON STREET · LONDON W1X 8JS
Tel: 01-499 4411 Cables: Armourer London W1 Telex: 269021 Gunner G

HOLLAND & HOLLAND ARE NOW KNOWN FOR MORE THAN THEIR GUNS AND RIFLES

For over one hundred and fifty years Holland & Holland big game and stalking rifles have been used all over the world -- from the Highlands of Scotland and the Himalayas to the jungles of India, Africa and South America and in the frozen wastes of the North American continent. Today, in addition to their world renowned guns and rifles, Holland & Holland offer a complete range of shooting clothing and accessories. The instructors from the Holland & Holland Shooting School, who make frequent instructional visits to America, have a deservedly high reputation. A visit to Holland & Holland will help you to prepare for every kind of hunting expedition. Please write for our new Gun and Rifle Price Lists, our Shooting and Clothing and Accessories Catalogue and the Holland & Holland Shooting School folder.

I AM SAMURAI

I AM UNIQUE
With a 3X built-in power zoom, I allow you to capture expressions and natural poses like no other point and shoot camera. Real snapshots of real life. My date back even allows you to record the date on every photograph.

I AM SIMPLICITY
Completely automatic, I focus and will compensate for back-light situations. I even decide when the flash is needed. My shape is ergonomically designed to fit the palm of your hand, like no other 35mm camera on the market today.

I AM THE NEW CONCEPT CAMERA
That introduces a revolutionary vertical film transport system, known as "Double 35" which enables you to get twice the pictures from every roll of film. SAMURAI: designed to make the most of every picture taking opportunity.

Double 35 SAMURAI

For more information on this exciting new concept contact:
KYOCERA CANADA INC.
7470 Bath Rd., Mississauga, Ont. L4T 1L2
(416) 671-4300

KYOCERA

THE NEW CONCEPT, DOUBLE 35 CAMERA

In *HUNTERS GUIDE to PROFESSIONAL OUTFITTERS*, the hunting season never ends. Each ad, each feature, every annual issue is entirely devoted to your interests as a big game hunter/sportsman.

Each edition takes you to the hunting continents of the world. Find out where to bag the best elephants, leopards, caribou, elk, sheep, pronghorns, bears and so much more. HUNTERS GUIDE provides a wealth of knowledge and explodes with magnificent photography. HUNTERS GUIDE introduces you to the legendary safari outfitters of Africa, Canada, the United States, Europe and Australia: Cotton Gordon, Robin Hurt, Lynn Castle, Glacier Guides, Nimrod Safaris, Spatsizi, Faunafrika, Hunting Spain...plus everything else you need to be a successful big game hunter.

Published by:
THE HUNTER'S GUIDE
17 Prince Arthur Avenue
Toronto, Ontario, Canada M5R 1B2
(416) 967-4319

Big game hunters/sportsmen who demand an up-to-date source book -- HUNTERS GUIDE is the book for you!

- **Big Game Outfitters**
- **Upland Game & Waterfowl Outfitters**
- **Fishing Outfitters**
- **Booking Agents**
- **Ammunition**
- **Rifles & Accessories**
- **Scopes & Binoculars**
- **Art & Investment**
- **Outfitters Directory**
- **Taxidermists**
- **Supplies**

HUNTERS GUIDE
TO
PROFESSIONAL OUTFITTERS

WORLDWIDE 1989 EDITION

HUNTERS GUIDE
TO
PROFESSIONAL OUTFITTERS

WORLDWIDE 1990 EDITION

FINALLY...
a source of outfitters and suppliers in a permanent form! No other book like it in the WORLD!

Taxidermists 9

First Place Winner —
Open Division 1988
FNAWS Taxidermy
Competition

DYNAMIC...DISTINCTIVE...
Personally Designed
for your Trophy Room

Animal Artistry

BY MIKE BOYCE

3921 GREENBRIAR CT., RENO, NV 89509 • (702) 827-9006, 826-6081

Animal
Artistry

BY MIKE BOYCE

3921 GREENBRIAR CT., RENO, NV 89509

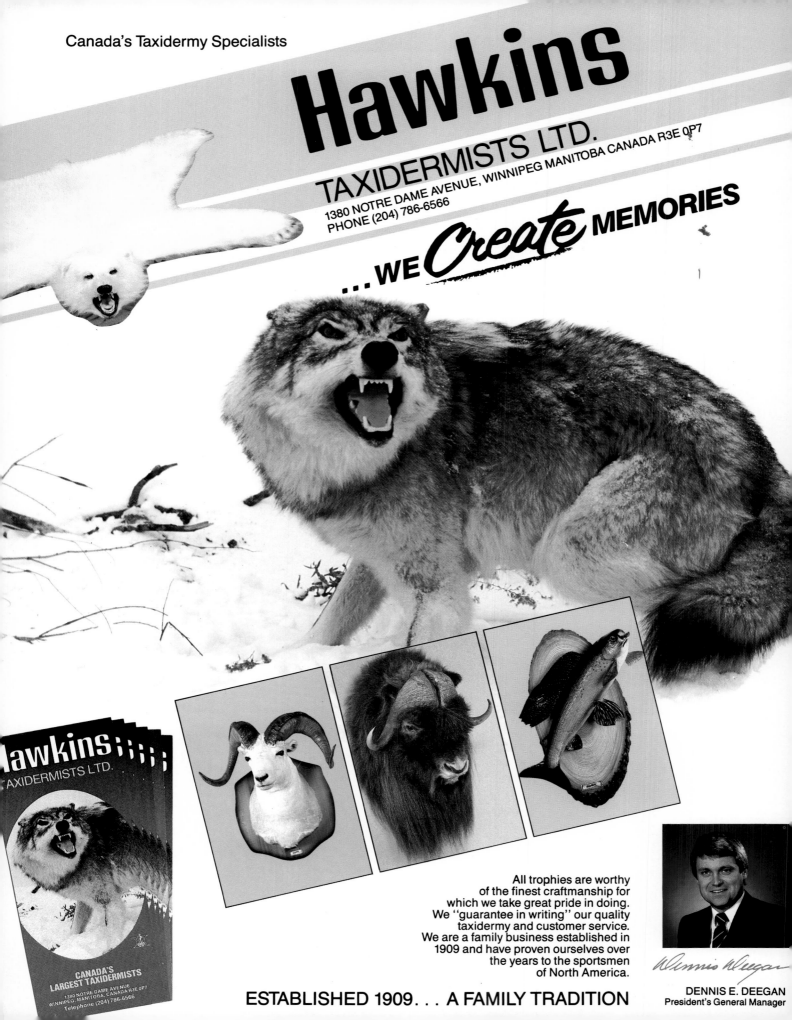

CARLSON TAXIDERMY LTD.

Serving hunters, museums and specimen buyers with high quality, lifesize big-game mounts, heads, rugs, birds, fish and novelties, since 1959

Box 329, Atlin, B.C. Canada V0W 1A0 Radio: Phone through Whitehorse - Yukon Operator JR3-7896 or JR3-7897 White Mountain Channel

The art of taxidermy is a craft few master. The taxidermist must have a keen sense of understanding regarding the actual animal or bird to be mounted.

We have a proven record of capturing the spirit of the subject and reflecting it in a finished product.

Taxidermy calls for a variety of skills. Our craftsmen sculpture mannequins, then stretch the hides upon them. We oil tan skins, taking 3 months to allow for best results and no cracking. These are just some of the things that add up to the perfect creation.

For the past 20 years, we have helped the autumn hunter and the serious safari gamesman alike.

We invite the local hunter to visit our facilities prior to going out on the hunt. Upon their visit, hunters will have the opportunity to view the care given to the ''prizes'' we create.

We know you respect and cherish the winged, webbed, and furred creatures of the wild. We give your trophy the same respect — taking the time necessary to create a quality masterwork.

CONROE TAXIDERMY

Rt. 1, Box 282 AS
Conroe, Texas 77385

25908 I-45 N
Spring, Texas 77386

(713) 367-2745

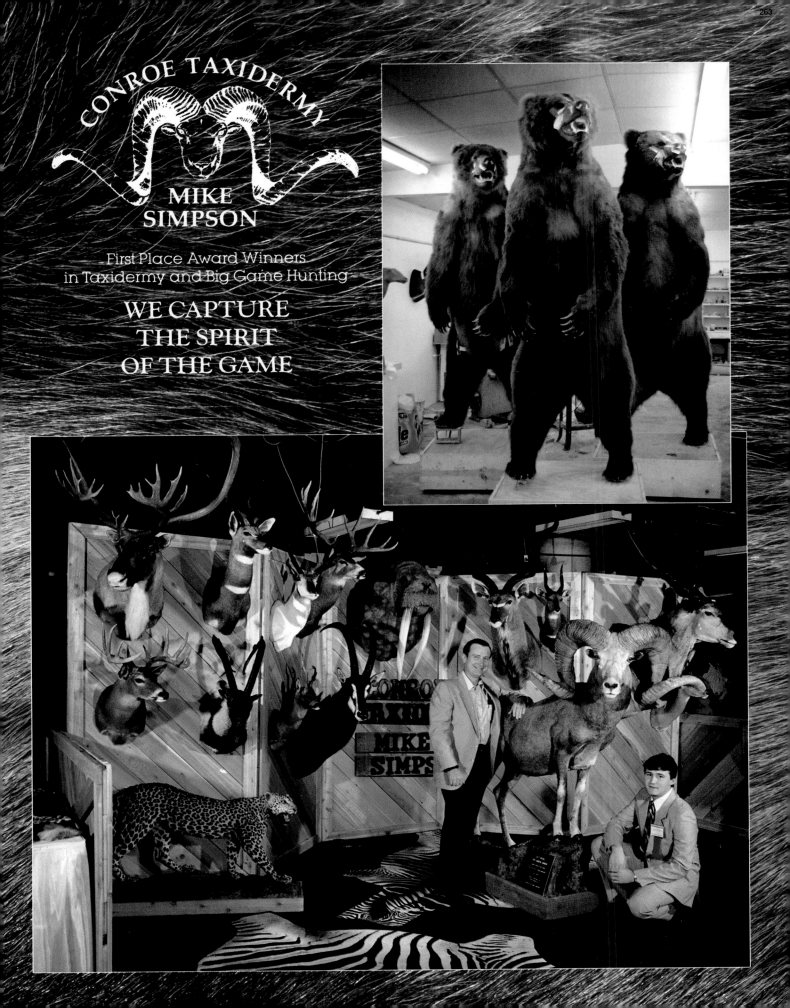

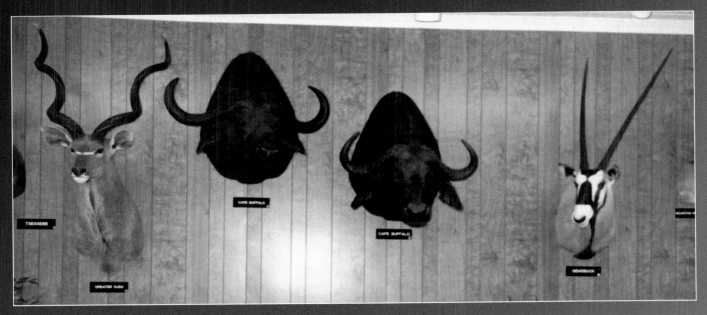

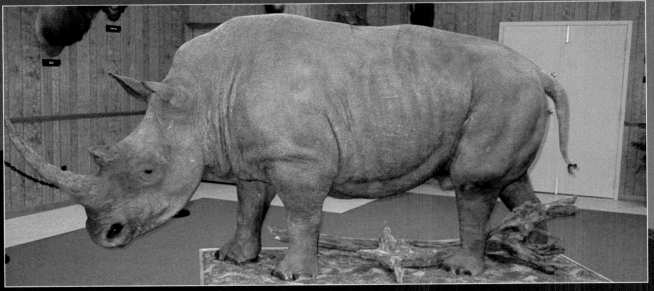

The art of taxidermy is a craft few master. The taxidermist must have a keen sense of understanding regarding the actual animal or bird to be mounted.

We have a proven record of capturing the spirit of the subject and reflecting it in a finished product.

Taxidermy calls for a variety of skills. Our craftsmen sculpture mannequins, then stretch the hides upon them. We oil tan skins, taking 3 months to allow for best results and no cracking. These are just some of the things that add up to the perfect creation.

For the past 20 years, we have helped the autumn hunter and the serious safari gamesman alike.

We invite the local hunter to visit our facilities prior to going out on the hunt. Upon their visit, hunters will have the opportunity to view the care given to the "prizes" we create.

We know you respect and cherish the winged, webbed, and furred creatures of the wild. We give your trophy the same respect — taking the time necessary to create a quality masterwork.

CONROE TAXIDERMY

Rt. 1, Box 282 AS
Conroe, Texas 77385

25908 I-45 N
Spring, Texas 77386

(713) 367-2745

First Place Award Winners
in Taxidermy and Big Game Hunting

**WE CAPTURE
THE SPIRIT
OF THE GAME**

Conroe **TAXIDERMY**

DEER PROCESSING
—IN BACK—

HeadsWest Taxidermy

4929 Ironton
Denver, Colorado 80239
(303) 371-8060

Capturing life in taxidermy

Uncommon animals from around the world are commonplace at HeadsWest. Record Book Trophies are entrusted to us and award winning mounts are returned in Record Time — while memories of the hunt are still fresh.

HeadsWest has in in house tannery where trophies receive individual attention by hand and never leave the studio.

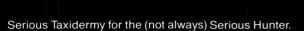

Serious Taxidermy for the (not always) Serious Hunter.

As a service to our clients HeadsWest will score trophies for Rowland Ward, Boone and Crockett, Pope and Young and Safari Club International.

GOOD HUNTING.

HeadsWest's dedication to the sport of hunting comes from the belief that proper game management is essential. We will not accept endangered animals without a CITIES Permit from the county of origin. Proof that the animal was legally taken is required for all protected animals.

GAME BIRDS • RUGS • TROPHY FISH

SACKVILLE TAXIDERMY
997 SACKVILLE DR., LOWER SACKVILLE
NOVA SCOTIA, CANADA B4E 1S3

Art and 10 Investments

Craig Bone is a wildlife artist living in a remote area of Zimbabwe, close to the Zambezi Valley. A specialist in wildlife paintings, he uses mostly oils on canvas. His time is divided between collecting material and ideas in the bush and painting at home. After leaving school in 1973, Craig studied commercial art for two years before deciding that his forte lay more in fine art than advertising. A further two years was spent exploring techniques and reaching for perfection. In 1977, Craig was drawn into the Rhodesian war that was raging in the country. He joined the elite Rhodesian Light Infantry. During this time he was injured on a military operation and was casevaced back to hospital in the capitol. Four and a half months and eight operations later, he was released form hospital. The love of painting soon saw the young artist hard at work again at the easel. Craig says, "There is only one kind of art for me -- realism with effect and atmosphere. This is the only combination worthy of a good painting." He once read that behind every artist there should be miles and miles of canvas. Craig has covered a lot of ground already and believes a lot lies ahead. He feels that "one cannot stop learning or taking on

WILDLIFE ART
BY
CRAIG BONE

P.O. BOX 35 RAFFINGORA
ZIMBABWE
AFRICA

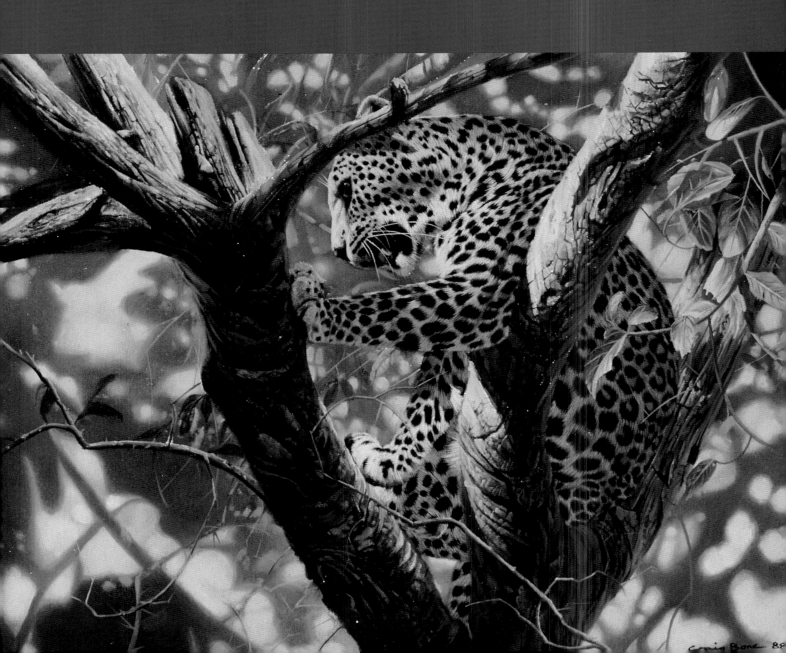

Being a hunter and outdoorsman, I have always been inspired by the beauty of nature and have tried to capture this in my subjects and material.

Dan Bridge
Box 16, Site 8 Airport
RR #1, Fort St. John
British Columbia, Canada V1J 4M6
604-785-5522

Title: 7 and 7
Size: 18" x 30"
Edition: 25

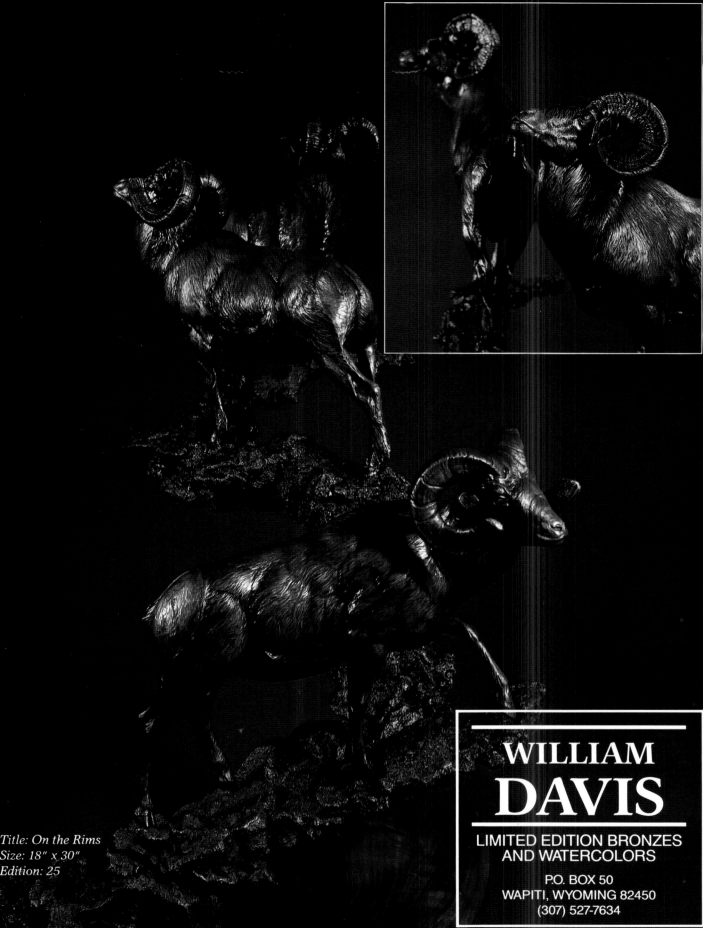

Title: *On the Rims*
Size: *18" x 30"*
Edition: *25*

Prairie Monarch
Edition: 25

Sonoran Summer
Edition: 30

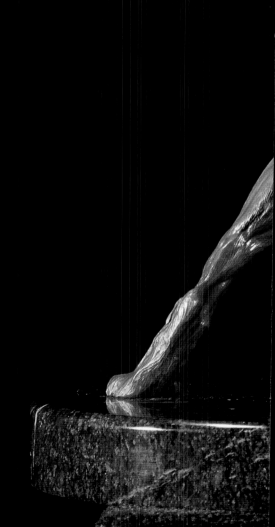

Thunder & Lightning
Edition: 25

THUNDER & LIGHTNING
BY WM. DAVIS

Trophy Hunter
Edition: 25

Bustin' It
Edition: 35

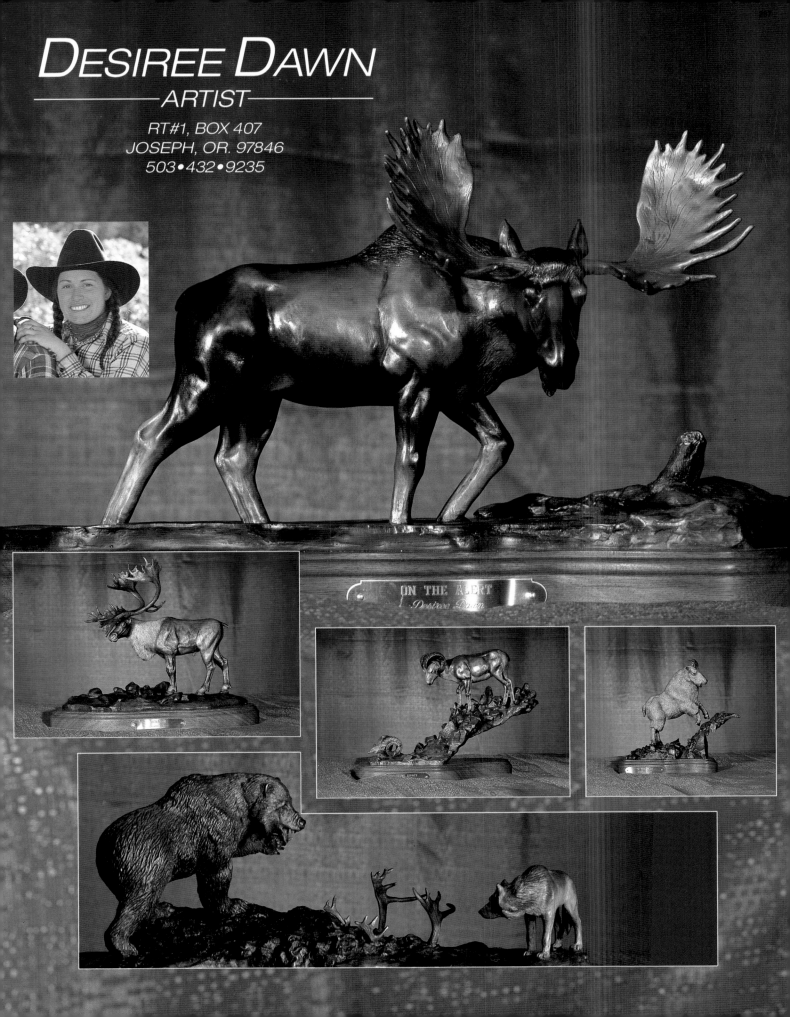

DESIREE DAWN
ARTIST

RT#1, BOX 407
JOSEPH, OR. 97846
503•432•9235

ON THE ALERT
Desiree Dawn

Romancing the Stone

Desert Nomads

Timberline Monarch

Cloud Dancers

MIKE FLANAGAN

SCULPTOR

WESTERN AND WILDLIFE ART

450 East Second P.O. Box 57 Dayton, Wyoming 82836

Mike Flanagan, nationally known sculptor and owner of the Packstring Gallery and Foundry, lives in Dayton, Wyoming. Nestled at the foot of the Big Horn Mountains, this area provides a natural setting for inspiration and research of Mike's bronzes. However, some research has found him as far north as Alaska and the Mackenzie range in the Northwest Territories of Canada. Mike specializes in western and wildlife bronzes. He handles mountain men, wild sheep and waterfowl with equal ease. He is noted for accurate detail, posture and proportion in his sculptures. Most recently, Mike has shown his special talent and sensitivity in doing the four North American Wild Sheep species in bronzes. The unique colorization through his sophisticated patina process make these wild sheep a collector's dream. Other accomplishments include a commissioned piece for the Cowboy Hall of Fame, a belt buckle for the late John Wayne, and a large portrait bronze of the renowned Wyoming Historical Painter John Clymer. Mike has had many one-man exhibits and currently takes his bronzes to major shows across the country. His sculptures can be found in many private collections throughout the US and in many foreign countries.

Great Blue Heron
28" x 14" Edition 21

Grand Slam Head Study

Grand Slam Head Study

Pintail Rhapsody

America's Pride

Track of the Grizzly

Trouble on the Wind
40" x 36" Edition 30

Lorenzo Ghiglieri

Enraged

With its great strength and treasure of ivory, this magnificent African bull elephant is enraged. This mighty pachyderm has been pushed to its limits. In a moment of great danger, he turns to face his challenge.

Now you can own a collection of truly distinctive art by Lorenzo. The intrinsic beauty of African wildlife has been captured by America's master artist in bronze limited edition sculptures. The elephant, rhino and lion, three of Africa's most exotic species are yours to collect. Settle for nothing less than these strikingly beautiful masterpieces. Discover the pleasure of collecting the best. They are authentic, of recognized value and enduring ...destined to become classics.

Enraged (23"x 30")
Edition 50 Bronze   Edition 50 Silver

In Full Charge (13"x 22")
Edition 20

Lion's Roar (16"x 26")
Edition 75 Bronze
Edition 10 Silver

Flying Home

A majestic eagle returns to its nest. Nature teaches us values of life and dramatically emphasizes the importance of our own survival.

Flying Home (60″x54″)
Edition 10

Bacchus

Bacchus reflects originality and artistic sensitivity in an exciting, exhilarating and traditional rendition in classical style.

Lorenzo's perspective and versatility are beyond the challenge of critics. He embraces inspiration and works from it, passing it on to us. As the eagle flies, his career soars. Each new bronze impression is created with mastery, accuracy and intricate detail. Lorenzo has earned the reputation of being an outstanding artist because he embraces the never ending process of creation.

Available now:
The Ghiglieri
Corporation
12993 Ehlen Road N.E.
Aurora, Oregon 97002
(503) 224-4123

Bacchus (42″x21″)
Edition 75

Bugle Call (19″x22″)
Edition 45

The rutting bull elk bugles his challenge to all rivals.

El Torro (14″x22″)
Edition 50 Bronze
Edition 50 Silver

Symbol of strength, energy and power.

The art of...

Emerging from his studio are the latest works of Lorenzo Ghiglieri. His realism and impressionism are unique in their style and cover a wide range of subjects from heroic sculpture to masterful paintings. His perspective and versatility are beyond the challenge of critics. Lorenzo embraces inspiration and works from it, thus he passes it on to us. As the eagle flies, his career soars. Ghiglieri continues to expand with energy and vigor to reach his goal and now introduces a new "Cowboy and Western Series." It is original, powerful and beautiful. Each new bronze impression is created with mastery and depicts history with accuracy and intricate detail. As Lorenzo has earned the reputation of being an outstanding artist it is because he embraces the never ending process of creation. His new heroic lion roars loudly —three times that of life...

Lion's Roar

Priced for the investing collector
Available now through:
The Ghiglieri Corporation
995 S.W. Highland Drive
Gresham, Oregon 97080
(503) 667-7776
(503) 224-4123

© All Rights Reserved 1988

Wind, Wings & Waves (Eagle) (26"X22")
Edition 50

Lorenzo Ghiglieri

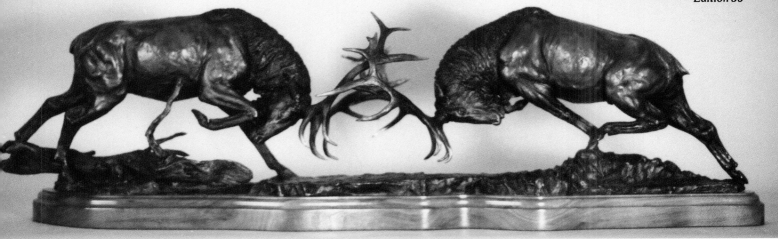

Royal Battle (Wapiti) (13"X41")
Edition 35

The Persistant General (General Howard)
(14"X17") Edition 45

Fight No more (Chief Joseph) (15"X17")
Edition 45

Vaquero (First Cowboy) (14"X17")
Edition 45

Powerful Exchange (Bull-N-Bear) (21"X32")
Edition 50

Lorenzo Ghiglieri

New*
Flight of
Glory

Lorenzo's beautiful eagle sculptures have become world renowned. This stunning eagle is the most recent of 32 unique interpretations of our national symbol and it represents a new beginning to our endeavors at home, in the world and in space. Enrich your collection with this sculpture "Flight of Glory," cast in approximately 395 troy ounces of .999 fine silver.

Available now through:
The Ghiglieri Corporation
12993 Ehlen Road N.E.
Aurora, Oregon 97002
(503) 224-4123

Flight of Glory (25"x22")
Edition 50 Bronze
Edition 50 Silver

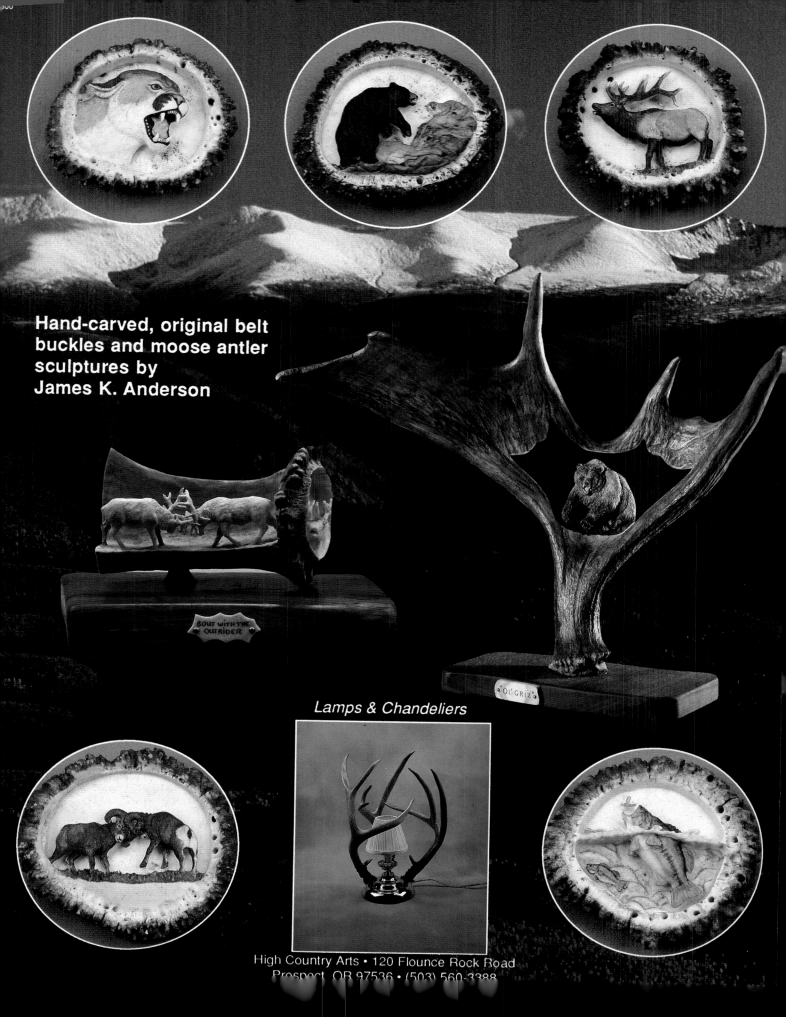

Hand-carved, original belt
buckles and moose antler
sculptures by
James K. Anderson

Lamps & Chandeliers

High Country Arts • 120 Flounce Rock Road
Prospect, OR 97536 • (503) 560-3388

HIGH COUNTRY ARTS

Presenting the artists' interpretations of the rugged beauty of the high country through wildlife carvings and sculpture

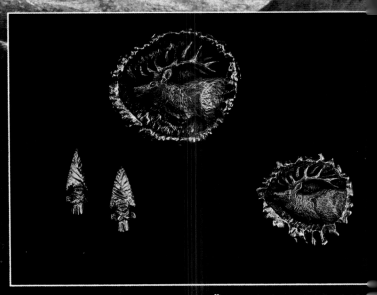

"Meeting the Challenge"
ed. of 250 by Don Burda
5" X 7"

"Undefeated"
ed. of 150 by Don Burda
6.5" X 7.5"

"Wapiti" limited ed. of 100
Silver & gold belt buckle and bolo tie by Don Burda

"Distant Relative"
ed. of 21 by Don Burda
12" X 8.75"

Thousands of years before this buffalo walked the plains, there lived a giant, long-horned cousin, *Bison Antiquus.* Erosion releases from the earth the skull of one of these relatives that had fallen prey to an early American hunter of the Folsom Culture.

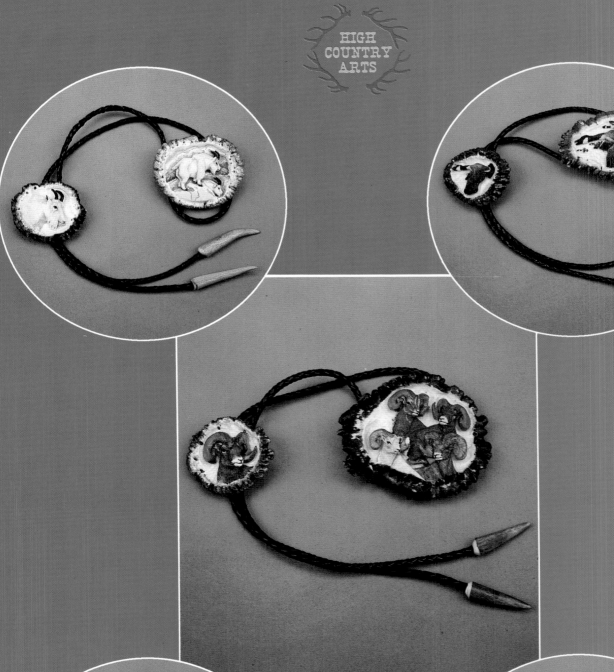

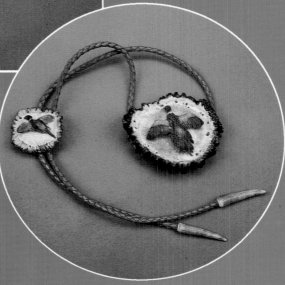

Hand-carved, original belt buckles and bolo ties by Kitty Burda

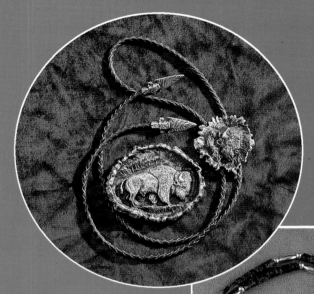

"Plains Nomad"
ed. of 100 by Don Burda

"Elk Fight"

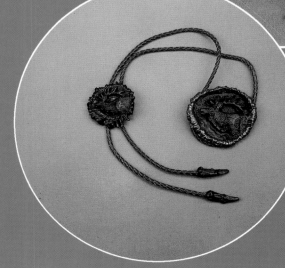

"Wapiti" ed. of 100 by Don Burda

Semi-precious stone inlays, limited-edition castings in silver or bronze, and gift items such as cribbage boards are a few examples of the items created by the Artists of High Country Arts.

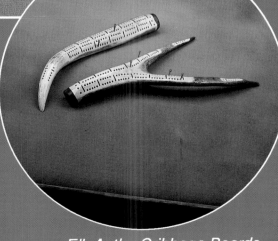

Elk Antler Cribbage Boards

SCULPTOR

Rain in the Face
41″ tall Ed. 12

1225 LAPWAI ROAD • LEWISTON, IDAHO 83501 • PHONE 208/746-0225
The Larry Casey Gallery • 7132 Stetson Dr. • Scottsdale, Arizona 85251

BRONZES by BURL JONES

Burl or Eunice Jones
Route 62, box 3110C
Livingston, Mt 59047
Home phone: 406-222-8719
Gallery phone: 406-222-3517

His Majesty
Edition: 10
Size: 32" X 32"

Custom frame to suit your decor!

2131

2132

DENNIS JONES

Dennis Jones has quickly earned a national reputation as one of the most premiere wildlife artists in America today. His skills have conveyed the power and beauty of wildlife around the world. "I try to make my work appear as if there is something going on outside the bronze itself. Each piece of art seems to draw your imagination away from the sculpture to a place or time that each of us as outdoorsmen have experienced."

Low editions, fine detail, powerful compositions and a high regard for accuracy make Dennis' bronzes a fine investment. Collectors and sportsmen from across the country have appreciated more the beauty of our wildlife heritage through the efforts of Dennis Jones.

Khayam, the 1½ lifesize bronze (above) was a project Dennis was commissioned by the city of Winston, Oregon and the Wildlife Safari to commemorate this beautiful animal. The cheetah truly is an investment worth considering.

Title — Survival on the Serengeti   Edition — 10   Size — 18" high, 31" high

Survival on the Serengeti portrays the beauty, power and elegance of this magnificent creature. The fastest animal on earth, the cheetah, is definitely an animal worthy of our appreciation.

Madleine Kay brings the eye and sensibilities of her
hunter's background to her art.
Each ebony and ivory carving is one of a kind.
Limited edition pieces are executed in 14-carat gold.

Write for catalogs at:
21787 Ventura Blvd.
Suite 194
Woodland Hills
California
91364
(818) 704-7666

MADLEINE KAY
ARTIST - HUNTER - JEWLER

VIC LEMMON
WESTERN and WILDLIFE SCULPTURE

Vic Lemmon was born in Silver City, Utah, and spent much of his youth helping his father, who was in the business of rounding up wild horses and promoting rodeos. Later years found Vic in Wyoming as an outfitter, guide and packer in the WInd River and Teton Mountains. That was where he met his close friend Joe Back, who encouraged Vic to promote his art. Years later they wrote a book together, titled "The Old Guide Remembers, The Young Guide Finds Out."

The success of artists or writers lies in their abilities as a storyteller. This ability can only come from experience. To this experience the artist adds love and respect for his subject. These ingredients show in the sculpture of Vic Lemmon. One look at his work and one knows Vic has experienced what he is creating. His love and feeling for horses, cowboys, wildlife and rodeos lives in each piece.

A naturally gifted and self-taught artist, Vic now lives in one of the beautiful towns left in America -- Dubois, Wyoming. His art has won many top awards in national art shows and he is represented in many private collections throughout the United States, including President Reagan's collection in the White House.

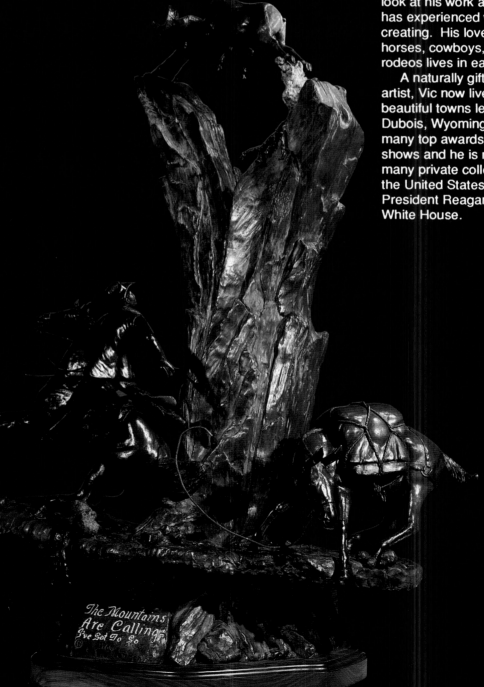

The Mountains
Are Calling
I've Got To Go

September Challenge
Edition: 21
17" high

Rocky Mountain Bighorn
Edition: 30
11" high

Showing off
Edition: 25
13" high

CURTIS ZABEL

39510 ROUTT CO. RD. 44
STEAMBOAT SPRINGS, COLORADO 80487
(303) 879-0144

I have a great deal of love and respect for wildlife and our western heritage. When I finish a sculpture of a big bull elk or a good looking horse I feel the same excitement that I do when I see them in real life. I hope my feelings are transmitted through my work for others to see and enjoy.

Escape Artist
By Curtis Zabel

Escape Artist
Edition: 21
18" high

Airlines & Travel 11

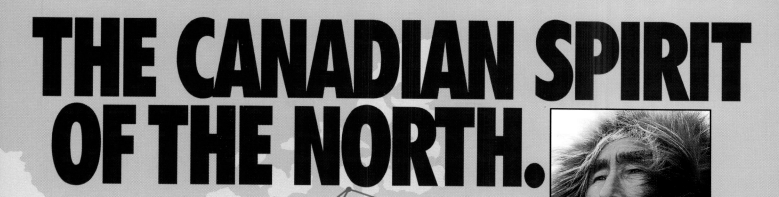

THE CANADIAN SPIRIT OF THE NORTH.

There's a spirit in the North. A spirit you'll find wherever Canadian Airlines International spreads its wings.

From Inuvik to Resolute to Iqaluit, the Canadian network flies to more destinations in the North than any other.

And of course, every time you fly with us you'll receive valuable Canadian Plus frequent flyer points.

Discover the spirit of the Canadian North. For reservations call your travel agent or Canadian Airlines.

Canadian
Canadian Airlines International

Big Game Outfitters Directory

Africa

Botswana

Assoc. of Hunting Safari Operators
Box 119
Maun
Botswana

McFarlane, R.
Box 1602
Gaborone
Botswana

Roussos, Nassos
Box 3658
Addis Ababa
Ethiopia

Vira Safaris Ltd.
Box 1602
Gaborone 372308
Botswana

Central African Republic

Sporting International Inc.
Box 24988
Nairobi
Kenya
882268
Robin Hurt

Namibia

Mount Etjo Safari Lodge
Box 81
Kalkfield 9000
Rep. of S.A.
06532-1602
J. Oelofse

Biggs, Russell
Box 30124, Pioneers Park
Windhoek 9000
Rep. of S.A.
061-41665

South Africa

AAA Hunting
Box 4789
Pretoria 0001
Rep. of S.A.
012-322120

Action Africa Safaris
Box 23232
Innesdale 0031
Rep. of S.A.
012-335-3535
FAX 012-762301
Johann W. Nortje

African Safaris Unlimited
Box 41332
Craighall 2024
Rep. of S.A.
880-1948
J. Brelsford

Ameland Safaris
Box 241
Potgietesrus 0600
Rep. of S.A.
C. van der Merwe

Angus Brown Safaris
Box 666
Ellisras 0555
Rep. of S.A.
015362 ask for 2912
A. Brown

Answa Safaris
Box 542
Silverton 0127
Rep. of S.A.
012-862312
J. Swart

Badenhorst, W.
Box 256
Mtubatuba 3933
Rep. of S.A.

Baobab Safaris
Box 512
Potgietersrus 0600
Rep. of S.A.
015332-830
FAX 01541-4492
J. Shoeman

Basson, J.C.
Box 315
Vaalwater 0530
Rep. of S.A.

Basie Maartens
Box 2501 Mountain Shadows
Paarl 7620
Rep. of S.A.
02211-623192

Beck, L. R.
Box 91252
Auckland Park 2006
Rep. of S.A.

Belvedere Safaris
Box 84
Bedford 5780
Rep. of S.A.
94632-2522 1120 Bedford
Willem de Klerk

Berry, Mark
Box 616
Kimberly 8300
Rep. of S.A.
0531-22919

BG Hunting Safaris
Box 733
Louis Trichardt 0920
Rep. of S.A.
01551-9762
Bertie Guillaume

Bivack Game Ranch
Box 61
Alldays 0909
Rep. of S.A.
01554-360
H.G. Wollert

Boehme, Keith
Box 583
Tzaneen 0850
Rep. of S.A.
015236-4-1157

Bonamanzi Game Ranches
Box 48
Hluhluwe 3960
Rep. of S.A.
03562 ask for 3530 or 143AH
Nigel Fairhead

Botha, Christo
Box 727
Potgietersrus 0600
Rep. of S.A.
01541-4710

Bowker & Scott Safaris
Box 80
Tarkastad
Rep. of S.A.
F. Bowker

Bowker, Francis
Box 442
Grahamstown 6140
Rep. of S.A.
0461-5203

Bredenkamp, P.
Posbus 114
Postmasburg 8420
Rep. of S.A.

Buffalo Safaris
Box 29050
Sunnyside 0132
Rep. of S.A.
012-465327
Kobus Prinsloo

Buffalo Safaris
Box 26292
Arcadia 0007
Rep. of S.A.
012-465327
Maj.-Gen. Minnaar

Calverly, Mark
P/Bag X070145
Wasbank 2920
Rep. of S.A.

Camdeboo Safaris
Box 427
Graaff Reinet 6280
Rep. of S.A.
23038
Lewes Tonks

Cormack, Gordon
Box 640
Hilton 3245 Natal
Rep. of S.A.
0331-34548

Carlstein, K.M.
32 St. Johns Wood Boeing Road
Bedfordview 2008
Rep. of S.A.

Chete Safaris
Box 10442
Aston Manor 1630 Transvaal
Rep. of S.A.
964-1025
F. Rademeyer

Ciskei Safaris
P.O. Box 59
Bisho
Rep. of Ciskei
0401-92191
FAX 0401-91333
Kevin, Jim or Charles

Coenraad Vermaak Safaris
Box 739
Dundee 3000
Rep. of S.A.
03425-729
D.A. Beattie

Costhuizen, Johyn C.
P/Bag X071
Marshalltown 2107
Rep. of S.A.
836-6525

D'Alton, M.J.
Box 400
Bredasdorp 7280
Rep. of S.A.
0264-42142

de Bruijn, Lud
Box 115
Somerset East 5850
Rep. of S.A.
042412-1820

Deane, Robert C.
Box 79
Hluhluwe 3960
Rep. of S.A.
03562 ask for 144

Dippenaar, C.R.
Box 1057
Nelspruit 1200
Rep. of S.A.
01311-22367

East Cape& Karoo Safaris
Box 1227
Plettenberg Bay 6600
Rep. of S.A.
04457-9442
Lud de Bruijn

Elite Hunting Outfitters
Box 157
Haenertsburg 0730
Rep. of S.A.
015-2222
Cassie de Bruin

Ellington Ranch
Box 207
Ellisras 0555
Rep. of S.A.
A. Brown

Big Game Outfitters Directory

Africa

Erasmus, Willem P.
Box 1414
Kempton PArk 1620
Rep. of S.A.

Ernst Dedekind Safaris
Box 14
Moolman 2387
Rep. of S.A.
013431 616.H 621.B

Esser, Franz J.
40 Morsim Road
Hyde Park 2196
Rep. of S.A.

Exclusive Safaris
Box 833
Krugersdorp 1740
Rep. of S.A.
669-9834
J.D. Marais

Executive Safaris
Box 12614
Clubview 0014
Rep. of S.A.

Engonyameni Safaris
Box 9
Kaapmuiden 1295 E. Transvaal
Rep. of S.A.
D. Van Graan

Faunafrika
Box 53
Vaalwater 0530
Rep. of S.A.
27-11-683-4350

Flanagan, Marge
Box 1510
Honeydew 2040
Rep. of S.A.
795-2133

Frans Van Straaten Safaris
P.O. Box 304
Marble Hall 0450
Rep. of S.A.
012020-2297
Frans or Lettie

Free State Safaris
Box 7
Kroonstad 9500
Rep. of S.A.
01411-23002
Theo Erasmus

Frylinck, Athol
Box 1822
Vryburg 8600
Rep. of S.A.
01451-4141

G.G. Viglietti
42 Caxton Way
Oakridge 7800
Rep. of S.A.
015352-144
L.J.C. Van Tonder

Game Bird Safaris
Box 299
Vryheid 3100
Rep. of S.A.
0386-667
T.D. Comins

Game Hunters' Safaris
P.O. Box 35
Steenbokpan 0533
Rep. of S.A.
01536-60241
Gerhard Steenkamp

Gary Kelly Safaris
11 Surrey Lane
Kloof 3610
Rep. of S.A.
27-31-7640137
Gary Kelly

Ghenzi, C.A.
Box 69748
Bryanston 2021
Rep. of S.A.
704-3060

Giuletti, F.
Box 232
Paulshof 2056
Rep. of S.A.

Goss, Ian L.
Box 10
Magudu 3160
Rep. of S.A.
03841 41167

Greater Kuduland Safaris
Box 45
Tshipise 0901
Rep. of S.A.
015539-720
B.Van Wulfften Palthe

Greer, Graham W.
Box 403
Paulshof 2056
Rep. of S.A.

Grobler, Donald K.
10 Rithleigh Drive
Westville 3630
Rep. of S.A.
031-821504

Guillaume, Bertie & Celia
Box 733
Louis Trichardt 0920
Rep. of S.A.
01551-9762

Halse, A.R.D.
Box 9
Sterkstroon 4025
Rep. of S.A.
04592-3311

Hannan, Edward A.D.
P/Bag X527
Mkuze 3965
Rep. of S.A.
03562 ask for Mkuze 1931

Harmse, Frans
Box 4124
Germiston South 1411
Rep. of S.A.

Harmse, Meil
Box 407
Maledane 1320
Rep. of S.A.
0131622-144

Haselau, G.R.
Box 2501
Paarl 7620
Rep. of S.A.

Havemann, Louis J.
P.O. Heatonville
Windy Ridge 3881
Rep. of S.A.
0351-23465

Hiles, Roland
Box 2269
Beacon Bay 5205
Rep. of S.A.

Hockley, Robin
Cullendale
Bedford 5780
Rep. of S.A.
04632-1303

Holbrow, Peter J.
11 Surrey Lane
Kloof 3600
Rep. of S.A.
031-741137

Hongoney Hunting Safaris
Box 18
Klaserie 1381
Rep. of S.A.
0131732-2802
G.P. Van Niekerk

Hunting Africa #111
Box 1775
Johannesburg 2000
Rep. of S.A.
27-11-290898
T. Shaw

Ingwe Safaris
Box 218
Hoedspruit 1380
Rep. of S.A.
0131732-3304
K.A. McCarter

Inkasa Safaris
Box 13876
Northmead 1511
Rep. of S.A.
849-2082
A. Grobbelaar

Inter-Africa Safaris Pty. Ltd.
Box 72
Klaserie 1381
Rep. of S.A.
0131732-2423
P. Otto

Intergame Africa Pty. Ltd.
Box 78495
Sandton 2146
Rep. of S.A.

Jaap Seegers Safaris Pty. Ltd.
Box 343
Vaalwater 0530
Rep. of S.A.
015352 ask for 96

Johnny Vivier Hunting Safaris
Box 514
Harrismith 9880
Rep. of S.A.
27-01436-22924

Johnson, P.G.
Box 460
Bergvlei 2012
Rep. of S.A.

Jones, P.A.
Box 72
Muldersdrift 1747
Rep. of S.A.

Joubert, Hendrik P.
Box 578
Germiston 1400
Rep. of S.A.
827-0970

Karise Farm & Pheasantry
Box 121
Eikenhof 1872
Rep. of S.A.
948-9739
E.J. Pittaway

Kelly, Garry
11 Surrey Lane
Kloof 3600
Rep. of S.A.
031-741137

Kelly, John W.
19 Homeford Drive
La Lucia 4051
Rep. of S.A.
031-525942

Kgama Safaris
Private Bag X2078
8670 MMBATHO
Bophuthatswana
South Africa
27-1401 24114 ext5144

Kido Safaris
Box 511
Pretoria 0001
Rep. of S.A.
2712-46-3156
P. Pienaar

Kliphoek Lodge/Palala Safaris
6 Tomkordale Bldg. Dekgras St.
Silvertondale
Rep. of S.A.
86-8005 86-8016

Big Game Outfitters Directory

Africa

Knott, Peter & Howard
Box 1385
Louis Trichardt 0920
Rep. of S.A.
01551-9663

Knowles, J.G.
Box 106
Letsitele 0885
Rep. of S.A.
01152332-2321

Kohrs, Karl
P/Bag X516
Mkuze 3965
Rep. of S.A.
03562 ask for Mkuze 1303

KWA - Maswazi
Box 152
Hectorspruit 1330
Transvaal
Rep. of S.A.
013134-980

Lamprecht, J.J.
Box 305
Ellisras 0555
Rep. of S.A.

Limpopo Hunting Safaris
Box 431
Howick 3290
Rep. of S.A.
03324-4525
J.R. Coleman

Lindsay, Donald C.
Box 227
Vanderbijlpark 1900
Rep. of S.A.
01617-330

Loubser Safaris Africa
Box 12026
Cape Town 8000
Rep. of S.A.
Francois Loubser

Louw, Gerrit J.R.
Box 494
Thabazimi 0380
Rep. of S.A.
015379 ask for 82630

Magnum Hunting Safaris
Box 611
Louis Trichardt 0920
Rep. of S.A.
01551-4069

Manning, Jack
Box 5
Mkuze 3965
Rep. of S.A.
03562 ask for 2831

Marais, Dr. J.T.
Box 2693
Pretoria 0001
Rep. of S.A.
012-215957

McDonald Wildlife Property Ltd.
Box 37
Tshipise 0901
Rep. of S.A.
015539-719
Sandy McDonald

McNeil, Hugh A.
Box 893
Johannesburg 2000
Rep. of S.A.
613-6777

Millican, R.R.
Box 128
Stanger 4450
Rep. of S.A.
0324-21288

Mkuze Falls Safaris
Box 236
Pongola 3170
Rep. of S.A.
038422-1604
A.J. Marais

Mmabolela Safaris
Box 29
Swartwater 0622
Rep. of S.A.
015432 ask for Masstown 704
J. Van Der Meulen

Mountain Shadows/Cape Safaris
P.O. Box 2501
Paarl 7620
Rep. of S.A.
02211-623192

Mountain View Farm
Klipfontein
Lydenburg 1120
Rep. of S.A.
A. de Jager

Mulobezi Safaris
Box 7466
Petic 1512
Rep. of S.A.
A. McCallum

Mziki Safaris
P.O. Box 98117
Sloane Park 2152
Rep. of S.A.
011-706-7454
FAX 011-706-2012
Pelham Jones

Nimrod Safaris
P.O. Box 241
Potgietersrus 0600
Rep.of S.A.
01541-2210
Dr. Choppie van der Merwe

North-Western Safaris
P/Bag X2626
Potgietersrus 0600 Transvaal
Rep. of S.A.
609-6808
I. Ritchie

Nyala Game Ranch
Box 73
Kwambonambi 3915
Rep. of S.A.
0352-876
R. Barnes

Nyalaveld Safaris Pty. Ltd.
Box 3741
Durban 4000
Rep. of S.A.
031-313403

Palala Safaris
Kliphoek Lodge
P.O. Melk Rivier 0541
Rep. of S.A.
01280-41167
Derick Van Staden

Pallamar, Werner A.
Box 781038
Sandton 2146
Rep. of S.A.
84-1327

Parkes, James
BGox 184
Graaff Reinet 6280
Rep. of S.A.
0491-23078

Peens, J.A.
Box 310
Potgietersrus 0600
Rep. of S.A.

Pro Nobis Hunting Service
Box 5
Hluhluwe 3960
Rep. of S.A.
03562 ask for 5
A. Meintjes

Rand Arms & Safaris PTy.
60 Eloff Street
Johannesburg 2001
Rep. of S.A.
331-5180
C.D. Smith

Ras, M.D.
Box 179 Tsuma Putego
Thabazimbi 0380
Rep. of S.A.
015379-724

Rautenbach, Sigi
85 Torquay St.
Benoni 1500
Rep. of S.A.
894-1966
Lakefield Ext. 21

Rooipoort Safaris
Box 616
Kimberly 8300
Rep. of S.A.
0531-22171 ext 233
A.J. Anthony

Roos, Peter C.
Box 276
Kroondal 0350
Rep. of S.A.

Roux, Daniel F.
Box 4443
Pretoria 0001
Rep. of S.A.

Rudling, Tony
Box 383
Alberton 1450
Rep. of S.A.
339-1814

Sabi Sabi
Box 1170
Johannesburg 2000
Rep. of S.A.
833-7481

Schimper, Frank
Box 343
Krugersdorp 1740
Rep. of S.A.
763-3851

Scott, William H.
Box 80
Tarkastad 5371
Rep. of S.A.
04582-4202

Seegers, Jaap
Box 343
Baalwater 0530
Rep. of S.A.
015352 assk for 96

Shepherd, Grant
Box 78
Klaserie 1381
Rep. of S.A.

Sinclair, C.A.
Box 135
Kouis Trichardt 0920
Rep. of S.A.

Skuilkrans Safaris
Box 73008
Fairland 2030
Rep. of S.A.
F. Hartzer

Smith, Stephen J.
105 Athol Road
Atholl 2199
Rep. of S.A.
783-5012

Sparks, Chappie
Box 557
Queenstown 5320
Rep. of S.A.
0451-2325

Sparrow, Ronnie
Box 381
Muldersdrift 1747
Rep. of S.A.
666-2507

Big Game Outfitters Directory

Africa

Stegmann, W.A.
Bourkestraat 71
Sunnyside 0002
Rep. of S.A.

Sussens, C.G.
Box 289
Hartbeespoort 0216
Rep. of S.A.
01211-31975

Swart, J.G.
Box 538
Thabazimbi 0380
Rep. of S.A.

Theron, A.M.
24 Stratton Avenue
Bryanston 2021
Rep. of S.A.

Theron, P.A.
149 Wilton Avenue
Bryanston 2021
Rep. of S.A.

Thomas, K.D.
Box 1424
Queenstown 5320
Rep. of S.A.

3 B Ranch
Elysium
Kiesel 0382
Rep. of S.A.
015379-921
D.G. Bubb

Tinley, Charles
Box 87
Tarkastad 5370
Rep. of S.A.
04582-5402

Tomkinson, A.J.
Box 657
Greytown 3500
Rep. of S.A.

Tout, Mark
Box 20
Mica 1380
Rep. of S.A.

Trophyland Safaris
Box 7611
Johannesburg 2000
Rep. of S.A.
838-4235

Tswana Game Ranch
Box 87
Taskastad 5370
Rep. of S.A.
04582-5211

Tumuga Safaris
Box 1427
Potgeitersrus 0600
Rep. of S.A.
01541-5254
Van Den Heever, Daan

Ubizane Game Ranch & Safaris
P.O. Box 102
3960 Hluhluwe
Zululand, Natal
Rep. of S.A.
03562-3602
Chris Wex

Van Coppenhagen, Lou
Box 29144
Sunnyside 0231
Rep. of S.A.
012-346-1135

Van Der Merwe, C.J.
Box 241
Potgietersrus 0600
Rep. of S.A.
01541-2710

Van Der Post, Alec
Box 35415
Northcliff 2115
Rep. of S.A.
678-1603

Van Greunen, Faan
P/Bag 2471
Potgietersrus 0600
Rep. of S.A.

Van Rooyen, Johann
Box 3789
Pietersburg 0700
Rep. of S.A.
01521-6379

Van Straten, C.J.
35 Second Road
Linbro Park 2199
Rep. of S.A.

Van Tonder, L.J.C.
Box 375
Vaalwater 0530
Rep. of S.A.
015352-144

Vimercati, Paulo
Box 372
Honeydew 2040
Rep. of S.A.
660-5640

Vira Safaris
P/Bag 1046
Waterpoort 0905
Rep. of S.A.
I.B. McFarlane

Wagendrift Safaris
Box 463
Piet Retief 2380
Rep. of S.A.
27-13431-860
C. Labuschagne

Waring, Neil
Box 54
Mkuze 3965
Rep. of S.A.

Wex, C.I.
Box 619
Umtentweni 4235
Rep. of S.A.

Wildlife Expeditions
Box 645
Bedfordview 2008
Rep. of S.A.
53-1814/53-8411
C. Walker

Wildspan Hunting
Box 5
Campbell 8360
Rep. of S.A.
0020 ask for Campbell 1330
Hendrik Van Eck

Wilkinson, Chris
12 York Road
Gillitts 3610
Rep. of S.A.
0381-4861

World Expedition & Safari
Box 11450
Secunda 2302
Rep. of S.A.
27-13-6344379
A. Hattingh

Zingela Safaris
Box 1057
Nelspruit 1200
Rep. of S.A.
T. Shaw

Zulu Bush Safaris
Box 832
Vryheid 3100
Rep. of S.A.
0381-4861
D.J. Paul

Zulu Nyala Safaris
Box 1775
Johannesburg 2000
Rep. of S.A.
27-11-290898
T. Shaw

Tanzania

Sporting International Inc.
Box 24988
Nairobi
Kenya
882268
Robin Hurt

Zambia

Busanga Trails
Box 31322
Lusaka
Zambia
216715
D. H. Price

Cotton Gordon Safaris
Tarryall River Ranch
Lake George CO, USA
80827
303-748-3255

Higgins, Darryl M.
Box 30275
Lusaka
Zambia

Kazuma Safaris Ltd.
Box 330793
Lusaka
Zambia
P. Swanepoel

United Safaris, Ltd.
Box 35370
Lusaka
Zambia
J. Chalansi

Zimbabwe

Baird, James
Box 18, Diamond Ranch
Kudoma
Munyati 2424
USA 219-464-8216

Hunters Tracks (Private) Ltd.
Box CH 4
Chisipite
736797 Harare
329 Arcturus

Nuanetsi Hunters
P. Bag 2008
Mwenezi
Don Price

Ngezi Safaris
Box 482
Kadoma
Doug Kok

Rosslyn Safaris
P. Bag 5934
Hwange
Hwange 70223

Safaris Connection, Inc.
9520 Fairview Ave.
Boise, ID 83704 USA
800-225-2502
Roger/Larry/Adrian

Vadoma Safaris
Box 296
Kwe Kwe
38764
F. Meyer

Westwood Wildlife Safaris
Box 21
Victoria Falls
469/31519

Big Game Outfitters Directory

Asia

Turkey

Pamfilya Hunting Org.
30 Augustos Cad. 54
Antalya 07100
Turkey
311-21401
Yasir Sobutay

Australia

Australia

Hunt Australia
72 Blanch Street
Shortland, 2307
N.S.W., Austalia
049-511198
Bob & Kay Penfold

Kingham Hunting Preserve
P.O. Box 53
Kilcoy 4515
Queensland, Australia
071-973115
Bill Webster

McCormack, Kevin
Fentondale, R.S.D.
Clarkefield, Victoria 3030
Australia
054-28-5372

Thomas, Murray
Hunters Lodge, 5 Tabor Street
Sunbury, Victoria 3429
Australia

Nimrod Safaris
Box 472
Darwin 5794
Australia
089-81-1633/1256
B. Lees

New Zealand

Angus Corporation Limited
Box 30069
Lower Hutt
New Zealand
NZ-04-663-329

Bimler, Harry
R.D.#2
Ngongotaha Rotorua
New Zealand
23457

Danks New Zealand Safaris &
Tours
Box 8066
Kensington Whangarei
New Zealand
A.C. Wilson

Humboldt Hunting Safaris
Box 153
Queenstown
New Zealand
Gary Mullings

Lilybank Safari Lodge
Box 60
Lakr Tekapo
New Zealand
064-5056-522
Gary Joll

New Zealand Wildlife Safaris
Box 4058
Christchurch
New Zealand
Terry Pierson

Vern Wilson Hunting & Shooting
Box 7057
Hamilton
New Zealand
64-71-435-664

Westland Guiding Services
Box 38
Franz Josef Glacier
New Zealand
Ph 750 Telex Thru 4349
S. Peterson

Wilderness Safaris
Box 761
Taupo
New Zealand
Tom Con

Europe

Austria

Vienna Hunt International
Auhofstrasse 65
A-1130 Vienna, Austria
43 222 82 33 53
Johannes Stiedl

Worldwide Safaris
Krass 15
A-9560 Feldkirchen
Austria
04276-3692
Werner Fleck

Bulgaria

Bulgaria-Murgash
11 Auguststrasse 25
Sofia 1000
Bulgaria

England

Hunting Safari Consultants of
London
83 Gloucester Place
London W1H 3PG
England
486-4774
Capt. J.C. Pollock

Safari Services International
Box 460
Windsor Berkshire SL44HN
England
07535-68341

France

Safaris Jacques Guin
34, Route de Vinsobres
Valreas 84600
France
J. Guin

Hungary

State Farm of Balatonnagybereki
Nimrod u. 1
Balatonfenyves
Hungary

Italy

Europa Caccia
50018 Scandicci
Florence
Italy
55-752267

Forum Travel Thirama Grandi Cacce
Via Veneto 23
Roma 00187
Italy

Portugal

Seia, Hugo Manuel
27685 Joao Do Estoril Apt. 22
Estoril Codex
Portugal

Urbanizacao Terplana
Lote 27 R/C D 2775
Parede
Portugal
246-4352
L.P. de Sa E Mello

Scotland

McCrave, Mike
Woodside
Gordon TD3 6JU
Scotland
057381-303

Big Game Outfitters Directory

Europe

Sport in Scotland Ltd.
22 Marketbrae
Inverness 1V2 3AB
Scotland
J. Ormiston

Spain

ACISA
Vereda de las Penas/La Moraleja
Alcobendas, Madrid
Spain
Sr. Bustamente

Cazagerica
Mes. 5, Talavera de la Reina
Toledo
Spain
925-80-51-83
M.R. Benz

Cazatur, CIC Delegation
Box 50.577
Madrid 28080
Spain
Ricardo Medem

Hunting Spain
Box 57
Majadahonda, Madrid
Spain
A. Fabres

Lalanne, Felix
JoséAbascal, 55
28003 Madrid
Spain
442 86 43

Spain Safaris
Box 752
Santiago
Spain
981-58-1885/4178
Dr. J. Varela-Duran

Rosich Martin, Francisco
17 Cardenal Reig, 2nd fl, #1
Barcelona 08028
Spain
240-80-43

Trofeos International
c./Antonio Lopez 170 2
Madrid 28026
Spain
T. Garcia

Trophy Hunt Iberica
Maria de Molina, 60
28006 Madrid
Spain
262-58-82
Javier Iniguez

West Germany

Weinhold, Dieter
Au der Hohe 1
5204 Lohmar
West Germany
02246-4941

Wengert-Windrose Safari Ltd.
Wiesensteigerstrasse .20
7341 Muehlausen
West Germany
37-7335-5204

North America

Canada

Alberta

Alberta Frontier Guiding/Outfitting
Box 83
Sundre, AL, Canada
T0M 1X0
403-638-2897

Alberta Trophy Hunters
52246 Rge. Road 232
Sherwood Park, AL, Canada
T8B 1C1
403-467-9598/8668

Alberta Trophy Hunts
Box 1563
Hinton, AL, Canada
T0E 1B0
403-865-3990
Ferlin Koma

Alberta Wilderness Guide Services
12439 96th Street
Edmonton, AL, Canada
T5G 1W6
403-988-8332
Terry Birkholz

Alstott, Edwin
Box 14
Caroline, AL, Canada
T0M 0M0

Ameri-Cana Expeditions Inc.
4707 106 A Ave. Suite 93
Edmonton, AL, Canada
T6A 1J3
403-468-1060
Pat Frederick

Anchor D Guiding & Outfitting
Box 656
Black Diamond, AL, Canada
T0L 0H0
403-938-2867

Antler Hill Guide & Outfitting
Box 321
Bowden, AL, Canada
T0M 0K0
403-224-3083
Ab Brewster

Artindale Guide Service
Box 2642
Olds, AL, Canada
T0M 1P0
403-335-8532
Doug Artindale

Ayers, Don
3015 109th Ave.
Edmonton, AL, Canada
T5W 0G2
403-433-5395

Babala, Randy
Cadomin, AL, Canada
T0E 0E0
403-692-3762

Bald Eagle Outfitters
Box 961
Stony Plain, AL, Canada
T0E 2G0
403-963-2868
Dean Dunbar

Barrier Mountain Outfitters
Box 69
Olds, AL, Canada
T0M 1P0
403-556-6778
W. Les Short

Bertagnoli, Alfred
General Delivery
Robb, AL, Canada
T0E 1X0
403-794-3853

Brewster Mountain Packtrain
Box 964
Banff, AL, Canada
T0L 0C0
403-762-5454

Broken Horn Packin' Outfitters
104 Temple Blvd.
Lethbridge, AL, Canada
T1K 5A3
403-381-8535
Ron Babin

Brown Bros. Guiding & Outfitting
Box 57
Torrington, AL, Canada
T0M 2B0
403-631-2391
Clarence & Allan Brown

Campbell, James & Nagy, Edith
Box 281
Didsbury, AL, Canada
T0M 0W0

Canada Maximas Outfitters
550 6th Ave. SW #900
Calgary, AL, Canada
T2P 0S1
403-261-3955
John Leonard

Chester Sands Guide & Outfitting
R.R.#1
Rocky Mtn. House, AL, Canada
T0M 1T0
403-845-6454

Cofield, Randi
Box 789
Nanton, AL, Canada
T0L 1R0
403-549-2330

Custom Guiding
Box 1172
Blairmore, AL, Canada
T0K 0E0
403-562-2173

Diamond Jim's Mountain Rides
Box 394
Rocky Mtn. House, AL, Canada
T0M 1T0
403-845-6859
Jim Colosimo

Dorey, Lyle
Box 1463
Rocky Mtn. House, AL, Canada
T0M 1T0
403-845-4633

Double Diamond Wilderness Trails
R.R.#3
Rimbey, AL, Canada
T0C 2J0
403-843-3582
John HAtala

Double W Guides & Outfitters
Box 743
Carstairs, AL, Canada
T0M 0N0
403-337-3461
Tom & Bill Windsor

Echo Canyon Outfitters Ltd.
Box 831
Rocky Mtn. House, AL, Canada
T0M 1T0
403-845-6131
Charlie Makofka

Big Game Outfitters Directory

North America

Everclear Guiding & Outfitting
Box 1377
Didsbury, AL, Canada
T0M 0W0

G&H Outfitting
70 Glenpatrick Rd.
Cochrane, AL, Canada
T0L 0W0
403-932-3246
Garry Gallup

Grosso, Clayton J.
Box 684
Rocky Mtn. House, AL, Canada
T0M 1T0
403-845-6840

Guinn, Rick E.
183 Huntwick Way NE
Calgary, AL, Canada
T2K 4H4

Hallett, Nayda
Box 1333
Rocky Mtn. House, AL, Canada
T0M 1T0
403-845-4358

Hartum, Bruce
2411-49 St.
Edmonton, AL, Canada
T6L 4P4

Highwood Outfitters
79 Cedardale Cresc.
Calgary, AL, Canada
T2W 4B2
403-938-5531

Holmes Outdoor Recreation
Box 570
Sundre, AL, Canada
T0M 1X0

Homeplace Guest Ranch/Pack Trips
R.R.#1
Priddis, AL, Canada
T0L 1W0
403-931-3245

Jake's Guide & Outfitting
Box 684
Sundre, AL, Canada
T0M 1X0
403-638-4071
D. Vennard

Jasper Wilderness Pack Trips
Box 550
Jasper, AL, Canada
T0E 1E0
403-852-3909
Gord Dixon

K Country Outfitting
Box 1343
Cochrane, AL, Canada
T0L 0W0
403-845-2197/6620
K. Koebisch

Kelly, George
Box 35
Hinton, AL, Canada
T0E 1B0
403-865-3295

Kostynuk, Sam
Box 636
Rocky Mtn. House, AL, Canada
T0M 1T0
403-845-6620

Leonard, Bazil
Box 818
Grande Cache, AL, Canada
T0E 0Y0
403-827-3246

Lost Guide Outfitters
R.R.#1
Sundre, AL, Canada
T0M 1X0
403-556-2984
Gary Bracken

McKenzie's Trails West
Box 971
Rocky Mtn. House, AL, Canada
T0M 1T0
403-845-4880/6810

Mitzel, Brett
Box 6
Lake Louise, AL, Canada
T0L 1E0
403-522-3770

Narraway River Outfitting
Box 177
Goodfare, AL, Canada
T0H 1T0
403-356-2650
Daryl Fettes

Ostashek, George
General Delivery
Brule, AL, Canada
T0E 0C0
403-865-7001

Pacific Rim Guide Service
2016 Sherwood Dr. #7
Sherwood Park, AL, Canada
T8A 3X3
R. D. Munroe

Panther Valley Outfitters
Box 96
Red Deer, AL, Canada
403-340-0292
Amos Neufeld

Porcupine Creek Outfitters
Box 2442
Pincher Creek, AL, Canada
T0K 1W0
403-627-2540
B. Sinclair

Regnier, Ed
Box 496
Edson, AL, Canada
T0E 0P0

Rifle Creek Guiding Service
10827 38 A Ave.
Edmonton, AL, Canada
T6J 0L6
D. Till

Rocky Mountain Outfitters
R.R.#1
Bon Accord, AL, Canada
T0A 0K0
403-921-2341
Leo Ferbey

Rocky Mountain Safaris Inc.
2020 105th St. #13
Edmonton, AL, Canada
T6J 5J2
403-437-3101

Rugged Mtn. Big Horn Guide O/F
635 Penbrooke Rd. SE
Calgary, AL, Canada
T2A 3S9
403-273-4216
Mike Smith

Saddle Peak Trail Rides Ltd.
Box 1463
Cochrane, AL, Canada
T0L 0W0
403-932-3299
Dave Richards

Sands, Chester V.
R.R.#1
Rocky Mtn. House, AL, Canada
T0M 1T0
403-845-6454

Sands, Sam
Box 568
Rocky Mtn. House, AL, Canada
T0M 1T0
403-845-6487

Silvertip Outfitters
Box 515
Midnapore, AL, Canada
T0L 1J0
403-256-5018
Eric Grinnell

Simpson, David D.
Box 511
Claresholm, AL, Canada
T0L 0T0
403-625-2931

Simpson, James F.
Box 190
Midnapore, AL, Canada
T0L 1J0
403-938-5434

Skyline Trail Rides
Brule, AL, Canada
T0E 0C0
403-865-4880

Smith & Overguard Outfitting
R.R.#1
Sundre, AL, Canada
T0M 1X0
403-638-2735

Solomon Mountain Outfitters
Box 1563
Hinton, AL, Canada
T0E 1B0
403-865-3295
Ferlin Koma

Sonset Enterprises
Box 340
Cremona, AL, Canada
T0M 0R0
403-637-2361
Duane Papke

Steve Cooper Outfitters
Box 1347
Edmonton, AL, Canada
T5J 2N2
403-477-6595

Storm Mountain Outfitters
98 Emberdale Way
Airdrie, AL, Canada
T48 1Y7
403-948-6656
Pat & Mike Bates

Timberline Guides & Outfitters Ltd.
104 Beddington Circle
Calgary, AL, Canada
T3K 1K6
Brian Oliver

Timberline Tours Ltd.
Box 14
Lake Louise, AL, Canada
T0L 1E0
403-552-3743
Paul Peyto

Trimble Outfitting
Box 209
Caroline, AL, Canada
T0M 0M0
403-722-2340
Janet Trimble

Trophy Hunting & Fishing Consultants
12 Cedardale Cr. SW
Calgary, AL, Canada
T2W 3Z5
403-251-3828
L.D. Biscope

Turner, Bobby
R.R.#2
Cochrane, AL, Canada
T0L 0W0
403-932-5504

Big Game Outfitters Directory

North America

British Columbia

Vinson, Tom
General Delivery
Brule, AL, Canada
T0E 0C0
403-866-3746

Wiens Whitetails Inc.
R.R.#2, Box 6, Site 1
Tofielde, AL, Canada
T0B 4J0
403-662-3963
E. Wiens

Alpine Ridge Guiding & Outfitting
R.R.#2 Site 4 - 15
Cranbrook, BC, Canada
V1C 4H3
604-489-4218
Allan Strauss

Alpine Mountain Outfitters
Box 821
Chetwynd, BC, Canada
V0C 1J0

Ashnola Guide-Outfitters
Box 122
Keremeos, BC, Canada
V0X 1N0
604-499-5853
C. Schneider

Aurora Outfitters
Box 4150
Smithers, BC, Canada
V0J 2N0
604-847-4848
K. Oysmueller

A/Z Ranch Ltd.
Box 86
Windermere, BC, Canada
V0B 2L0
Bill Dubois

Baldy Mountain Outfitters
General Delivery
Wardner, BC, Canada
V0B 2J0
604-429-3985
Harry Levenberger

Bear Paw Guides & Outfitters
General Delivery
Sinclair Mills, BC, Canada
V0J 3M0
D. Smith

Big Game Guide & Outfitters
General Delivery
Dome Creek, BC, Canada
V0J 1H0
K.W. Hooker

Big Nine Outfitting
10532 Alaska Road
Fort St. John, BC, Canada
V1J 1B3
Barry Tompkins

Bougie Mountain Outfitters
Box 30 RR#1 Mile 308
Fort Nelson, BC, Canada
V0C 1R0
P. Gillis

Caribou Mountain Outfitters
Box 4010
Quesnel, BC, Canada
V2J 3J2
604-747-3334
B. Bowden

Carson, John & Rita
Box 1977
Grand Forks, BC, Canada
V0H 1H0
604-442-2406

Christina Falls Outfitters
Box 6640N
Fort St. John, BC, Canada
V1J 4J1
604-787-9624
Darwin Watson

Diamond M Outfitters Ltd.
Box 297
Atlin, BC, Canada
V0W 1A0
Radio Ph.2M8464 White Mtn.
Jim Mattarozzo

Doern, Wally
586 Edkins Street
Quesnel, BC, Canada
V2J 1X9
604-992-2287

Double Eagle Guides & Outfitters
Box 11 SS#1
Granisle, BC, Canada
V0J 1W0
Mr. S. Berg

Driftwood Ventures
SS#3 Comp. 1 Sykes Road
Prince George, BC, Canada
V2N 2S7
604-964-2467
S.S. Schielke

East Kootenay Outfitters
14-21st Avenue South
Creenbrook, BC, Canada
V1C 3H1
604-426-2834
J. Juozaitis

Elk Valley Bighorn Outfitters Ltd.
Box 414
Ferney, BC, Canada
V0B 1M0
604-529-7209
B. Fontana

Fawnie Mountain Outfitters
General Delivery
Anahim Lake, BC, Canada
V0L 1C0
503-575-1152

Finlay River Outfitters
549 Lampson Street
Victoria, BC, Canada
V9A 5Z8
604-385-3649

Fort Graham Lodge
Box 238
Hudson's Hope, BC, Canada
V0C 1V0
604-783-5248
Ken Kyllo

Frontier Hunting
Box 4491
Quesnel, BC, Canada
V3J 3J4
D. Davis

Gana River Outfitters Ltd.
Box 1178 Station A
Kelowna, BC, Canada
V1Y 7P8
604-763-0685
G. Koopman

Glenora Guest Ranch Ltd.
Telegraph Creek, BC, Canada
V0J 2W0
Radio Ph. JJ3-7079 Meehause
Nancy Hall

Graham River Outfitters Ltd.
Fort St. John, BC, Canada
V1J 4H9
604-785-4250/Radio YJ3-6280
Audrey Tompkins

Grizzly Basin Outfitters
Site 15 C71
Cranbrook, BC, Canada
V1C 4H4
604-426-5043
Wilf Boardman

Hawkins Outfitters
Box 187
Eureka, MT, USA, BC, Canada
59917
406-296-2642

Indian River Ranch
Box 360
Atlin, BC, Canada
V0W 1A0
D. Smith

Kettle River Guides
RR#1
Oliver, BC, Canada
O0H 1T0
M. Kilback

Kimsquit Fishing Outfitters
RR#4 Site 17 Comp 17
Prince George, BC, Canada
V2N 2J2
G. Pitman

Kinbasket Lake Outfitting
14210 Marine Drive
White Rock, BC, Canada
V4B 1A8
604-426-5043
Richard Hark

Lamoureux Outfitters Ltd.
General Delivery
Fort Ware, BC, Canada
V0J 3B0
Radio Ph. 2M3827 Ft. Ware
M. Lamoureux

Leake, Herb
Pink Mtn. Alaska Hwy.
BC, Canada
V0C 2B0

Len's Guide Service
Box 825
Prince George, BC, Canada
V2L 4T7
N698736 Radio Op.
L. Pickering

Love Bros. & Lee Ltd.
RR#1 Kispiox Road
Hazelton, BC, Canada
V0J 1Y0
604-842-6350
Ron Fleming

Mitchell-Cross Outfitters
Box 402
Radium, BC, Canada
V0A 1M0
604-347-9013
Lance McLean

Monashee Guide Service
RR#1
Lumby, BC, Canada
V0W 1A0
J. Langton

Moon Lake Outfitters Ltd.
Box 161
Atlin, BC, Canada
V0W 1A0
604-651-7515
E. Smith

Norwest Guiding & Outfitting
Box 29
Fort Steele, BC, Canada
604-426-5230
Jeff Beckley

Ottertail River Outfitting
S.S.#2, Site #12, Comp. 120
Fort St. John, BC, Canada
V1J 4M7
403-242-9209
Alan & Mary Young

Pallister River Guides & Outfitters
Box 238
Radium, BC, Canada
V0Z 1M0
604-347-9274

Big Game Outfitters Directory

North America

Prophiet & Muskwa Outfitters
General Delivery
Pink Mountain, BC, Canada
V0C 2B0
H.C. Leake

Purcell Wilderness Guiding & O/F
Box 6 Site 5 SS#1
Kimberley, BC, Canada
V1A 2Y3
604-427-7295
G. Hansen

Ram Creek Outfitters
General Delivery
Wardner, BC, Canada
V0B 2J0
604-429-3445
R. Fahselt

Red Sorensen Outfitting
Box 6067 Dept. SG
Victoria, BC, Canada
V8P 5L4
604-785-6473

Rocky Mountain High Outfitter/Guide
Box 65
Wardner, BC, Canada
V0B 2J0
604-429-3560
B. Scott

Rocky Mountain Outfitters
Box 4132
Golden, BC, Canada
V0A 1H0
604-344-2633
Carmen Dempsey

Ruby Range Outfitters Ltd.
Box 4874
Williams Lake, BC, Canada
V2G 2V8
604-398-7686/296-4305
John Drift

Sheep Mountain Outfitters
Box 577
Fernie, BC, Canada
V0B 1M0
604-423-7136

Simons, Charlie
Box 141
Horsefly, BC, Canada
V0L 1L0

Skeena Mountain Outfitters
6821 Lilac Crescent
Prince George, BC, Canada
V2K 3H2
604-962-7995
V. Carson

Sorensen, R.
Box 40
Muncho Lake, BC, Canada
V0C 1Z0

Spatsizi/Collingwood Bros. Guides
Box 3070
Smithers, BC, Canada
V0J 2N0
604-847-9692/846-9196

Steciw, I.
Box 2665
Smithers, BC, Canada
V0J 2N0
604-847-3055

Stein River Outfitters Ltd.
Box 494
Hope, BC, Canada
V0X 1L0
604-869-9532
Leo Ouellet

Stone Mountain Safaris
Mile 422 Alaska Highway
Toad River, BC, Canada
V1G 4J8
604-232-5469
D. Wiens

Taku Safari Inc.
Box 268
Atlin, BC, Canada
V0W 1A0
G. Anttila

Taseko Lake Outfitters
Box 4834
Williams Lake, BC, Canada
V2G 2V8
Radio N424967 Pr. George
S. Henry

Toby Creek Guides & Outfitters
304 9th Avenue S.
Cranbrook, BC, Canada
V1C 2M5
604-489-3006
Lloyd Harvey

Turnagain Holding LTd.
Box 130
Watson Lake, Yukon, Canada
Y0A 1C0
403-536-7942

Tweedsmuir Park Guides
Box 569
Vanderhof, BC, Canada
V0J 3A0
B. Nielsen

Wild Horse River Outfitters
Box 233
Cranbrook, BC, Canada
V1C 4H7
604-426-2688

Labrador

Lobstick Lodge
Box 86
Churchill Falls, Labrador, Canada
A0R 1A0
709-925-32235
Ray Cole

Reid, R.
Box 791
Cornerbrook, Labrador, Canada
A2H 6G7
709-639-7258

Manitoba

Mantagao Outfitters Inc.
15 Wiltshire Bay
Winnipeg, Man., Canada
R2J 2L6
204-235-0557

New Brunswick

Al Hunting Camp
RR#2 North View Road
Plaster Rock, NB, Canada
E0J 1W0
506-356-2575
Albert Deleaney

Al's Log Cabin
305 Fulkton Avenue
Fredericton, NB, Canada
E3A 2B9
506-472-3268
Allen A. Francis

Andy's Cabin
97 Queensway
St. Stephen, NB, Canada
E3L 1L6
506-466-5755
Andrew Mosher

Armondale Vacations, Outfitter
RR#1
Hartland, NB, Canada
E0J 1N0
506-375-4078
G. R. Henderson

Auberge du Summit
8P-Tisco Park
Edmundston, NB, Canada
E3V 3K5
506-735-7662
Robert Y. LaFrance

Barney Brook Hunting & Fishing
Box 1 Site 7
Grand Falls, NB, Canada
E0J 1M0
506-473-2226/3180
Albert & Mario Cote

Base plein-air du Yukon d'or
C.P. 487
St. Quentin, NB, Canada
E0K 1J0
506-235-2405/2645
Yvon & Gilles Quimper

Bass Creek Outfitter
RR#3
Oromocto, NB, Canada
E2V 2G3
506-357-3835/3012
Graham Currier

The Bear's Den
364 York Street
Fredericton, NB, Canada
E3B 3P7
506-458-0102/367-5032
Corey, Haines, Assoc.

Beaver Lodge
RR#1 Riley Brook
Plaster Rock, NB, Canada
E0J 1W0
506-356-2392/328-3524
James B. Parrish

Big Buck Lodge
Prince William, NB, Canada
E0H 1S0
506-363-5111
Brian McLean

Big Cedar Lodge
CC.P. 88
St. Quentin, NB, Canada
E0K 1J0
506-235-3428
Gaston Cote

Birch Lodge
RR#2
St. Stephen, NB, Canada
E3L 2X9
506-466-4427
E. Arsenault

Black Bear Lodge
Box 1888 161 Charles Street
Woodstock, NB, Canada
E0J 2B0
506-328-6969
Donald Sarchfield

Black's Hunting & Fishing Camps
RR#1
Plaster Rock, NB, Canada
E0J 1W0
506-356-2429
Juanita Black

Black Mountain Camps
Arthurette, NB, Canada
E0J 1C0
506-273-3738
John A. MacKellar

Big Game Outfitters Directory

North America

Bodell Lodge
Box 336
Perth-Andover, NB, Canada
E0J 1V0
506-273-2187
Harold Demerchant

Boiled Owl
Box 597
Plaster Rock, NB, Canada
E0J 1W0
506-356-2206
Donald Taylor

Broken Feather Lodge
Box 69
Red Bank, NB, Canada
E0C 1W0
506-836-2876
Wilfred I. Ward

The Buck Stops Here
102 Downey Avenue
Riverview, NB, Canada
E1B 1W5
506-386-2687
Glenn Jonah

Cains River Enterprises Ltd.
775 Hillsborough Road
Riverview, NB, Canada
506-386-3604/843-6301
R.W.W. Brown

Cambridge-Narrows Lodge
Cambridge-Narrows, NB, Canada
E0E 1E0
506-488-3302/832-3143
Charles B. Darling

Campbell's Fishing Camps
RR#1
Upper Blackville, NB, Canada
E0C 2C0
Mary Arbeau

Canaan Game Lodge
Coles Island, NB, Canada
E0E 1G0
506-382-5324
Donald A. Black

Canoose Camps
RR#3
St. Stephen, NB, Canada
E3L 2Y1
506-466-4586
Tom Mosher

Chickadee Lodge
Prince William, NB, Canada
E0H 1S0
506-363-2759/2288
Vaughn D. Schriver

Chickamoor Lodge
489 Island Road
Lunenburg, MA, USA
01462
617-582-4868
Paul Williams

Coakley's Camps
Newcastle Bridge, NB, Canada
E0E 1K0
506-472-5980/327-6419
A. Coakley

Condor Lodge
Box 801, Woodstock Road
Fredericton, NB, Canada
E3B 5B4
506-455-5537
Conrad Mead

Country Inns Renaissance Hotel
44 Arron Court
Riverview, NB, Canada
E1B 4C4
506-356-8821

Craigs Sporting Lodge & Camps
Box 1412
Woodstock, NB, Canada
E0J 2B0
506-328-3736
Dale & Brian Craig

Cranberry Lake Lodge
RR#1
Moores Mills, NB, Canada
E0G 2L0
506-466-3646
Leonard H. Way

Crockett's Sport Camp
RR#1
Codys, NB, Canada
E0E 1E0
506-488-2684
David L. Edwards

Curtis Fishing Camps
RR#1
Upper Blackville, NB, Canada
506-843-2569
John D. Curtis

Darrold Hunting Camp
RR#1
Plaster Rock, NB, Canada
E0J 1W0
506-273-2610
Darrold Taylor

Deerville Camps
RR#1
Lakeville, NB, Canada
E0J 1S0
506-276-3235
W. Alton Morrison

Donovan's Den
1 Raymond Avenue
Fredericton, NB, Canada
E3A 1S7
506-472-7784/367-3032
A. Donovan

Do-Ray Chalets
Box 251
Rexton, NB, Canada
E0A 2L0
506-523-9553
Doreen & Ray Burns

Dorrington Hill Outfitter
Box 131
Canterbury, NB, Canada
E0H 1C0
Shaun & Joy Collicot

D.P. Cole Rod & Gun
Box 2209
Sussex, NB, Canada
E0E 1P0
506-485-2989
David Cole

Dyer's Hunting & Fishing Camps
Box 216
Plaster Rock, NB, Canada
E0J 1W0
506-553-6587
Lawrence A. Dyer

The Eagle's Nest Sporting Camps
Canterbury, NB, Canada
E0H 1C0
506-279-2114
Arnold F. Drost

Eagle's Rest
9 Myles Drive
Saint John, NB, Canada
E2J 3E1
506-696-1273

Edmond Hemphill Outfitter
Glassville, NB, Canada
E0J 1L0
506-375-8707

Finnie's Canteen
RR#3
Harvey Station, NB, Canada
E0H 1H0
506-366-5222
Vernon Finnie

Flemming's Outfitters
RR#1
Debec, NB, Canada
E0J 1J0
506-277-6570
Bill & Joan Flemming

Fraser's Hunting Lodge
Box 1432
Sussex, NB, Canada
E0E 1P0
506-433-2122
Harland Fraser

Fundy Lodge
St. George, NB, Canada
E0G 2Y0
506-755-2963/328-3571
Sid & Lynette Weinman

Fundy Outfitters
Box 16
Hillsborough, NB, Canada
E0A 1X0
506-734-2424
Malcolm Rossiter

Gary Hunting Camp
RR#3
Bath, NB, Canada
E0J 1E0
506-278-5561
Gary Kearney

Geneau & Son Outfitter
RR#2
Plaster Rock, NB, Canada
E0J 1W0
506-553-6587

Gerald's Place
RR#1
Codys, NB, Canada
E0E 1E0
506-488-2737
Gerald C. Sarchfield

Green Acres Camp
RR#1
Canterbury, NB, Canada
E0H 1C0
506-894-2486
Mrs. J. Higgs

Governor's Table Camps
Box 282
Hartland, NB, Canada
E0J 1N0
506-246-5333/5466
Hugh B. Smith

Guimac Camps
RR#4
Hartland, NB, Canada
E0J 1N0
506-375-4711
Ralph Orser

Hanson's Lodge
Box 877 RR#5
Perth-Andover, NB, Canada
E0J 1V0
506-273-2844
Murray Hanson

S. Harrison Long Lake Sporting
Camps
RR#1
Plaster Rock, NB, Canada
E0J 1W0
506-551-1083/356-2362
Steve Harrison

Hector View Camp
Coles Island, NB, Canada
E0E 1G0
506-534-2985
Wayne W. Black

Big Game Outfitters Directory

North America

Henderson's Hunting Camps Ltd.
RR#1
Hartland, NB, Canada
E0J 1N0
506-375-4078
Robert A. Henderson

Herb's Sporting
Box 83
Centreville, NB, Canada
E0J 1H0
506-276-4768
Herbert Pryor

Hide Away Lodge
Box 820
Woodstock, NB, Canada
E0J 2B0
506-894-2412/328-9143
Brian Hayden

Highbridge Camps
Box 100
Newcastle, NB, Canada
E1V 3M2
506-622-0722

Hill, Gordon D.
RR#4
Hartland, NB, Canada
E0J 1N0
506-375-6488

Hilltop Lodge
RR#1
Plaster Rock, NB, Canada
E0J 1W0
506-356-2392
David R. Parish

Hinchey Pond Lodge
SS#1 (Silverwood)
Fredericton, NB, Canada
E3B 5M7
506-369-7208/454-4440
Leslie I Hull

Hotel/Motel Victoria
St. Quentin, NB, Canada
E0K 1J0
506-235-2002
Laura Perron

Howard's Camp
RR#1
Riley Brook, NB, Canada
E0J 1W0
506-356-2481
Ralph & Gladys Howard

Hudson Brook Fishing Club
Blackville, NB, Canada
E0C 1C0
506-843-6510/2802
Richard Underhill

Indian Island Vacation
RR#2
Texton, NB, Canada
E0A 2L0
506-523-9676
R. Garfield Barlow

Inn by the Pond
Box 114
Doaktown, NB, Canada
E0C 1G0
506-365-7942
Percy Jagoe

Joe's Place
57 Round Road
Lunenburg, MA, USA
01482
617-582-7707
Joe Williams

Juniper Lodge
Juniper, NB, Canada
E0J 1P0
506-246-5223
Frank MacDonald

Keith Robertson Sporting Camp
RR#1
Plaster Rock, NB, Canada
E0J 1W0
506-356-2677
Keith Robertson

Kelly's Lodge
Doaktown, NB, Canada
E0C 1G0
506-365-7602
Keith Betts

Kelly's Sporting Lodge
RR#6
Fredericton, NB, Canada
E3B 4X4
506-363-4435/672-0867
Allan Kelly

Kings County Outfitter
Plumweseep
Kings County, NB, Canada
E0E 1P0
506-433-1240

Lakeview Camps
St. Croix, NB, Canada
E0H 1K0
506-784-2918/207-788-3875
Kenneth F. MAson

Larry's Corner Outfitter
RR#4
Burtts Corner, NB, Canada
E0H 1B0
506-622-7389/363-2302
Lawrence Burtt

L & W Fishing & Hunting Lodge
Box 47
Blackville, NB, Canada
E0C 1C0
506-843-7772
Winston J. Curtis

Lindsay Sporting Camps
RR#4
Millville, NB, Canada
E0H 1M0
506-463-2639
Charles Lindsay

Little Bald Peak Lodge
RR#1
Plaster Rock, NB, Canada
E0J 1W0
506-356-2354
Allison King

Log Sluice Camp
Riley Brook
Plaster Rock, NB, Canada
E0J 1W0
506-356-2223
Gordon B. Workman

Long Meadow Cabins
Harvey Station, NB, Canada
E0H 1H0
506-366-2043
Dell Johnston

Loon Bay Lodge Ltd.
Box 101
St. Stephen, NB, Canada
E3L 2A1
506-466-1240
David Whittingham

The Lucky 7 Camp
RR#1
Plaster Rock, NB, Canada
E0J 1W0
506-356-8311
David E. Parish

The Lyons Den
Doaktown, NB, Canada
E0C 1G0
506-365-4619
Calvin O. Lyons

MacFarlane Sporting Camps
Millville, NB, Canada
E0H 1M0
506-463-8102
Dixon MacFarlane

Magaguadavic River Diversion
RR#4
Harvey Station, NB, Canada
E0H 1H0
506-366-2124
James & Bonnie Smith

Mamozekel Lodge
RR#1
Plaster Rock, NB, Canada
E0J 1W0
506-356-2256
Robert Miller

Manuel's Hunting & Fishing Camps
RR#1
Hartland, NB, Canada
E0J 1N0
506-375-8812/6197
Dale & Sheldon Manuel

McIntyre's Motor Hotel & Restaurant
Waterborough, NB, Canada
E0E 1S0
506-362-2913
Derwyn McIntyre

McCrea Farms Hunting & Fishing
RR#2
Hatfield Point, NB, Canada
E0G 2A0
506-475-2753
James & Anna McCrea

Melvin's Hunting-Fishing Lodge
Box 481
Plaster Rock, NB, Canada
E0J 1W0
506-473-4058
Melvin B. Sirois

Mic Mac Salmon CLub
Box 43
Tabusintac, NB, Canada
E0C 2A0
506-779-9250
Clive W. Wishart

Millet's on the Cains
Blackville, NB, Canada
E0C 1C0
506-843-2869/2411
Millet Underhill

Miramachi Camps Ltd.
Juniper, NB, Canada
E0J 1P0
506-246-5291
Earl F. Boyd

Miramichi Inn
RR#2
Red Bank, NB, Canada
E0C 1W0
506-836-7452
Andre Godin

Miramichi Lodge
C.P. 462
Lac St. Charles, P.Q. Canada
G0A 2H0
418-849-5134
Gilbert Lemay

Miramichi Salmon Club
Doaktown, NB, Canada
E0C 1G0
506-365-2289

Mountain Spring Lodge
RR#2
Plaster Rock, NB, Canada
E0J 1W0
506-356-8848
Mildred Yeomans

Mountain View Cottage
RR#1
Plaster Rock, NB, Canada
E0J 1W0
506-356-2514
Delores Jenkins

Mountain View Hunting & Fishing
RR#2
Plaster Rock, NB, Canada
E0J 1W0
506-356-7214
Collins Hudnut

Big Game Outfitters Directory

North America

Mohannes Camp
Box 1 Site 8 SS#1
St. Stephen, NB, Canada
E3L 2Y4
506-466-3325
Wilfred M. Davidson

Napadogan Lodge
Mapadogan, NB, Canada
E0H 1E0
506-367-2475
Michel E. Order

Nash Bar Lodge
RR#4 D57 398 Caledonia Road
Moncton, NB, Canada
E1C 8J8
506-843-6597
Dan Fowler

Neilson's Sporting Camps
Plaster Rock, NB, Canada
E0J 1W0
506-356-2391
Neil C. Neilson

Nepisiguit River Camps
Box 345 RR#5
Bathurst, NB, Canada
E2A 3Y8
506-546-5873
Kenneth Gray

Nerepis Lodge
RR#2
Westfield, NB, Canada
E0G 3J0
506-757-8871
Reginald Fredericks

Newburg Lodge
RR#5 Newburg Road
Woodstock, NB, Canada
E0J 2B0
506-328-2959
Robert Clark

Northern Pine Hunts
Box 631 RR#2
Plaster Rock, NB, Canada
E0J 1W0
506-356-2412

Northern Wilderness Lodge
Box 571
Plaster Rock, NB, Canada
E0J 1W0
506-356-8327
William Linton

North Lake Guiding Service
RR#1
Canterbury, NB, Canada
E0H 1C0
506-894-2235
Mrs. E. Fredericks

North View Hunting & Fishing Lodge
Box 593
Plaster Rock, NB, Canada
E0J 1W0
506-3356-7212
Queenie Deleavey

Odell Lodge
RR#1
Arthurette, NB, Canada
E0J 1C0
506-356-2521
Jean Louis Page

Old Mill Boat & Gun Club
Red Bank, NB, Canada
E0C 1W0
506-836-7759/7818
Eugene Gillis

Old River Lodge
RR#2
Doaktown, NB, Canada
E0C 1G0
506-365-7568
Alex Mills

Out Back Camp
RR#6
St. Stephen, NB, Canada
E3L 2Y3
506-466-2247
Wayne Townsend

Oven Rock Camp
RR#1
Riley Brook, NB, Canada
E0J 1W0
506-356-2330
Joseph Glaneuski

Palfrey Lake Lodge
Box 386
McAdam, NB, Canada
E0H 1K0
506-784-2817
Mrs. Larry G. Day

Parson's Hunting & Fishing Camp
RR#4
Hartland, NB, Canada
E0J 1N0
506-375-4347
Lloyd Parsons

Phillips Fishing & Hunting Camp
118 Fawn Crescent
Fredericton, NB, Canada
E3B 6H7
506-455-2708/894-2271
Earlin Phillips

Pond's Chalet Resort
Porter Cove Road
Ludlow, NB, Canada
E0C 1N0
506-369-2612
Keith Pond

Pond's (Porter Kove) Kamps
Box 8
Ludlow, NB, Canada
E0C 1N0
506-369-2228
Mrs. Charles Pond

Portobello Cedars
RR#2
Fredericton, NB, Canada
E3B 4X3
506-357-8013
Eric W. Moxon

Pro-Guides
Box 39
St. Leonard, NB, Canada
E0L 1M0
506-423-6689
Ephrem Michaud

Riley Brook Camps Ltd.
RR#1
Plaster Rock, NB, Canada
E0J 1W0
506-356-2315
Ivan McAskill

River de Chute Lodge
Box 641
Plaster Rock, NB, Canada
E0J 1W0
506-356-2242
Don Hollins

River Side Guest Home
Doaktown, NB, Canada
E0C 1G0
506-365-4685
Thomas Sturgeon

Rivers Inlet Lodge
RR#1
Albert, NB, Canada
E0A 1A0
506-882-2601
Grant I. Woodworth

River View Camp
RR#1
Plaster Rock, NB, Canada
E0J 1W0
506-356-8351
Donald McAskill

Romeo's Maple Lodge
RR#2
New Denmark, NB, Canada
E0J 1T0
506-356-2239
Romeo Rossignol

Ruff's Sporting Camps
RR#1
Plaster Rock, NB, Canada
E0J 1W0
506-356-2438
Edward & John Ruff

Salmon River Lodge Ltd.
Box 253
Chipman, NB, Canada
E0E 1C0
506-339-6556
Monte Farrell

Shogomoc Camps
RR#3
Mackawic, NB, Canada
E0H 1P0
506-272-2171
Willard Way

Skiff Lake Inn Sporting Camps
RR#1 Skiff Lake
Canterbury, NB, Canada
E0H 1C0
506-279-2119
Albert E. Conklin

Slipp Bros. Ltd. Hunting & Fishing
Central Blissville, NB, Canada
E0G 1M0
506-368-7882/7747
Ron & Duane Slipp

Southridge Sporting Camp
Florenceville, NB, Canada
E0J 1K0
506-392-5318
W.A. Prosser

Spring Brook Camps
Tracy, NB, Canada
E0G 3C0
506-368-2509
Eugene O'Neill

Sunset Shangri-La Hunting & Fishing
Doaktown, NB, Canada
E0C 1G0
506-365-7956
Donald Lyons

Sunset View Lodge
RR#1
McAdam, NB, Canada
E0H 1K0
506-784-2928
Jack H. Grant

Sutherland Hunting Camp
RR#1
Plaster Rock, NB, Canada
E0J 1W0
506-356-2467
William Sutherland

Sutter Lodge
Box 96
Doaktown, NB, Canada
E0C 1G0
506-365-4572/4607
Kaye Lyons

Tamarack Lodge
Box 137
Canterbury, NB, Canada
E0H 1C0
506-277-6598
John Davidson

Big Game Outfitters Directory

North America

Tardif Sporting Camp
Box 237 Enterprise Road
Plaster Rock, NB, Canada
E0J 1W0
506-356-2298
Larry Tardif

Thornton's Sporting Camps
Box 452
Hartland, NB, Canada
E0J 1N0
506-375-6632
Beatrice S. Thornton

Three Brook Camps
RR#2
Plaster Rock, NB, Canada
E0J 1W0
506-356-2245
Dale Tomkins

Timberline Lodge
25 Davenport Avenue
Saint John, NB, Canada
E2K 4C4
506-657-2853/534-2515
Edward J. Soucy

Tobique & Serpentine
RR#1
Plaster Rock, NB, Canada
E0J 1W0
506-356-2215
Edythe McAskill

Tobique River Lodge
RR#1
Plaster Rock, NB, Canada
E0J 1W0
506-356-2000
Jim & Lena Lacey

Tobique View Motel & Sporting
Camps
Box 571
Plaster Rock, NB, Canada
E0J 1W0
506-356-6327
William Linton

Trecartin's Sporting Camps
RR#4
Hartland, NB, Canada
E0J 1N0
506-375-6238
Jerry A. Trecartin

Tuckaway Lodge
Box 91
Boiestown, NB, Canada
E0H 1A0
506-369-2294
Vincent Swazey

Victor Hunting Camp
RR#1
Plaster Rock, NB, Canada
E0J 1W0
506-356-2372
John Merritt

Webb, Fred A. & Sons
RR#1 Nictau
Plaster Rock, NB, Canada
E0J 1W0
506-356-8312

Williams Hunting & Fishing
RR#3
Harvey Station, NB, Canada
E0H 1H0
506-366-5646
Gary Williams

Wilson's Sporting Camps Ltd.
McNamee, NB, Canada
E0C 1P0
506-365-7963
Keith Wilson

Winchester Arms Sporting Camps
RR#1
Mactaquac, NB, Canada
E0H 1N0
506-363-3550
David Winchester

Windy Hill Lodge
Riley Brook, NB, Canada
E0J 1W0
Albert Scafordi

Yukon d'Or Camp & Lodge
Box 1222
Grand Falls, NB, Canada
E0J 1M0
506-473-1190/356-2241
Riley Brook

Newfoundland

Blue Mountain Outfitters
Box 126
Cow Head, NFLD, Canada
A0K 2A0
709-243-7278/2422
Carol Paynew

Deer Pond Camps Ltd.
Box 9
Corner Brook, NFLD, Canada
A2H 6C3
709-634-2347
A.N. Wenzell

Long Range Outfitters
Highlands, NFLD, Canada
A0N 1N0
709-645-2789
Gerry Pumphrey

MacInnis, Don
Highlands, NFLD, Canada
A0N 1N0
709-639-7309

Pumphrey, Gerry
Highlands, NFLD, Canada
A0N 1N0
709-639-7309

Reid, R.
Box 791
Corner Brook, NFLD, Canada
A2H 6G7
709-639-7258

Shanadithit Camps Ltd.
Box 733
Corner Brook, NFLD, Canada
A2H 6G7
709-634-2505
Joe Peddie

Nova Scotia

Beaver Island Lodge
Box 402 Milton
Queens County, NS, Canada
B0T 1T0
902-354-4354
Don Breen

Bras d'Or Lakes Outfitters
RR#2 Boisdale, Christmas Island
Cape Breton, NS, Canada
B0A 1C0
902-871-2549
Earl Rudderham

Clearwater Outfitters
RR#2
Annapolis, NS, Canada
B0S 1A0
902-638-3509
Robert & Marie

Eastern Valley Outfitters
Box 40
Sherbrooke, NS, Canada
B0J 3C0
902-522-2235
Aubrey Beaver

Lansdowne Lodge
Upper Stewiacke Valley
NS, Canada
B0N 2P0
902-268-2749
Tom & Marion Kennedy

North Mountain Outfitters
Box 149
Middleton, NS, Canada
B0S 1P0
902-825-4030/6629
Roger Ehrenfield

River View Lodge
Greenfield
Queens County, NS, Canada
B0T 1E0
902-685-2423/2378/2376
Moyal Conrad

Sentinel Safety Consultants
RR#3 Meisner's Section
New Germany, NS, Canada
B0R 1E0
902-644-3015
Ron Seney

Stewiake Valley Outfitters
RR#3 Brookfield
Colchester County, NS, Canada
B0N 1C0
902-673-2023
David Kennedy

Turner's West Branch Lodge
RR#1 Aspen
Guysborough County, NS, Canada
B0H 1E0
902-833-2303
Phillip Turner

Northwest Territories

Arctic Fishing Lodges & Outfitters
Box 806
Yellowknife, NWT, Canada
X1A 2N6
403-873-4036/3626
Yvonne Quick

Arctic Red River OutfittersLtd.
Box 1457
Lloydminster, AL, Canada
S9V 1K4
403-875-0560
R. Woodward

Canada North Outfitting Inc.
Box 1230 SA
Waterdown, Ont., Canada
L0R 2H0
416-689-7925

Canada North EXpeditions
Box 2435
Yellowknife, NWT, Canada
X1A 2P8
403-920-2196
Bill Tait

Guided Arctic Expeditions
Box 2120
Inuvik, NWT, Canada
X0E 0T0
403-979-2408
T. Cook

J Group Co. Ltd.
Box 447
Yellowknife, NWT, Canada
Z1A 2V7
403-920-4654
Jim Peterson

Mackenzie Mountain Oufitters Ltd.
Box 124
Norman Wells, NWT, Canada
X0E 0V0
403-587-2255
S. Stevens

Nahanni Butte Outfitters Ltd.
Box 879
Nanton, AL, Canada
T0L 1R0
403-646-5768
G. Williams

Big Game Outfitters Directory

North America

NWT Outfitters Ltd.
Box 1144
Glenwood, AL, Canada
T0K 2R0
403-626-3279
D. Nelson

Ramhead Outfitters Inc.
Box 89
Warburg, AL, Canada
T0C 2T0
403-848-7578/2502
S. Simpson

Redstone Mountain Trophy Hunts
Box 608
Banff, AL, Canada
T0L 0C0
403-762-5241
Tim & Hugh MacAuley

South Nahanni Outfitters Ltd.
Box 586
Cardston, AL, Canada
T0K 0K0
403-653-2562
B. Woodward

True North Safaris
36 Morrison Dr.
Yellowknife, NWT, Canada
X1A 1Z2
403-873-8533
G. Jaeb

Webb-Qaivvik Ltd.
441 Church Rd.
Landsdale, PA, USA
19446
215-362-1510

Ontario

Black Ghost Outfitters
146 4th Avenue
Sudbury, Ont., Canada
P3B 3R8
705-560-6802
Kris Fielding

Camp Asgard
Svant Lake, Ont., Canada
P0V 2S0
804-584-2923

Canada North Outfitting Inc.
Box 1230 SA
Waterdown, Ont., Canada
L0R 2H0
416-689-7925

French River Bear Outfitters
RR#2
Alban, Ont., Canada
P0M 1A0
705-857-2951
Trevor Spooner

Hay Lake Lodge
Box 189H
Whitney, Ont., Canada
K0J 2M0
613-637-2675
Phil Morlock

Koivukoski, Kai
Box 1304N
Sioux Lookout, Ont., Canada
P0V 2T0
807-737-1707

Northern Lights Resort
Box 79A
Loring, Ont., Canada
705-757-2554
Mr. H. Streoher

Pine Acres Bear Camp & Outfitters
Box 59H
Vermilion Bay, Ont., Canada
P0V 2V0
807-227-2073

Polar Bear Camp & Fly-In Outfitters
Box 396 22-5th Street
Cochrane, Ont., Canada
P0L 1C0
705-272-5890/4672
Mr. S. Konpelly

Red Pine Hunting & Fishing Camp
1402 Altona Road
Pickering, Ont., Canada
L1V 1M1
416-286-2994

Windy Bay Lodge
RR#1
Rainy River, Ont., Canada
P0W 1L0
807-488-5723
Tony & Lynn Beyak

Quebec

Arctic Adventures
8102 Trans Canada Hwy.
Montreal, Quebec, Canada
H4S 1R4
514-332-0880
S. Cantafio

Cargair Ltd.
Box 370
St Michel-des-Saints, Que., Canada
J0K 3B0
514-833-6836

Cerf-Sau Inc.
Dept. G, 40 Racine St.
Loretteville, Quebec, Canada
G2B 1C6
418-843-0173
Gilles Shooner

Club Cesar, Inc.
7602 Blvd. Marie-Victoire
Brossard, Quebec, Canada
J4W 1B2
514-672-1103
Benoit Brossard

Domaine Omega Inc.
Route 323
Montebello, Quebec, Canada
J0V 1L0
819-423-5023
Mr. Spengler

Hunt River Camps Ltd.
Box 307, Stn. A
Goose Bay, Labrador, Canada
A0P 1S0

Laurentian Ungava Outfitters Ltd.
250 Dunany Rd.
Lachute, Quebec, Canada
J8H 3W8
514-562-3832
Jack Hume

Mistassini Lake Outfitting Camps
Baie de Poste
Via Chibougamau, Quebec, Canada
G0W 1C0
A. Matoosh

Montagnais Fishing & Hunting Club
6357, Des Citelles
Orsainville, Quebec, Canada
G1G 1E3
418-627-4165

Nordik Adventure Inc.
Box 203 succ. LaSalle
LaSalle, Quebec, Canada
H8R 3V2
514-366-7421

Normanic Inc. - Pourvoiries
2323 N. Versant Blvd. #103
Sainte-Foy, Quebec, Canada
G1N 4P4
418-681-1258
F. Lacombe

Pourvoiries des 100 Lacs, Inc.
603 Boul. Ste-Elisabeth, #A
La Prairie, Quebec, Canada
J5R 1V5
514-659-4155

Pourvoyeurs de la R. Delay Inc.
C.P. 1540
Schefferville, Quebec, Canada
G0G 2T0
418-585-3475

Richer Lodge (Echouani)
110 Cavanaugh
Maniwaki, Quebec, Canada
J9E 2P8
819-449-1613
Raymond Richer

Toundratour Inc.
319 E., St-Zotique
Montreal, Quebec, Canada
H2S 1L5
514-270-7266
Henri Poupart

Twin River Lodge
4101 Radisson St.
Montreal, Quebec, Canada
H1M 1X7
514-254-6159
Robert Threlfall

Tuktu Fishing & Hunting Club
Box 427
Ancienne-Lorette, Quebec, Canada
G2E 4W6
418-872-3839

Saskatchewan

KOO-STO Wilderness Outfitters
807 N. 6th Street
Bismarck, ND, USA
58501
701-223-8127
Mike Dolbel

Saskatchewan River Hunting Camps
1529 East Heights
Saskatoon, Sask, Canada
S7J 3B4
306-653-2650
Glen Hill

Sportsmen's Adventures Inc.
94 Empress Drive
Regina, Sask, Canada
S4T 6M6
306-522-6381

Yukon

Cassiar Mountain Outfitters Ltd.
Box 267
Watson Lake, Yukon Canada
Y0A 1C0
403-536-7536
K. Funnell

Ceaser Lake Outfitters
Box 484 Dept. 1
Watson Lake, Yukon Canada
Y0A 1C0
403-536-2174
Terry Wilkinson

Desrosiers, Belle
Box 4804
Whitehorse, Yukon Canada
Y1A 4N6
403-633-2146

Dickson, R.A. (Dick)
708 Minto Rd.
Whitehorse, Yukon Canada
Y1A 3X9
403-633-2228

Big Game Outfitters Directory

North America

Herb Sievers Outfitters Ltd.
503 Hoge St. Ste. 206
Whitehorse, Yukon Canada
Y1A 1W3
403-668-7219
Herb Sievers

High Country Safaris Ltd.
Teslin, Yukon Canada
Y0A 1B0
Radio JJ 36454 Swift River
Ed Dolhan

Jenson, Pete
58 Alsek Rd.
Whitehorse, Yukon Canada
Y1A 3K4
403-667-2030

Koser, Werner
General Delivery
Ross River, Yukon Canada
Y0B 1S0
403-969-2210

Kusawa Outfitters Ltd.
28 Alsek Rd.
Whitehorse, Yukon Canada
Y1A 3K2
403-667-2755/2379
K. Heyman

Laberge Ranch & Outfitters
Box 4458
Whitehorse, Yukon Canada
Y1A 2R8
403-633-6606

Low, Doug J.
General Delivery
Taglish, Yukon Canada
Y0B 1T0
403-399-3171

MacMillan River Outfitters, Inc.
Box 5088
Whitehorse, Yukon Canada
Y1A 4S3
403-668-5072
D. Coleman

Nisutlin Bay Outfitters
General Delivery
Teslin, Yukon Canada
Y0A 1B0
403-390-2557
B. Hassard & P. Smith

Ostashek Outfitting Ltd.
Box 4146 Dept. NA
Whitehorse, Yukon Canada
Y1A 3S6
403-668-7323
J.L. Ostashek

Pelly Mountain Outfitters
Box 4492
Whitehorse, Yukon Canada
Y1A 2R8
403-633-6606
Clay Martin

Reynolds, Stan
Box 108
Dawson City, Yukon Canada
Y1B 1G0
Radio SQ 787

Rogue River Outfitters
General Delivery
Ross River, Yukon Canada
Y0B 1S0
403-969-2250
Cam Drinan

Ruby Range Outfitters
General Delivery
Destruction Bay, Yukon Canada
Y0A 1H0
604-398-7686
J. Drift

Teslin Outfitters
General Delivery
Teslin, Yukon Canada
Y0A 1B0
403-390-2559
Doug Smarch

Widrig Outfitters Ltd.
Box 5390
Whitehorse, Yukon Canada
Y1A 4Z2
403-668-2752
Chris Widrig

Young, David
Site 12 Comp 24 R.R.#1
Whitehorse, Yukon Canada
Y1A 4Z6
403-668-4518

Yukon Hunting &Guiding Ltd.
#25 - 5 Klondike Rd.
Whitehorse, Yukon Canada
Y1A 3L7
403-667-7182
Rick Furniss

Yukon Outfitting
Box 5364
Whitehorse, Yukon Canada
Y1A 4Z2
403-667-2712
Rick Furniss

Mexico

Alcampo Hunting Adventures
Dr. Noriega Y Garmandia 108
Hermosillo, Sonora, Mexico
83000
621-2-32-39

Big Game Outfitters
Sauzales No. 44
Mexico, D.F.
14330
671-1177/2064
C. G. Hermosillo

Ron's Mexico Safaris
Box 83B Rte. 2
Mission, TX, USA
78572
512-581-1680

Solimar Hunting Safaris
Box 41
Guaymas, Sonora, Mexico
622-2-70-39
Ernesto Zaragoza

Sonora Outfitters
Aguascalientes 132
Hermosillo, Sonora, Mexico
52-621-48703
Leon Hoeffer

United States

Alaska

AAA Alaskan Outfitters Inc.
Box 110-774
Anchorage, AK, USA
99511-0774
907-345-0399

Alaska Bush Adventures
610 W. 91st Avenue
Anchorage, AK, USA
99515
907-522-1712

Alaska Hunts
607 - 2900 Boniface Parkway
Anchorage, AK, USA
99504
907-333-5214
Audrey Engle

Alaska King Salmon Adventures
Box 294
Oak Creek, WI, USA
53154
414-425-1838/483-8870

Alaska Rainbow Lodge
Box 1711
Anchorage, AK, USA
99510
907-248-2880/287-3059
Ron Hayes

Alaska Trophy Hunts
Box 878 Mystic Lake Lodge
Palmer, AK, USA
99645
907-745-3168
George & Marty Palmer

Alaskan Trophy Hunting
Box 193
Willow, AK, USA
99688
907-495-6434
Dick Gunlogson

Arctic Alaska Safaris
Box 57
Kotzebue, AK, USA
99752
907-442-3592
John A. Walker

Bailey, James K.
Box 770695
Eagle River, AK, USA
99577
907-688-2163

Black, Stephen W.
Box 4323
Kenai, AK, USA
99611

Branham, Chris
Box 6184
Anchorage, AK, USA
99502

Branham, Mike
Box 190128
Anchorage, AK, USA
99519-0128

Brooks Range Arctic Hunts
Parks Highway Mile 329 Route 1
Nenana, AK, USA
99760
E. Witt

Canoe Bay Outfitters
Box 176
Sand Point, AK, USA
99661
907-383-2381/3844
S. Hakala, Sr.

Carlson, Dick
3900 Greenland Drive
Anchorage, AK, USA
99517

Castle, Lynn
Box 517
Denali Park, AK, USA
99755

Cinder River Lodge
1820 Rebel Ridge Drive
Anchorage, AK, USA
99504
G. King Jr.

Deneut, Michael C.
Pope & Vannoy Landing
Iliamna, AK, USA
99606

Englund, Des
Box 6881
Anchorage, AK, USA
99502

Erickson, John E.
Box 101
Tok, AK, USA
99780

Big Game Outfitters Directory

North America

Exclusive Alaskan Hunts
Box 8860 Route C
Palmer, AK, USA
99645
A. Runyan

Fair Chase Hunts
Box 10-2104
Anchorage, AK, USA
99510-2104
907-274-3996
J. Hendricks

Fait, Gary
507 - 1013 East Diamond Blvd.
Anchorage, AK, USA
99502
907-345-1731

Fanning, Ken
Box 80929
College, AK, USA
99708

Farmen, Darrell
1228 - 1200 East 76th Avenue
Anchorage, AK, USA
99518

Fejes, Samuel T.
Box 111394
Anchorage, AK, USA
99511

Fitzgerald, Bill
Box 93
Talkeetna, AK, USA
99676

Fitzgerald, Kevin
Box 375
Talkeetna, AK, USA
99676

Flynn, David H.
9800 Tolsona Circle
Anchorage, AK, USA
99502

Flynn, Howard D.
4203 Minnesota Drive
Anchorage, AK, USA
99503

Frazier, Jay
Box 1331
Delta Junction, AK, USA
99737

Frost, Stan
Box 112449
Anchorage, AK, USA
99511

Gaedeke, Bernd
Box 80424 Farmers Loop Road
Fairbanks, AK, USA
99708

Gay, Kirk D.
Box 6583
Anchorage, AK, USA
99502

Gerlach, Robert
Box 23
Talkeetna, AK, USA
99676

Gillis, Melvin B.
847 East 74th Street
Anchorage, AK, USA
99502

Glacier Guides Inc.
Box 66
Gustavus, AK, USA
99826
907-697-2252
J. Rosenbruch

Grasser, Ed
Box 1350
Palmer, AK, USA
99645

Gray, Charles Lee
311 Slater Street
Fairbanks, AK, USA
99701

Guthrie, Richard A.
Box 24-0163 9530 Albatross Drive
Anchorage, AK, USA
99524
907-243-7766

Hancock, Lee
Nabesna Road
Slana, AK, USA
99586

Hankerd, Hank
Box 873668
Wasilla, AK, USA
99687

Hannon, Bob
Box 22 General Delivery
Koyuk, AK, USA
99753
907-963-3221

Hansen, David
1511 Atkinson
Anchorage, AK, USA
99504

Harms, Dennis
Box 670071
Chugiak, AK, USA
99567

Harrower, Jim
13830 Jarvis Drive
Anchorage, AK, USA
99515

Hautanen, Nelson
3157 64th Avenue
Anchorage, AK, USA
99502

Helmericks, Hermon
930 9th Avenue
Fairbanks, AK, USA
99701

Herscher, Rick
Box 8376
Anchorage, AK, USA
99508
907-279-9874

High Adventure Air Charter & O/F
Box 486
Soldotna, AK, USA
99669
907-262-5237
W. Bell

Holleman, Dan Foy
Box 80085
Fairbanks, AK, USA
99708

Hunt Alaska
Chisana, AK, USA
99588
T. Overly

Ingledue, F.W.
4815 Glacier Highway
Juneau, AK, USA
99801

Israelson, Arnold J.
Box 467
Yakutat, AK, USA
99689

Jacobson, Jake
Box 124
Kotzebue, AK, USA
99752

Jacobson, Patricia A.
Box 1313
Kodiak, AK, USA
99615

Jensen, Marcus F.
Box 2220
Juneau, AK, USA
99802

Johnson, Don L.
Box 152
Kenai, AK, USA
99611

Johnson, Keith
3646 North Point Drive
Anchorage, AK, USA
99515
907-243-5087

Johnson, Warren
Bear Lake Lodge
Port Moller, AK, USA
99571

Jones' Guide & Outfitting
HCR 33675 Jones Drive
Homer, AK, USA
99603
907-235-6455

Kahn, Steve
SR Box 26192
Wasilla, AK, USA
99687

Katmai Guide Service
Box 313
King Salmon, AK, USA
99613
907-246-3030
Joe Klutsch

Keeline, Jim
Box 1333
Juneau, AK, USA
99801
712-336-5124/225-2168

Keen, Rocky
SRA Box 6316
Palmer, AK, USA
99654

King Jr., Gary
1820 Rebel Ridge Drive
Anchorage, AK, USA
99504

Knutson, Howard
211-555 W. Northern Lights Blvd.
Anchorage, AK, USA
99503

Kuskokwim Guide Service
2 - 1608 Tamarack Street
Fairbanks, AK, USA
99701
P. Shepherd

Lamoureux, Gus & Frenchy
Box 4-444-S
Anchorage, AK, USA
99509
907-248-4971/3021

Lane, Karl E.
Box 295
Juneau, AK, USA
99802

LaRose, Gary B.
Box 3412
Palmer, AK, USA
99645

Latham, John H.
Box 254
Yakutat, AK, USA
99689

Lazer, David L.
SRA Box 6877
Palmer, AK, USA
99645
907-745-4504

Lee, Jack
Box 4-2495
Anchorage, AK, USA
99059

Big Game Outfitters Directory

North America

Lee, Tony
Box 771224-S AP
Eagle River, AK, USA
99577

Leonard, Dave
Box 1426
Kenai, AK, USA
99611

Lovin, Lloyd K.
Box 81429
College, AK, USA
99708

Mark's Guide Service
3942 Cosmos Drive
Anchorage, AK, USA
99517
907-248-1452
Mark Sandland

Masterson Charters
Box 34173
Juneau, AK, USA
99803
907-789-9061
Don Masterson

Matfay, Larry
Box 2
Old Arbor, AK, USA
99643

McNutt, Ray
Box 10
Sterling, AK, USA
99672

Metheny, Jim
Box 40015
Clear, AK, USA
99704

Midnight Sun Adventures
1306 East 26th Avenue
Anchorage, AK, USA
99508
P. Driver

Morgan, Rocky
Box 870649
Wasilla, AK, USA
99687

Mountain Monarchs of Alaska
Box 1426
Kenai, AK, USA
99611
907-283-4010/694-1569
D. Leonard

Neel, Dave
Box 6303
Anchorage, AK, USA
99502

Norman, Edward M.
Box 770588
Eagle River, AK, USA
99577

Northwest Outfitters
4127 Rasberry Road
Anchorage, AK, USA
99502
Chris Goll

Nunivak Outfitters
Box 2
Mekoryuk, AK, USA
99630
F. Don

Oney, Tony
2631 West 100th Avenue
Anchorage, AK, USA
99515

Owens, Dennis C.
Box 61
Moose Pass, AK, USA
99631

Pahl, Gerlad
Box 516
Glennallen, AK, USA
99588

Park Munsey, Michael
Amook Pass
Kodiak, AK, USA
99615

Pinnell, Bill
Olga Bay
Kodiak, AK, USA
99615

Ptarmigan Lake Lodge
1001 Lake View Terrace
Fairbanks, AK, USA
99701
907-456-6967
Urban E. Rahoi

Rainer, Dennis E.
Box 55454
North Pole, AK, USA
99705

Rainy Pass Lodge
430 - 200 West 34th Avenue
Anchorage, AK, USA
99503
907-349-4976
C. Vernon Humble

Rivers, Larry R.
Box 107
Talkteetna, AK, USA
99676
907-733-2471

Rohrer's Bear Camp
Box 2219
Kodiak, AK, USA
99615
907-486-5835
Richard Rohrer

Running W Outfitters
Box 1848
Homer, AK, USA
99603
907-235-6616
Dennis Wade

Runyan, Andy
SRC Box 8860
Palmer, AK, USA
99645

Sage, C. Michael
5108 Strawberry Road
Anchorage, AK, USA
99502

Schetzle, Harold
Box 670790
Chugiak, AK, USA
99567

Schoonover, Ken
Box 136
Hoonah, AK, USA
99829

Shavings, Ed
Box 31
Mekoryuk, AK, USA
99630

Sheep River Hunting Camps
Box 87-1721
Wasilla, AK, USA
99687
E. Stevenson

Smith, Tarleton F.
Box 1132
Sitka, AK, USA
99835

Spiridon Camp
Box 483
Kodiak, AK, USA
99615
907-486-5436
L. Francisco

Stoney River Lodge
Box 670577
Chugiak, AK, USA
99567
907-688-2187
C. Warren

Swiss's Alaska Trophy Hunts
129 F Street
Anchorage, AK, USA
99501
907-272-1725
John Swiss

Talaheim Lodge
205 - 4505 Spenard Road
Anchorage, AK, USA
99517
907-733-2815
Mark Miller

Talifson, Morris
Olgha Bay
Kodiak, AK, USA
99615

Timberline Outfitters
Box 134 Dept. 49T
Chugiak, AK, USA
99567
907-688-2722
E.E. "Red" Beeman

Tinker, Mike
Box 197
Ester, AK, USA
99725

Troutman, Donald
2453 Homestead Drive
North Pole, AK, USA
99705

Vrem, Kelly
Box 670742
Chugiak, AK, USA
99567
907-688-3736

Vrem, Tracy
Box 520623
Big Lake, AK, USA
99652

Wapiti Inc. NX Bar Ranch
Box 667
Shindam, WY, USA
82801
307-750-2427/672-6178
Brian MacCarty

Waugaman, William
Box 80589
College, AK, USA
99708

Webber, Mike
Box 670748
Chugiak, AK, USA
99567

Wetzel, Dan L.
Box 10224 22 Mile Creeks Road
Fairbanks, AK, USA
99710

White, Ben
1513 F Street
Anchorage, AK, USA
99501

Wirschem, Chuck
6608 Blackberry Street
Anchorage, AK, USA
99502
907-243-1649

Worker, Matt
Box 871574
Wasilla, AK, USA
99687

Big Game Outfitters Directory

North America

Arizona

Adams, Robert
618 Park Place
San Manuel, AZ, USA
85631

Allen, Paul
Box 1043
Pinetop, AZ, USA
85935

Althauser, Timothy
Box 34 Route 180 E
Alpine, AZ, USA
85920

Anderson, John
Box 1056 Price CN RN
Douglas, AZ, USA
85607

Arizona Trophy Hunting
Box 1021
Flagstaff, AZ, USA
86002
602-525-9206
Randall Shelton

Ash Creek Guiding & Outfitting
Box 26002
Phoenix, AZ, USA
85068
602-841-1261/253-3451

Baker, Otis
2100 North Second Street
Flagstaff, AZ, USA
86001

Baldwin, Michael
2037 East Warwick
Mohave Valley, AZ, USA
86440

Ballard, Jack
5733 North 32nd Avenue
Phoenix, AZ, USA
85021

Barney, Ollie
611 East Paseo Paloma
Rio Rico, AZ, USA
85621

Bechtel, Robin
1705 South Catarina Circle
Mesa, AZ, USA
85202

Beck, Robert
8901 North 17 Line
Phoenix, AZ, USA
85021

Bedlion, James
Box 304 HC31
Happy Jack, AZ, USA
86024

Bemel, William
Box 145 2230 East 2nd Avenue
Apache Junction, AZ, USA
85217

Beneze, Nathan
1588 Country Club Drive
Rivier, AZ, USA
86442

Bennett, John
Box 183
Springerville, AZ, USA
85938

Bettis, Ronald
Box 465
Taylor, AZ, USA
85939

Boggess, Tom
1301 W. Hatcher Road
Phoenix, AZ, USA
85021

Brimhall, Gail
2423 East Glencove
Mesa, AZ, USA
85203

Brown, William
Box 773 RR#1
Lakeside, AZ, USA
85929

Buschschulte, Steve
Box 472
Heber, AZ, USA
85928

Carr, Dale
Box 2400
Pinetop, AZ, USA
85935

Castleberry, Olin
4127 West Puget Avenue
Phoenix, AZ, USA
85021

Catchings, Junior
Box 25
Marble Canyon, AZ, USA
86036

Chamberlin, Arthur
14804 Del Cambre Avenue
Fountain Hills, AZ, USA
85268

Cimellaro, Peter
5118 East Flower
Phoenix, AZ, USA
85018

Cissel, Neal
8715 East Amelia Avenue
Scottsdale, AZ, USA
85251

Cloudt, Jean
801 East Ox-bow
Payson, AZ, USA
85541

Coon, Gene
Box 1464
Showlow, AZ, USA
85901
602-537-7164

Cox, Daniel
Box 5875
Mohave Valley, AZ, USA
86440

Crilley, Anthony
Box 5121
Scottsdale, AZ, USA
85251

Cummelin, Ronald
Box 561
Flagstaff, AZ, USA
86002

Curiel, Albert
Box 588
Miami, AZ, USA
85539

Daws, Bryan
4230 East Wilshire Drive
Phoenix, AZ, USA
85008

Day, Gregory
3627 West Topeka Drive
Glendale, AZ, USA
85308

Dent, Arthur
5621 Harbour View Road
Parker, AZ, USA
85344

Despain, Douglas
63 Princess Avenue
Flagstaff, AZ, USA
86004

Dickerson, Richard
4001 West Lone Cactus
Phoenix, AZ, USA
85308

Dieringer, Nicolas
Box 1100 South Access Road
Camp Verde, AZ, USA
86322

Dodd, Jerry
4402 West Poinsettia
Glendale, AZ, USA
85304

Dotson, Dave
Box 536
Bagdad, AZ, USA
86321

Dover, David
Box 457
Claypool, AZ, USA
85532

Ellison, Nathan
Box 2443
Globe, AZ, USA
85502

Elmer, Jeff
Box 3381
West Sedonia, AZ, USA
86340

Elmer, Jay Jr.
Box 3862
Sedona, AZ, USA
86340

Epperson, Randall
Box 2316
Cottonwood, AZ, USA
86326

Estes, Corwin
Box 92
Eagar, AZ, USA
85925

Fisk, George
1061 North Delmar
Mesa, AZ, USA
85203

Flamme, Robert
3346 North Wayman Street
Flagstaff, AZ, USA
86001

Fleming, Leon
Box 1024
Patagonia, AZ, USA
85624

Flory, Douglas
1816 North Daley
Mesa, AZ, USA
85203

Foshee, Don
549 Ramar
Bullhead City, AZ, USA
86442

Francis, William
5220 North 28th Drive
Phoenix, AZ, USA
85017

Frost, Clinton
6057 East Risner
Sierra Vista, AZ, USA
84635

Garard, Kenneth
2526 Carefree Circle
Flagstaff, AZ, USA
86004

Big Game Outfitters Directory

North America

Gassaway, Henry
4166 West Nidito Place
Tucson, AZ, USA
85705

G Bar C Outfitters
Box 414
Pinetop, AZ, USA
85935
602-368-6471
George Curbello

Glenn, Marvin
Box 1195
Douglas, AZ, USA
85608

Glenn, Warner
Drawer 1039
Douglass, AZ, USA
85608

Golightly, Michael
3900 East Huntington
Flagstaff, AZ, USA
86001

Gomez, Richard
2408 East Hale
Mesa, AZ, USA
85203

Goswick, George
Box 74
Humboldt, AZ, USA
86329

Graf, Stan
Box 121T RR#2
Hereford, AZ, USA
85615

Gragg, Jerry
7010 West Purdue
Peoria, AZ, USA
85345

Grant, William
Box 7619 RR#3
Showlow, AZ, USA
85901

Griffin, Charles
Box 160 RR#2
Casa Grande, AZ, USA
85222

Grounds, H.
Box 4118
Kingman, AZ, USA
86402

Guglielmo, Joe
340 Pinal Street
Globe, AZ, USA
85501

Gunn, Terry
Box 36
Marble Canyon, AZ, USA
86036

Haggitt, Donald
Box 324
Lakeside, AZ, USA
85929

Hale, Van
Box 1573
Eagar, AZ, USA
85925

Hankerson, Dennis
4626 North 66 Street
Scottsdale, AZ, USA
85251

Hardy, Patrick
3039 East Corrine
Phoenix, AZ, USA
85032

Harlow, Christopher
6741 West Highland Avenue
Phoenix, AZ, USA
85033

Harvey, Henry
3302 West Citrus Way
Phoenix, AZ, USA
85017

Haskell, Roy
5849 East Burns
Tucson, AZ, USA
85711

Havener, Philip
4539 North 48th Drive
Phoenix, AZ, USA
85031

Havener, Rolland
3048 West Greenway
Phoenix, AZ, USA
85203

Haws, Allen
Box 412
Snowflake, AZ, USA
85937

Heathington, Lawrence
Box 367A Route 2
Casa Grance, AZ, USA
85222

Higgs, James
Box 728 HC30
Prescott, AZ, USA
86301

Homen, Manuel
5798 East Pas Cimarron
Tucson, AZ, USA
85715

Hopkins, John
Box 300 HC21
Happy Jack, AZ, USA
86024

Howell, Gary
1051 South Milton
Flagstaff, AZ, USA
86001

Hur, Donald
2775 Typhoon
Lake Havasu City, AZ, USA
86403

Jagermeister Guide Service
Box 240
Taylor, AZ, USA
85939
602-536-7608
Don McBride

James, Marvin
Box 964
Sedona, AZ, USA
86336

James, Russel
Box 41
Lakeside, AZ, USA
85929
602-368-5525

Jerome, Jerry
Box 962 RR#1
Flagstaff, AZ, USA
86004

Johnson, Royce
Box 505
Miami, AZ, USA
85530

Johnson, Jack
1701 North 40th Drive
Showlow, AZ, USA
85901

Joy, John
Box 875
Springerville, AZ, USA
85938

Kaibab Outfitters
Box 2642
Flagstaff, AZ, USA
86003
602-774-5008/4318
B. Dixon

Kane, Ross
Box 494
Patagonia, AZ, USA
85624

Keeler, Aubrey
Box 2771
Globe, AZ, USA
85502

Kessinger, James
19202 East Cloud Road
Queen Creek, AZ, USA
85242

Kibler, Jonathon
Box 1099
Willcox, AZ, USA
85644

Kiggins, Kenneth
216 North Mud Springs Road
Payson, AZ, USA
85541

Kinley, Robert
Box 72294
Martinez Lake, AZ, USA
85365

Klump, John
Box 316
Bowie, AZ, USA
85605

Knagge, Peter
Box 4078 CRB
Tucson, AZ, USA
85738

Krank, Floyd
Box 372 HC02
Globe, AZ, USA
85501

Lafuze, Terry
1019 East Minnezona
Phoenix, AZ, USA
85014

Lann, Donald
Box 206 Eagle Creek Route
Clifton, AZ, USA
85533

Larabell, Leonard
18803 East Viadearboles
Highley, AZ, USA
85236

Lawrence, James
2550 North 14th Avenue
Tucson, AZ, USA
85703

Lawson, Neil
1802 East Campobello
Phoenix, AZ, USA
85022

Lawson, Tom
5651 East Spring Street
Tucson, AZ, USA
85712

Ledin, Gerry
903 Pineview Street
Payson, AZ, USA
85541

Lee, Robert
2127 Holly Avenue
Lake Havasu City, AZ, USA
86403

Leon, Richard
Box 357B Route 1
Laveen, AZ, USA
85339

Big Game Outfitters Directory

North America

Levy Brothers Outfitters
4615 North Camino Nuestro
Tucson, AZ, USA
85745
Seymour & John Levy

Lewis, John
Box 1043
Claypool, AZ, USA
85532

Lisak, Frank
5623 West Beck Line
Glendale, AZ, USA
85306

Marks, Justin
Box 65
Blue, AZ, USA
84922

Marshall, William
Box 1332
Payson, AZ, USA
85547

Martin, W.H.
Hewitt Station Road
Superior, AZ, USA
85273

Martin, William
Box D
Superior, AZ, USA
85273

Martin & Workman Guide Service
Box D
Superior, AZ, USA
85273
602-689-2891

Mast, Jerry
7501 West Banff
Peoria, AZ, USA
85345

McBride, Donald
Box 240
Taylor, AZ, USA
85939

McCasland, James
Box 6042 Route 1
Lakeside, AZ, USA
85929

McCord, Thomas
5102 East Blanche
Scottsdale, AZ, USA
85254

McKown, Robert
2334 West Tonto
Phoenix, AZ, USA
85009

Mecey, James
Box 1215 Route 1
Lakeside, AZ, USA
85929

Meeske, Ernie
2608 West Bulla
Payson, AZ, USA
85541

Midler, Marshall
2935 Indian Land Drive
Lake Havasu City, AZ, USA
86403

Miller Brothers Outfitters
319 North Tucson Boulevard
Tucson, AZ, USA
85712
602-327-8673/721-1220
Chris & Mike Miller

Miller, Ray
Box 22971
Tucson, AZ, USA
85734

Miller, Mark
433 North Center Street
Mesa, AZ, USA
85201

Mitchell, Joe
8730 West Virginia
Phoenix, AZ, USA
85032

Moreland, Chester
1775 Riverside Drive
Piviera, AZ, USA
86442

Morton, Ted
17427 North 35th Place
Phoenix, AZ, USA
85032

Murphy, Bill
Box 1060 HC30
Prescott, AZ, USA
86301

Nason, Stanley
6241 North Misty Lane
Tucson, AZ, USA
85743

Nelson, Allen
Box 3041
Flagstaff, AZ, USA
86003

Molande, Albert
Portal Star Route
San Simon, AZ, USA
85632

Nossaman, Ralph
1020 9th Avenue
Yuma, AZ, USA
85634

Oberdin, Geroge
1451 Orilla Lane
Bullhead City, AZ, USA
86430

Ohaco, Mike
Box 1047
Winslow, AZ, USA
86047

Ortiz, Raymond
Box 1043
Oracle, AZ, USA
85623

Parker, Dennis
Box 861
Patagonia, AZ, USA
85624

Parton, William
1310 Soldier Pass
Sedona, AZ, USA
86336

Peggegatti, Michael
Box 41128
Phoenix, AZ, USA
85050

Perkins, Marion
501 South 12th Street
Williams, AZ, USA
86046

Preas, Floyd
2283 East Broadway
Apache Junction, AZ, USA
85219

Price, George
2244 East Jacaranda
Mesa, AZ, USA
85203

Priest, Dean
1911 East Karen Drive
Phoenix, AZ, USA
85022

Priest, Dan
3837 West Townley
Phoenix, AZ, USA
85021

Priest, Elvis
5107 West Harmont Drive
Glendale, AZ, USA
85302

Pulsifer, David
Box 913
Springerville, AZ, USA
85938

Reeves, Robert
Box 93
Camp Verde, AZ, USA
86322

Reidhead, Ernest
Box 235
Nutrioso, AZ, USA
85932

Riddle, Michael
Box 1474K Route 2
Phoenix, AZ, USA
85029

Rim Country Guided Hunts
Box 183
Springerville, AZ, USA
85938
602-333-4174
John Bennett

Rincon Creek
2390 South Window Rock
Tucson, AZ, USA
85710
602-886-6437

Ritchie, Howard
3924 West Westcott
Glendale, AZ, USA
85308

Rogers, Robert
13041 North Victor Hugo
Phoenix, AZ, USA
85032

Romero, Raymond
1100 - 1 East Camelback
Phoenix, AZ, USA
85012

Rossi, Thomas
2415 West Morningside
Phoenix, AZ, USA
85023

Row, James
3320 East University
Mesa, AZ, USA
85203

Russell, Stanford
Box 638 Route 1
Pine, AZ, USA
85544

Sanders, Gary
Box 17526
Tucson, AZ, USA
85731

Schaal, Perry
3319 West Harmont Drive
Phoenix, AZ, USA
85051

Schmidt, Ted
13044 North 8th Avenue
Phoenix, AZ, USA
85029

Schultz, James
5015 Lake Country
Flagstaff, AZ, USA
86001

Seddon, Tony
13044 North 55th Drive
Glendale, AZ, USA
85304

Big Game Outfitters Directory

North America

Shaff, James
3100 East Mount Elden
Flagstaff, AZ, USA
86001

Smith, Loyd
11000 Old Spanish Trail
Tucson, AZ, USA
85748
602-886-0645

Smith, Gerald
2390 South Window Rock
Tucson, AZ, USA
85710

Smith, Marvin
650 West 22nd Avenue
Apache Junction, AZ, USA
85220

Snead, Larry
703 - 805 North 4th Avenue
Phoenix, AZ, USA
85003

Snyder, Dorsie
3050 Rustler Drive
Lake Havasu City, AZ, USA
86403

Sportsman's Adventures
10809 North 99th Street
Scottsdale, AZ, USA
85260
602-860-8835/991-9282
F. Romley

Starr, Douglas
Box 756
Mayer, AZ, USA
86333

Stodghill, Travis
Box 981
Pine, AZ, USA
85544

Strasburg
Box 2699
Page, AZ, USA
86040

Sullivan, Floyd
Box 945
Mammoth, AZ, USA
85618

Sullivan, John
Badger Creek
Marble Canyon, AZ, USA
86036

Sullivan, Bill
Box 563
Claypool, AZ, USA
85532
602-467-2445

Sutherland, Charlie
Box 2737
Showlow, AZ, USA
85901
602-437-2811

Swan, Gordon
2630 Camino Del Rio
Bullhead City, AZ, USA
86442

Swindle, Gerald
R2 - 6416 South 122nd Avenue
Tolleson, AZ, USA
85353

T Inverted F Western Adventures
Box 1001
Thatcher, AZ, USA
85552
602-428-6890
Tommy Freestone

Thomas, Ronald
1830 West Ahmed
Tucson, AZ, USA
85704

Thompson, Maurice
7616 North 33rd Drive
Phoenix, AZ, USA
85051

Thornton, John
16690 Coronado Forest
Tucson, AZ, USA
85704

Tinnin, Glenn
Box 64
Marble Canyon, AZ, USA
86036

Todd, Tommie
Box 1550 RR#1
Willcox, AZ, USA
85643

Uhley, Alan
901 Cataract Drive
Lake Havasu City, AZ, USA
86403

Ulibarri, Phillip
3700 North Grand View
Flagstaff, AZ, USA
86002

Underwood, John
E102 - 15620 North 25th Avenue
Phoenix, AZ, USA
85023

Vancas, Mark
305 North Main Street
San Manuel, AZ, USA
85631

Vivian, Kenneth
4805 South Terrace
Tempe, AZ, USA
85282

Wantland, Patrick
Box 175 HC62
Camp Verde, AZ, USA
86322

Weigel, Marshal
5555 North Cumberland Drive
Tucson, AZ, USA
85704

Weisser, Stephen
Box 55, Route 1
Salome, AZ, USA
85348

Whelan, Michael
Box 1521
Cottonwood, AZ, USA
86326

White Mountain Apache Tribe
Box 220
Whiteriver, AZ, USA
85941
P. Stago, Jr.

White, Richard
Box 717
Happy Jack, AZ, USA
86024

Whitmore Outfitters
Box 143 Badger Ranch
Marble Canyon, AZ, USA
86036
Barbara & Dale

Willoby, Johyn
1030 Shorewood Drive
Lake Havasu City, AZ, USA
86403

Wright, Steven
Box 953
Sedona, AZ, USA
86336

Wyckoff, Donald
2527 North 29th Street
Phoenix, AZ, USA
85008

Arkansas

Duppy's Duck Hunting
Box 124 Route 2
DeWitt, AR, USA
72042
501-946-2057
Charles Dupslaff

California

Bow 'n' Bore Ranch
Box 2102
Livermore, CA, USA
94550
408-897-3262
S. Swart

Burrows Ranch, Inc.
12250 Colyer Sprints Road
Red Bluff, CA, USA
96080
916-529-1535
Bill Burrows

California Outfitters
135 - 5285 E. Kings Canyon Road
Fresno, CA, USA
93727
209-456-0663/916-824-2850
G. Flournoy, Jr.

California Ram Hunts
Box 54
Lockwood, CA, USA
93932
408-385-3005
Lester Patterson III

Clallam River Guide Service
Route 2
Clallam Bay, CA, USA
98326
206-963-2526
Bernie Paque

Deel, Boyd B.
P.O. Box 5909
San Jose, CA, USA
95150
408-866-4672

East Africa Safari Consultants, Ltd.
8235 Soledad Canyon Road
Acton, CA, USA
93510
805-268-0322
W. Dougherty

Handrich, Dave
6474 Stagecoach Road
Santa Barbara, CA, USA
93015
805-964-2965

John Gibson Safaris
Dept. SK 4055 Wilshire Blvd #52
Los Angeles, CA, USA
9001

Lainoff Robbins Safaris
Box 40181 4111 Illinois Street
San Diego, CA, USA
92104
619-283-1162

Matthew, Tom
3481 Lupine Drive
Redding, CA, USA
96002
916-223-6424

Modoc Licensed Guide
406 E. First St.
Alturas, CA, USA
96101
916-233-5286
Leo Kennedy & sons

Big Game Outfitters Directory

North America

Multiple Use Managers, Inc.
Box L
West Point, CA, USA
95255
209-293-7087

Ngezi Safaris
12066 Horely Avenue
Downey, CA, USA
90242
R. Comstock

Penland Guide Service
Box 303
Big Bend, CA, USA
96011
916-337-6471/547-4952

Rancho San Lucas
Box 100
San Lucas, CA, USA
93954
408-382-4321

Sacramento Hunting Club
12945 Orange Road
Wilton, CA, USA
95693
916-687-6380/455-7608
Andy Penn

Safaris Jacques Guin
1301 Rossmoyne Avenue
Glendale, CA, USA
91207
818-246-6077
J. Perkins

Schmidt, Nessen
Box 105 Oasis Road
King City, CA, USA
93930
805-472-9165

Sporting Adventures
20211 Patio Dr. #240
Castro Valley, CA, USA
94546
415-886-5544
Lee Bohner

Tony de Casta's Safari Headquarters
Box 264
Lompoc, CA, USA
93438
805-736-1098

Colorado

Adams Lodge
2400 County Road 12
Meeker, CO, USA
81641
303-878-4312

Alpine Outfitters
1640 M Road
Fruita, CO, USA
81521
303-858-3352
Jack Cassidy

Altenburg Bros. Outfitting
1333 Emery Street
Longmont, CO, USA
80501
303-772-8420
Eugene Altenburg

Anderson's Sportsmen Guide Service
10632 West Highway 374
Del Norte, CO, USA
81132
719-657-3113

Avalanche Creek Outfitters
11382 Highway 133
Carbondale, CO, USA
81623
303-963-2942
Michael Schilling

B & J Hunting Camps
55452 Highway 13-79
Meeker, CO, USA
81641
303-824-6458
Robert Wells

Bill Law Guide Service, Inc.
Box 87
Mesa, CO, USA
81643
303-268-5536
Bill Law

Blue Creek Outfitters
Box 153
Uravan, CO, USA
81436

Broadacres Guest Ranch
Box 39
Creede, CO, USA
81130
303-658-2291

Buford's Western Adventures
176 - 1699 S. Trenton Street
Denver, CO, USA
80231

Capitol Peak Outfitters
17893 Highway 82
Carbondale, CO, USA
81623
303-963-0211
Steve Rieser

Cache Creek Outfitters
Box 609
Parachute, CO, USA
81635
303-285-7346
Jim & Martha DeKam

C Bar Land & Cattle Co.
Box 117, Route 4
Victoria, TX, USA
77904
512-573-2667
Malcolm Calaway

Challenge Outfitters
Box 5092
Steamboat Springs, CO, USA
80477
303-879-0595
D. Elder

Chuck Davies Guide Service
3461 F 3/4 Road
Clifton, CO, USA
81520
303-464-7421

Cimmaron Outfitters & Packers
School
72834 Kinikin Road
Montrose, CO, USA
81401
303-249-7174
B. Lane

Colorado High Guide Service
1759 S. Ironton
Aurora, CO, USA
80012
303-751-9274/524-7900
Dennis Bergstad

Colorado Safaris
2263 S. Beech Way
Lakewood, CO, USA
80228
303-986-2578

Colorado Trail Riders & Outfitters
7806 County Road 1
Montrose, CO, USA
81401
303-249-5872
Ruth Ann Robinson

Cotton Gordon Safaris Ltd.
Tarryall River Ranch
Lake George, CO, USA
80827
303-748-3255

D & G Horses
1631 County Road 293
Rifle, CO, USA
81650
303-625-0234
Dale Coombs

D Bar J Outfitters
Box 147
Grand Junction, CO, USA
81502
303-434-9520
Donald Cardin

Deep Creek Outfitters
Box 1921
Montrose, CO, USA
81402
303-249-2183
Maple Taylor

Dick Pennington Guide Service, Ltd.
2317 H Road
Grand Junction, CO, USA
81501
303-242-6318
Richard Pennington

Dilley's Guide Service
47055 County Road F
Center, CO, USA
81125
303-754-3521
Dale Dilley

Don's Guide & Outfitting
111 South 8th Street
Gunnison, CO, USA
81230
303-641-0475
Donald French

Double Diamond Outfitters
Box 282
Old Snowmass, CO, USA
81654
303-927-3404

DTD Outfitters
391 Rodell Drive
Grand Junction, CO, USA
81503
303-243-0837
John Lowe

East Divide Outfitter
Box 1055
Glenwood Springs, CO, USA
81602

Fair Chase Safaris
1130 Main Avenue
Durango, CO, USA
81301
800-243-9658/303-259-3831

Fossil Ridge Guide Service
711 Ranch
Parlin, CO, USA
81239
303-641-0666
Rudy Rudibaugh

Gamefinders
2713 Ponderosa Road
Franktown, CO, USA
80116
303-841-8736/5314
L. Durbin & P. Varnak

Garvey Bros. Outfitting & Guides
Box 555
Nucia, CO, USA
81424
303-824-2243
Stan Garvey

Geneva Park Outfitters
2821 W. 64th Avenue
Denver, CO, USA
80221
303-429-5932
Terry Sandmeier

Big Game Outfitters Directory

North America

Gordon Blay Western Co. Outfitters
18315 6500 Road
Montrose, CO, USA
81401
303-249-8877

Grizzly Creek Guide Services
2911 Four Corners Park
Grand Junction, CO, USA
81503
T. Wood

Gunnison Country Guide Service
Box 1443
Gunnison, CO, USA
81230
303-641-2830
John Nelson

Gunnison River Pleasure Park
Box 233
Lazear, CO, USA
81420
303-872-3543
LeRoy Jagodinski

G.W.Peterson Outfitting
10825 N. County Road 15
Ft. Collins, CO, USA
80524
303-568-7396

High Lonesome Guide & Outfitter
Box 1059
Kremmling, CO, USA
80459
303-724-9685
William Hillier

High Plains Safaris Inc.
Box 430
Evans, CO, USA
80620
303-678-5548
Gerald W. Backhaus

High Valley Hunts
Box 1297
Alamosa, CO, USA
81101
303-589-9727
Mike & Bev McIntyre

High West Outfitters
2136 H Road
Delta, CO, USA
81416
303-874-8177
Richard Kim Miller

Hofman Hunting Guide Service
61278 East Monroe
Montrose, CO, USA
81401
303-249-2363/9551
M. Holman

Holman's High Country Outfitters
14686 - 6000 Road
Montrose, CO, USA
81401
303-249-5851
Buddy Holman

Horn Fork Guides
29178 Co. Rd. 361
Buena Vista, CO, USA
81211
719-395-8363
Glen Roberts

Hubbard Park Pack Station
3461 F 3/4 Road
Clifton, CO, USA
81520
303-464-7421
Chuck Davies

Hyatt Guides & Outfitters
Box 1288
Montrose, CO, USA
81402
303-249-9733
Harold Hyatt Jr.

International Adventures Unlimited
Box 1157
Gunnison, CO, USA
81230
303-641-5369
M. Grosse

Jack Owens Guide Service
Box 87
Rico, CO, USA
81332
303-963-1273

J & J Guides & Outfitters
107 County Road 22
Craig, CO, USA
81625
303-824-9611
Gerald Wollsey

J & Ray Colorado High Country, Inc.
8360 - 6400 Road
Montrose, CO, USA
80401
303-323-5155
Ronald Franks

J/B Adventures & Safaris, Inc.
330N - 6312 S. Fiddler's Green
Englewood, CO, USA
80111
303-771-0977

JML Outfitters
8563 E. Davies Avenue
Englewood, CO, USA
80112
303-770-2541

K & W Outfitters
Box 24
Maher, CO, USA
81421
303-921-3234
Drew Kissire

K. E. Schultz Guide & Outfitting
0010 Ponderosa Drive
Glenwood Springs, CO, USA
81601
303-945-7120
Kurt Schultz

Lamicq Guides & Outfitting
635 - 19 1/2 Road
Grand Junction, CO, USA
81503
303-243-1082
John Lamicq

Lazy J C Ranch
Box 43
Rand, CO, USA
80473
303-723-4357
William Ogburn

Little Creek Ranches
Box 171
Collbran, CO, USA
81624
303-487-3321/241-7272
A. L. Baier

Lobo Outfitters
Box 9A Route 2
Pagosa Springs, CO, USA
81147
303-264-5546
Dick Ray

Loncarich, Chris
950 R. Road
Mack, CO, USA
81525

Lost Creek Guides
1900 Co. Road 12
Meeker, CO, USA
81641
303-878-5214/5161
Lance & Rick Edinger

McLeod Outfitters
Box 132
Crawford, CO, USA
81415
303-921-7731/625-7261
Tom McLeod

Meadowlark Ranch-San Juan
Mountains
19786 Co. Road 501
Bayfield, CO, USA
81122
303-884-2966
Dale Sundblom

Mountain Goat Outfitting Services
Box 830
Durango, CO, USA
81302
R.D. Scarlett

Mountain Mesa Safaris
Box 15836
Colorado Springs, CO, USA
80935
303-597-4062
J. Snyder

Mountain West Expeditions, Inc.
2558 East Nichols Circle
Littleton, CO, USA
80122
303-796-9635
T. Tietz

Mountain West Outfitting
Box 514
Conifer, CO, USA
80433
303-674-4439
Tom Tietz

96 Ranch
Box 248
Parachute, CO, USA
81635
303-285-9600/7477

North Star Outfitters
Box 3185
Boulder, CO, USA
80307
303-440-4064/444-1155

Osborne, Kenneth
6567 County Road 41
Hamilton, CO, USA
81638
303-824-9262/602-682-7268

O.T.S. Guide & Outfitters
Box 791
Olanthe, CO, USA
81425
303-323-5022

Outback Outfitters & Guide Service
Box 667
Monte Vista, CO, USA
81144

Outdoor Recreation Consultants
Box 1304
Carbondale, CO, USA
81623
303-963-1273/1-800-367-5805

Outfitters West of Saddle Mountain
4536 East 50 Drive
Crawford, CO, USA
81415
303-921-6321
Arnold Watson

Outpost Wilderness Adventure, Ltd.
Box 7
Lake George, CO, USA
80827
303-636-0635/687-1800
David Appleton

Over The Hill Outfitters
3624 County Road 203
Durango, CO, USA
81301
303-247-9289/259-2834
John Neely

Big Game Outfitters Directory

North America

Peters Hunting Service
28310 R C Road 31
Oak Creek, CO, USA
80467
303-879-5095
Harley Peters

Popejoy, Andy
Box 903
Rangely, CO, USA
82648

Powderhorn Area Hunting Assoc.
481 County Road 25
Powderhorn, CO, USA
81243
303-641-2717
Yosef Lutwak

Puma Mountain Outfitters
Box 101
Hayden, CO, USA
81639
303-276-3434
Roy Best

Quaking Aspen Guides & Outfitters
Box 485
Gunnison, CO, USA
81230
303-641-0529
D. Mapes

Quarter Circle Circle Ranch
26100 County Road 17GG
Gunnison, CO, USA
81230
John Judson

Ragged Mountain Outfitters
1526 Blake Avenue
Glenwood Springs, CO, USA
81601
303-945-6265
Dion Lake

Ram's Horn Guides & Outfitter
Box 5619
Woodland Park, CO, USA
80866
719-687-3618
Al Vallejo

Rancho Del Rio/Monarch Outfitters
4199 Trough Road
Bond, CO, USA
80423
303-653-4431
Mark Bernhardt

Rawhide Adventures
Box 3802
Evergreen, CO, USA
80439
303-674-7285
Fred Ellis

Redwing Outfitters
Box 149
Gardner, CO, USA
81040
303-746-2269

Rendezvous Outfitters & Guides, Ltd.
16073 Hiland Circle
Brighton, CO, USA
80601
303-654-1428
Russ Eby

Rocky Mtn. Back Country Outfitter
7788 Greenleaf Lane
Denver, CO, USA
80221
303-665-8773
Gerald Risner

Rocky Mountain Riders
3885 FS 7 Road
Whitewater, CO, USA
81527
303-241-3860

Rough Creek Outfitters, Corp.
821 Ranney Street
Craig, CO, USA
81625
303-824-5535
Philip Pinnt

Saddle Mountain Guide Service
Star Route
Crawford, CO, USA
81415
303-921-3651
L. Zeldenthius

Saddle Tramp Outfitters
1531 - 335 Road
New Castle, CO, USA
81647
303-876-2960
Thomas Bullock

Sammons Brothers Guides &
Outfitters
Box 1346
Grand Junction, CO, USA
81502
303-241-1183/244-9852

Samuelson Outfitters
Box 868
Fraser, CO, USA
80442
303-726-8221
Richard Samuelson

Sangre de Christos Outdoors, Inc.
Box 586
Westcliffe, CO, USA
81252
303-783-9343/2265
Bill Schulze

San Juan Outfitters
120 Beaver Meadows Road
Bayfield, CO, USA
81122
303-884-2731
T. Mike Murphy

San Juan Ranch
2882 Highway 23
Ridgway, CO, USA
81432
303-626-5360
Scott MacTieman

Schultz, K.E.
0010 Ponderosa Drive
Glenwood Springs, CO, USA
81601
303-945-7120

Seven Lakes and Ranch
738 County Road 39
Meeker, CO, USA
81641
Rocky & Joan Rockwell

Seven W Guest Ranch
3412 County Road 151
Gypsum, CO, USA
81637
303-524-9328
Floyd Beard

Shamrock Ranch Corp.
175 Paragon Drive
Boulder, CO, USA
80303
303-499-1141
Gary Peschel

Slater Creek Outfitters
206 - 6 Abilene Street
Aurora, CO, USA
80011
303-690-1017/800-445-7685

Sombrero Ranches, Inc.
3100 Airport Road
Boulder, CO, USA
80301
303-422-0258
Rex Ross Walker

Sperry's Huntsman Ranch
Box 265
Eckert, CO, USA
81418
303-835-3630/929-667'
Joe Sperry

Stadjduhar Ranches
Snowmass, CO, USA
81654
303-963-0195

Steele, Rudy
Box 2503
Glenwood Springs, CO, USA
81601
303-945-6000

Steward Ranch Outfitter
4385 County Road 207
Durango, CO, USA
81301
303-247-8962
Laverne Gwaltney

Sunset Ranch
Box 876
Steamboat Springs, CO, USA
80477
303-879-0954
Patsy Scherar

Taylor Creek Ranch
51440 Elk River Road
Steamboat Springs, CO, USA
80487
303-879-9072
Vic Taylor

The Taylor Ranch
Box 96
San Luis, CO, USA
81152
303-672-3580
R.J. McGrath

Toneda Outfitters
Box 336
Moffat, CO, USA
81143
303-256-4866
Ed Wiseman

Tony Hoza Guide & Outfitting
Box 285
Borwood, CO, USA
81423
303-327-4305
Tony Hoza

Trapper's Lake Lodge
7700 Trappers Lake Road
Meeker, CO, USA
81641
303-878-3336
Dale Hopwood Jr.

Trujillo, J.C.
Box 1616
Steamboat Springs, CO, USA
80477

Twin Pines Outfitting
2880 County Road 3
Marble, CO, USA
81623
303-963-1220
Larry Darien

2V Outfitters, Ltd.
Box 57
Glade Park, CO, USA
81523
303-245-4636
Miles Keogh

Ute Trail Guide Service
10615 County Road 150
Salida, CO, USA
81201
303-539-4097
Glenn Everett

Wallace, Bill & Fred
Box 296
Collbran, CO, USA
81624
303-487-3235

Big Game Outfitters Directory

North America

Walz Guide Service
882 Legion Street
Craig, CO, USA
81625
303-824-3943/4861

West Elk Outfitters
Box 971
Crested Butte, CO, USA
81224
303-349-5885
John Hatlern

Western Colorado Outfitters
18315 6500 Road
Montrose, CO, USA
81401
303-249-8877
Gordon Blay

White River Resort, Inc.
21679 East Otero Place
Aurora, CO, USA
80016
303-690-6627
Jack Harrison

Wilderness Connection Outfitters
Box 1406
Wheatridge, CO, USA
80034
303-238-1127
Don Snyder

Wild Horse Outfitters
1819 County Road 329
Ignacio, CO, USA
81137
303-883-2356
Harry Landers

Willow Creek Ranch
Box 261
Lake George, CO, USA
80827
303-748-3687
Ray Hill

World Trek Inc.
2648 McCormick Ave.
Pueblo, CO, USA
81001
303-546-2121
Dirk Neal

Vadoma Safaris
Box 441
Hayden, CO, USA
81639
303-276-3885
D. Gore

Vadoma Safaris Ltd.
545 Estes Street
Lakewood, CO, USA
80226
303-237-2110
Robert Woodfill

Vickers Enterprises, Inc.
Box 96
Lake City, CO, USA
81235
303-944-2249
Larry Vickers

Wapiti Outfitter & Guides
Box 932
Gunnison, CO, USA
81230
303-641-2603/3220
J. Garfall

Waterways West, Ltd.
Box 40071
Grande Junction, CO, USA
81507
303-241-8188
E. Glade

ZX Ranch & Lodge
Box 250
Paonia, CO, USA
81428
303-929-6591
Dean Lampton

Connecticut

M'Dalla Safari Company
Oak Point Club
New Milford, CT, USA
06776
203-355-1945
T.M. Sweeney

Florida

Argentina Hunting & Fishing
Box 1349
Big Pine Key, FL, USA
33149
305-554-8875
R. Ortega

Caravelle Ranch
Box 168 Star Route 19
Palatka, FL, USA
32077
904-325-0032
J.W. Gorab

Dixie Wildlife Safaris
4431 Walk-in-Water Road
Lake Wales, FL, USA
33853
813-696-3300
M. Acreman

Eric Wagner Safaris Inc.
2065 NE 125th Terrace Road
Silver Springs, FL, USA
32688
904-625-2100

G. & W. Adventures
822 3rd Avenue South
Tierra Verde, FL, USA
33715
813-866-3189/867-0893
B. Grant

Issacs, Bill
Box 79
Everglades City, FL, USA
33929

Pinney, Richard
Box 14318
Gainnesville, FL, USA
32604
904-378-3000

Safari De Colombia
8166 150th Place North
Palm Beach Gardens, FL, USA
33410
305-747-8230

Sohrada Safaris
1455 Tolson Road
Deland, FL, USA
32720
904-738-3295
B. Agnew

Trophy Hunters Safaris Inc.
#1407 - 1000 Quayside Terrace
Miami, FL, USA
33138
305-893-1162
B. Jones Levitz

Whitetail, Inc.
2280 SW 66 Terrace
Davie, FL, USA
33317
305-475-9040

Georgia

Burnt Pine Plantation Inc.
#112 - 2250 Newmarket Parkway
Marietta, GA, USA
30067
404-953-0326
Cindy Robinson

Custom Hunts
404 Tripp Street
Americus, GA, USA
800-223-4868/912-924-8318

Professional Adventure Consultants
404 Tripp Street
Americus, GA, USA
800-223-4868

Idaho

Alpine Mountain Outfitters
Box 1561
Pocatello, ID, USA
83204
Gary Brown

Anderson Outfitting
5646 Sorrell Drive
Pocatello, ID, USA
83202
208-237-6544/2664
Robert Anderson

Barker River Trips
2124 Grelle
Lewiston, ID, USA
83501
208-743-7459
J. Barker

B Bar C Outfitters
Box 265
Orofino, ID, USA
83544
208-476-7074
Mike Stockton

Beamer's Heller Bar
Box 1223
Lewiston, ID, USA
83501
208-743-4800
M. Beamer

Bear Creek Outfitters
Box 5B Route 2
Weippe, ID, USA
83553
208-435-4610
Lyle Phelps

Bear Path Outfitters
Box 63
Kendrick, ID, USA
83537
208-289-4301
Bradley Dammerman

Bear River Outfitters
Box 1450 Star Route 1
Montpelier, ID, USA
83254
208-847-0263
Marriner Jensen

Beitelspacher Outfitting Service
Box 415
Grangeville, ID, USA
83530
208-983-2535
Ron Beitelspacher

Bighorn Outfitters
366-B Mill Creek Road
Hamilton, MT, USA
59840
406-961-3736
Curt Thompson

Birch Creek Outfitters
Box 650
Challis, ID, USA
83226
208-879-5240
David Peterson

Big Game Outfitters Directory

North America

Boulder Creek Outfitters
Box 119
Peck, ID, USA
83545
208-486-6232/839-2282
Tim Craig

Butler, Bruce
Box 478
Hailey, ID, USA
83333
208-788-2468

Castle Creek Outfitters
Box 2008
Salmon, ID, USA
83467
208-344-6600
Dick McAfee

Cat Track Outfitters
113 East Avenue C
Jerome, ID, USA
83338
208-324-3337
T. Molitor

Chamberlain Basin Outfitters
Box 240A Route 1
Salmon, ID, USA
83467
208-756-3715
Ed McCallum

Chilly Ranch
Star Route
Mackay, ID, USA
83251
208-588-2584
Milt Butler

C Lazy Three Outfitters
Box 107
Ovando, MT, USA
59854
406-793-5773
Dave Hettinger

Clearwater Outfitters
4088D Canyon Creek Road
Orofino, ID, USA
83544
208-476-5971

Cold Meadows Outfitters
Box 1955
Salmon, ID, USA
83467
208-756-3817
Cal Stoddard

Cole, Robert L.
3815 Rickenbacker
Boise, ID, USA
83705
208-342-7888

Coolwater Outfitters
Box 63 HC 75
Kooskia, ID, USA
83539
208-926-4707
Don Wilson

Cross Outfitters
310 South 3rd East
Preston, ID, USA
83263
208-852-1038
Larry Cross

Custom River Tours
Box 7071
Boise, ID, USA
83707
208-343-3343
K. Masoner

Dave Williams Guide Service
Box 8
Carmen, ID, USA
83462
208-756-2018
David Williams

Diamond D Ranch, Inc.
Box 36005
Grosse Pointe, MI, USA
48236
313-773-5850
Thomas Demorest

Dixie Outfitters, Inc.
Box 33
Dixie, ID, USA
83525
208-842-2417
W. Emmett Smith

D Double S Outfitter
2742 NW Fourth Avenue
Fruitland, ID, USA
83619
208-452-3932
Don Dressen

Double Fork Lodge & Outfitters
Box 911
Challis, ID, USA
83226
208-879-5270
David Peterson

Eakin Ridge Outfitters Inc.
Box 1382
Salmon, ID, USA
83467
208-756-2047
Lamont Anderson

Elk River Outfitters
Box 265
Orofino, ID, USA
83544
208-476-7074
Mike Stockton

Epley's Idaho Outdoor Adventures
Box 987
McCall, ID, USA
83638
208-634-5173
Ted Epley

Fall Creek Outfitters
3875 Ballantine Road
Eagle, ID, USA
83616
208-939-0469
Ron Sherer

Five Bears Outfitters
1360 NE Summerdale Road
Corvallis, MT, USA
59828
406-961-4778
Gary Peters

5-B Elk Ranch
Box 783
Challis, ID, USA
83226
208-879-2208
Ron & Pat Bricker

Flying Resort Ranches, Inc.
Box 770
Salmon, ID, USA
83467
208-756-6295
William R. Guth

4-4 Outfitters
Box 25
Ellis, ID, USA
83235
208-876-4487

F M & R Outfitters
Box 300 HCR 01
Naples, ID, USA
83847
208-267-5993/8903
Jack Riddle

G & L York's Outfitters, Inc.
Box 98R Route 1
Lenore, ID, USA
83541
208-836-5756
Gladys L. York

Garden Valley Outfitters Inc.
Garden Valley, ID, USA
83622
208-462-3751
Dan Rotthoff

Gerald Richie & Son Outfitters
Star Route Stage 1
Darby, MT, USA
59829
406-349-2499
Gerald Richie

Gilmore Ranch Outfitters & Guides
Box 641 Route 2
Orangeville", ID, USA
83530
208-983-2196
Chuck Neill

Gospel Mountain Outfitters
Box 363
Lucile, ID, USA
83542
208-628-3553
Jim Daude

Happy Hollow Vacations
Box 14 Star Route
Salmon, ID, USA
83467
208-756-3954
Martin Capps

Harrah's Middle Fork Lodge
3815 Rickenbacker
Boise, ID, USA
83705
208-342-7888/7941
Nick Stuparich

Heinrich & Smith Outfitters
3334 Upper Ford Creek
Orofino, ID, USA
83544
208-476-5011

Idaho Big Game, Inc.
Box 2501
Salmon, ID, USA
83467
208-756-4407
Jon Goodman

Idaho Guide Service Inc.
Box 1230
Sun Valley, ID, USA
83353
208-726-3358
Olin Gardner

Idaho Outfitters & Guides Assoc.
Box 95-17
Bois, ID, USA
83701
208-342-1438

Idaho Wilderness Camps, Inc.
Box 1516A
Salmon, ID, USA
83467
208-756-2850
Garry Merritt

Indian Creek Ranch
Box 105 Route 2
North Fork, ID, USA
83466
Salmon Op. ask for 24F211
Jack W.Briggs

Big Game Outfitters Directory

North America

Iron Horse Outfitters
Box 1346
Hamilton, MT, USA
59840
406-821-4474
Art Griffith

Jack Atcheson & Sons
3210 Ottawa Street Dept. H
Butte, MT, USA
59701
406-782-2382/3498

Juniper Mountain Outfitters
Box 50 Route 3
Caldwell, ID, USA
83605
208-454-1172
Stan Meholchick

Keating, Earl R., Jr.
Box 3
Gibbonsville, ID, USA
83463
208-865-2252

Lakeview Guest Ranch
2905 Harrison
Butte, MT, USA
59701
406-494-2585
Keith Rush

Lazy J Outfitters
Route 1
Kuna, ID, USA
83634
208-922-5648
L. Jarrett

Lemburg's Priest Lake Outfitters
Box 411
Nordman, ID, USA
83848
208-443-2685
Randall Lemburg

Little Wood River Outfitters
Box 425
Carey, ID, USA
83320
208-823-4414/4488
Robert Hennefer

Lochsa River Outfitters
Box 30 Route 2
Potlatch, ID, USA
83855
208-875-0620/926-4149
Jack Nygaard

Lost Lake Outfitters, Inc.
Box 226 HCR 66
Kooskia, ID, USA
83539
208-926-4988
Al Latch

MacKay Bar Corporation
3190 Airport Way
Boise, ID, USA
83705
208-344-1881
Garn Christenson

McManus, Jim
Box 442
Pierce, ID, USA
83546
208-464-2118

Meadow Creek Outfitters
Box 264 Route 2
Kooskia, ID, USA
83530
208-926-4759
Cheryl Bransford

Merritt's Saddlery
Box 1516
Salmon, ID, USA
83467
208-756-4170
Garry Merritt

Middle Fork Lodge, Inc.
3815 Rickenbacker
Boise, ID, USA
83705
208-342-7888
Nick Stuparich

Middlefork Ranch, Inc.
Box 7594
Boise, ID, USA
83707
415-329-0260 (Palo Alto CA)
Ben Grammar

Mile Hi Outfitters
Box 1066
Challis, ID, USA
83226
208-879-4403
Jerry Jeppson

Moose Creek Outfitters
Box 1181
Orofino, ID, USA
83544
208-476-5227
Richard Norris

Moyie River Outfitters
Box 54 HCR 85
Bonners Ferry, ID, USA
83805
208-267-2108
Stanley A. Sweet

Mystic Saddle Ranch
Box 2624-0
Hailey, ID, USA
83333
208-788-3055
Jeff Bitton

Norman Guth Inc.
Box D
Salmon, ID, USA
83467
208-756-3279

North Star Outfitters
Box 301
Darby, MT, USA
59829
406-821-3110
Kenneth Wolfinbarger

Paradise Outfitters
Box 74 HCR 11
Kamiah, ID, USA
83536
208-935-0859
Rich Armiger

Pioneer Mountain Outfitters
Box 5476 Route 2
Twin Falls, ID, USA
83301
208-734-3679
Thomas Proctor

Potts, Stanley
Box 1122
Hailey, ID, USA
83333
208-788-4584

Quarter Circle A Outfitters
Star Route Iron Creek
Salmon, ID, USA
83467
208-894-2451
Rick Hussey

R & R Outdoors, Inc.
2755 Aspen Cove
Meridian, ID, USA
83642
208-888-4676
Robert D. Black

Red River Corrals
Box 18 Star Route
Elk City, ID, USA
83535
208-842-2228
Archie George

Red Woods Outfitter
Box 580 HC 2
Pollock, ID, USA
83547
208-628-3673
N.F. Woods

Renshaw Outfitting, Inc.
Box 1165
Kamiah, ID, USA
83536
208-935-0726/2829
Jim Renshaw

Revell Enterprises
Box 674
Soda Springs, ID, USA
83276
208-547-3016
Phil Revell

Ridge W. Taylor Outfitters
Box 2356
Jackson, WY, USA
83001
307-733-9041

Rivers Navigation
Box 1223
Lewiston, ID, USA
83501
208-743-4800
Wally Beamer

Robson, Dale R.
Box 44
Felt, ID, USA
83424
208-456-2861

Rock'N H Packers
West Fork Road Route 1
Darby, MT, USA
59829
406-821-3815
Robert Stewart

Rugg, Ray
Box 58G Route 1
St. Ignatius, MT, USA
59865
406-745-4160

Running Creek Ranch
Box 509
Hamilton, ID, USA
59840
208-382-4336
Jerry L. Gifford

Salmon Meadows Lodge
Box 3410 HC 75
New Meadows, ID, USA
83654
208-347-2357
Jim Thrash

Salmon River Lodge Inc.
Box 348
Jerome, ID, USA
83338
208-324-3553
David Glles

St. Joe Hunting & Fishing Camp, Inc.
10405 Newport Highway
Spokane, WA, USA
99218
509-487-5971
Don Dixon

Big Game Outfitters Directory

North America

St. Joe Outfitters & Guides
Box 190 HCR 2
Harrison, ID, USA
83833
208-689-3528
Ed Hunt

S & S Outfitters
912 Burrell
Lewiston, ID, USA
83501
208-746-3569
David Bream

Sawtooth Wilderness Outfitters
730 West Greenhurst
Nampa, ID, USA
83651
208-466-8323
Leo Jarvis

Seal, Ray
Busterback Ranch
Ketchum, ID, USA
83340
208-788-4809/774-2217

Selway Lodge
Star Route Iron Creek
Salmon, ID, USA
83467
208-894-2451
Rick Hussey

Selway-Magruder Outfitters
Box 135
Corvallis, MT, USA
59828
406-961-4323
Don Habel & Sons

Seven Devils Outfitters Inc.
Box 5446
Boise, ID, USA
83705
208-343-7729
Jinny Hopfenbeck

Sevey Guide Serivice Inc.
Box 1527
Sun Valley, ID, USA
83353
208-774-2200
Bob Sevey

Shattuck Creek Ranch & Outfitters
Box 165
Elk River, ID, USA
83827
208-826-3405/3284
Andre Molsee

Shepp Ranch Idaho
Box 5446
Boise, ID, USA
83705
208-343-7729
Paul Resnick

Simons Outfitters
84 Mullan Gulch Road
St. Regis, MT, USA
59866
406-649-2329
Jack Simons

62 Ridge Outfitters & Guides
4239 Old Ahsahka Grade
Ahsahka, ID, USA
83520
208-476-7148
Ken & Elizabeth Smith

Stanley Potts Outfitters
Box 1122
Hailey, ID, USA
83333
208-788-4584
Stan Potts

Stover's Outfitters
Box 604
Council, ID, USA
83612
208-253-4352
John Stover

Sulphur Creek Ranch
7153 W. Emerald
Boise, ID, USA
83704
208-377-1188
Tom Allegrezza

Sun Valley Wilderness Outfitters
Box 303
Sun Valley, ID, USA
83353
208-622-5019/726-9449
R.J. Lewy

Taylor Ranch Outfitters
Box 4023 HC 82
Challis, ID, USA
83226
208-879-4718
Con Hourihan

Teton Ridge Ranch
Box 1732 Route 1
Tetonia, ID, USA
83452
208-456-2896
Albert Tilt, III

Trapper Creek Outfitters
Salmon River Air Route
Cascade, ID, USA
83611
Tony Popp, Jr.

Triple O Outfitters
Box 21
Pierce, ID, USA
83546
208-464-2349
Harlan Opdahl

Vaughn Haderlie & Sons
Box 126
Freedom, WY, USA
83210
208-873-2353
Vaughn Haderlie

Wally York & Son, Inc.
Box 319
Elk City, ID, USA
83525
208-842-2367
W. Travis York

War Eagle Outfitters & Guides
Box 1009 HC 61
Malta, ID, USA
83342
208-645-2455
Ken Jafek

Weitas Creek Outfitters
Box 115 C Route 2
Potlatch, ID, USA
83855
208-875-1190/0450
Steve Jones

White Cloud Outfitters
Box 217
Challis, ID, USA
83226
208-879-4574
Michael Scott

Whitewater Outfitters
Salmon River Air Route
Cascade, ID, USA
83611
208-382-4336
Lester "Zeke" West

Whitten Guide Service
Box 498
Riggins, ID, USA
83549
208-628-3862
Harvey Whitten

Wilderness Recreation Outfitter
1376 Walenta Drive
Moscow, ID, USA
83843
208-882-5367
Harry Vaughn

Wildlife Outfitters
992 Pleasant View Drive
Victor, MT, USA
59875
406-642-3262/3462
Jack Wemple

Illinois

Adventure Safaris Ltd.
747 - 3 First Nat'l Plaza
Chicago, IL, USA
60602
312-782-4756
P. Merzig

ISI Worldwide Adventures, Ltd.
P.O. Drawer 440
Carpentersville, IL, USA
60110
312-428-3311
George Daniels

Iowa

Hitzhusen Hunts & Sporting Goods
Box 420 304 Main Street
Rockwell, IA, USA
50469
515-822-4688/3300
D. Hitzhusen

Keeline, Jim H.
Box 7044
Spirit Lake, IA, USA
51360
712-336-5124/225-2168

Louisiana

EWW Safari Innovators
Box 258 Route 3
Tallulah, LA, USA
71282
318-574-1230
E.W. Williams

International Tours & Expeditions
3749 Perkins Road
Baton Rouge, LA, USA
70808
504-344-9476/800-222-0387

Laguna Vista
Box 580
New Roads, LA, USA
70760
504-638-8682/800-233-3985
D. Williams

Maine

Foggy Mountain Guide Service
Box 103 RFD#2
Dover-Foxcroft, ME, USA
04426
207-564-3404
W.A. Boswicz

Gentle Ben's Lodge
Box 212 SI
Rockwood, ME, USA
04478
207-534-2201
B. Pelletier

Hooke's Guide Service
Box 257 Route 4
Strong, ME, USA
04983
207-684-4178
T. Hooke

35

Big Game Outfitters Directory

North America

Mountain View Lodge
Box 20 HCR 76
Greensville, ME, USA
04441
207-695-3882
D. Peters

Northern Pride Lodge & O/F
Box 588 HCR 76
Kokadjo, ME, USA
Paul R. Loade

Patten Hunting Lodge
c/o 38 Preble Street
Portland, ME, USA
04101
207-772-0548/657-3867
B. Finney

Reid, Raymond
Box 820
Thorndike, ME, USA
04986
207-568-3165/709-639-7258

Maryland

Loeffler, Capt. Ron Sr.
Box 108 Route 1
Rock Hall, MD, USA
21661
301-639-2128

Wings at Dawn Gunning Service
1805 Trout Farm Road
Jarrettsville, MD, USA
21084
301-557-8068
Lee Peters

Massachusetts

Boston Safaris Ltd.
Shrewsbury Street
West Boylston, MA, USA
01583
617-835-6057

Michigan

International Big Game Safaris
100 S. Waverly Road
Holland, MI, USA
49423
616-392-6458

Outdoor Adventures Unlimited
296 Randall
Troy, MI, USA
48090
313-689-6715
Fred J. Smith

Renegade Ranch
Dept. NAH 2690 Riggsville Road
Cheboygan, MI, USA
49721
616-627-7232

Safari Adventures Ltd.
1929 Lone Pine Orad
Bloomfield Hills, MI, USA
48013
313-851-1707
C. Bazzy

Minnesota

Mason's Outdoor Adventures
819 East Clear Avenue
St Paul, MN, USA
55106
612-774-7930

Missouri

High Adventure Game Ranch, Inc.
#205 - 8330 Watson Road
St. Louis, MO, USA
63119
314-849-5700/894-3776

Rio Arriba Trophy Hunts
11 Solano Circle Gulf Hills
Ocean Springs, MS, USA
39564
601-875-6888

Montana

A Lazy H Outfitters
Box 729
Choteau, MT, USA
59422
406-466-5564
Al Haas

Avalanche Basin Outfitters
Box 17B
White Sulphur Springs, MT, USA
59645
406-547-3962
Doug & Zita Caltrider

Babcock Creek Outfitting
Box 1564
Kalispell, MT, USA
59901
406-862-7813
LeRoy Books

B Bar 2 Outfitters
Box 32
Dell, MT, USA
50724
406-276-3239
Phil & Deb Page

Baldwins Archery Outfitters
900 Ave. D NW
Great Falls, MT, USA
59404
406-761-0945

Bar 44 Outfitters & Guide School
Box 493
Hamilton, MT, USA
59840
406-363-3522
J.V. Rose

Bartlett Creek Outfitters
1190 Quililn Road
Deer Lodge, MT, USA
59722
406-693-2433
Miek Smith

Bassett, Al
Box 4
Melstone, MT, USA
59054
406-358-2360

Bear Creek Outfitters & Guest Ranch
Box 151
E. Glacier, MT, USA
59434
406-226-4489
Bill Beck

Beardsley Outfiiter & Guide Service
Box 360
Ennis, MT, USA
59729
406-682-7292
Tim & Kristy Beardsley

Bear's Den Outfitting
Box 941
Livingston, MT, USA
59047
406-222-0746

Beartooth Plateau Outfitters
Box 28
Roberts, MT, USA
59070
406-445-2293
Ronnie L. Wright

Big Horn Outfitters
Box 487
Manhattan, MT, USA
59741
406-284-3702
Arthur Vadon

Big Sky Pack Trips
Box 15
Stanford, MT, USA
59479
406-566-2486
M.G.Pride

Big Cir Lodge
Box 167
Deborgia, MT, USA
59830
406-678-4364
Stan Cirspinski

Billingsley Ranch Outfitters
Box 768
Glasgow, MT, USA
59230
406-367-5577
Jack Billingsley

Black Mountain Pack & Guide
Box 352
Florence, MT, USA
59833
406-273-6419
Bruce Scott

Blue Rock Outfitters
Tongue River Stage
Miles City, MT, USA
59301
K. Hughes

Box Marshall Wilderness Ranch
Seeley Lake, MT, USA
59868
406-754-2285

Bridger Outfitters
15100 Rocky Mountain Road
Belgrade, MT, USA
59714

Broken Hart Ranch
73800 Gallatin Road
Gallatin Gateway, MT, USA
59730
406-763-4279

Buckhorn Ranch Outfitters
Box 84
Eureka, MT, USA
59917
406-889-3762
H.T. Workman

Buffalo Horn Outfitters
205 Buffalo Horn
Gallatin Gateway, MT, USA
59730
406-995-4283
Jim Walma

Bull Buffalo Outfitters
Box 658-B
Emigrant, MT, USA
59027
406-848-7570
L. Britton

Bull River Outfitters
Box 40 E. Fork Bull River
Noxon, MT, USA
59853
Doug Peterson

Camp Baker Outfitters
913 Smith River Road
White Sulphur Springs, MT, USA
59645
406-547-2173
Don Johnston

Big Game Outfitters Directory

North America

Catron's Outfitting & Guide Service
Box 3204
Bozeman, MT, USA
59772
406-586-4796

Cayuse Outfitters, Inc.
Box 1218
Livingston, MT, USA
59047
406-222-3168
Larry Lahren

Circle KBL Outfitters
Box 25 Dept. R
Stevensville, MT, USA
59870
406-777-5969
Bob Lamberson

Circle R. Outfitters
St. Mary, MT, USA
59417
406-732-4453
Jack Ray & Tim Lytle

Climbing Arrow Outfitters
31000 Francis Road
Belgrade, MT, USA
59714
406-388-1305
Frank & Meg Anderson

Copenhaver Outfitters
Box 111
Ovando, MT, USA
59854
406-793-5557
Howard, Copenhaver

Crow Creek Outfitters & Guides
Box 5
Toston, MT, USA
59643
406-266-3742
M. Parsons

Curtiss Outfitters
3260 Bench Drive
Kalispell, MT, USA
59901
406-257-6215

Deep Creek Outfitters
1605 14 Street SW
Great Falls, MT, USA
59404
406-452-7365
Gary Anderson

DL Elk Outfitters, Inc.
282 Ten Mile Road
Cascade, MT, USA
59421
406-468-2642
Dennis LeVeque

DN & 3 Outfitters
Box 4116 Giltedge Route
Lewistown, MT, USA
59457
406-538-8591
Eldon & Barb Snyder

Doonan Gulch Outfitters
Box 501 S. Pumpkin Creek Road
Broadus, MT, USA
59317
406-427-5474
Russell Greenwood

Double Arrow Outfitters
Box 495
Seeley Lake, MT, USA
59868
406-677-2317
Jack & C.B. Rich

Double W Outfitters
Box 507
Darby, MT, USA
59829
406-821-3007/3802
Bill & Billy White

Eightmile Outfitters
Box 189
Ennis, MT, USA
59729
406-682-7494
Rick Matzick

Elk Creek Outfitters
Box 2213 Route 38
Livingston, MT, USA
59047
406-222-3637/578-2216

Elk Range Outfitters
1557 Colorado Gulch
Helena, MT, USA
59601
406-442-9124
Bill & Cindy Montanye

Elk Valley Game Ranch
Box 430
Hardin, MT, USA
59034
406-665-1215
Stan Hall

Five Bears Outfitters
Box 325
Carvallis, MT, USA
59828
406-961-4778
G. Peters

Great Bear Outfitters
Box 79
East Glacier, MT, USA
59434
406-226-9220
Brent Wyrick

Grimm, Kent "Jake"
Box 191 Canyon Route
Gallatin Gateway, MT, USA
59730
406-995-4630

H & H Outfitters
Box 632
Lincoln, MT, USA
59639
406-362-4581
Dave & Becki Harrington

Hawkins Outfitters
Box 187
Eureka, MT, USA
59917
406-296-2642

Hawley Mountain Guest Ranch
Box 4
MeLeod, MT, USA
59052
406-932-5791

Hidden Lake Outfitters
Box 1233
Big Timber, MT, USA
59011
406-932-6582
Bob Bovee

Hidden Valley Ranch
Augusta, MT, USA
59410
406-562-3622
A. Weikum

Hole in the Wall Lodge
Box 134
Alberton, MT, USA
59820
406-728-5203
Jeffry Freeman

Holland Lake Lodge
Condon, MT, USA
59826
406-754-2282
D.K. Mitchell

Horse Creek Outfitters
Box 667 (S6) Route 1
Emigrant, MT, USA
59027
406-848-7144

I.C.R. Outfitters
Box 974
Ennis, MT, USA
59729
406-682-7223
Wade Durham

Imperial Outfitters
Box 145
Kila, MT, USA
59920
406-854-2274

Jack Atcheson & Sons, Inc.
3210 Ottawa Street
Butte, MT, USA
59701
406-782-2382

Johnson, Edwin L.
Box 896
Corwin Springs, MT, USA
59021
406-848-7758

Johnson Outfitters
Mox 185 Jardin Route
Gardiner, MT, USA
59030
406-848-7256
Kathryn Johnson

Judith River Ranch
Hilger, MT, USA
59451
406-462-5654
Steve & Bethany Mosick

K Lazy Three Ranch
Box 267
Lincoln, MT, USA
59639
406-362-4258
Kenny Hoeffner

Koocanusa Outfitters
3435 US Highway 37
Libby, MT, USA
59923
406-293-7548
Lynn Berland

Lapham Outfitter
Box 795
Jackson, MT, USA
59736
406-834-3134
Max Lapham

Lazy T4 Outfitters
Box 116 B
Victor, MT, USA
59875
406-642-3586
Spence Trogdon

Lone Tree Hunting Club
LTHC 80 Fagan
Hillsborough, CA, USA
94010
415-981-2655

Lone Willow Creek Guide Service
Box 775
Livingston, MT, USA
59047
406-222-7155
Mark Baumeister

Lone Wolf Guide Service
Box 631
Livingston, MT, USA
59047
406-222-7155

Big Game Outfitters Directory

North America

Lost Creek Outfitters
107 South Main
Livingston, MT, USA
59047
406-222-7861
Don Wright

Lost Wolf Enterprises
Box 418
Thompson Falls, MT, USA
59873
406-827-3491
Brian W. Ray

Malson, Jerry
22 Swamp Creek Road
Trout Creek, MT, USA
59874
406-847-5582

McAfee Lodge
Box 27744 Rt. 1 Yaak River Rd.
Troy, MT, USA
59935
406-295-4880
Bill & Judy McAfee

McDonough, N.L. & Sons
Wolf Creek, MT, USA
59648
406-235-4205

Medicine Lake Outfitters
Box 3663 R
Bozeman, MT, USA
59715
406-388-4938
Tom Heintz

M Hanging Cross Outfitters & Guides
Box 788
Choteau, MT, USA
59422
406-466-2523
Chip Gollehon

Miller Outfitters
663 Vaughn S. Frontage Rd.
Great Falls, MT, USA
59404
406-761-5184

M.B.K. Outfitters
4155 W. Kootenai Road
Rexford, MT, USA
59930
406-889-3297

Montana Adventure Trips
West Fork Route
Darby, MT, USA
59829
406-821-3763
K. Allaman

Montana Wilderness Outfitters
4420 Watt Lane
Stevensville, MT, USA
59870
406-777-3673
David & Tena Kozub

Monte's Guiding
16 North Fork Road
Townsend, MT, USA
59644
406-266-3515
LaM. J. Schnur

Mountain Trail Outfitters
Box 2249 Route 38
Livingston, MT, USA
59047
406-222-2734

Muscat, Jim
Box 255
Big Sky, MT, USA
59716
406-995-4089

Pine Hills Outfitters
Box 282
Lincoln, MT, USA
59639
406-362-4664
Mike Barthelmess

Pintler Wilderness Outfitting
Box 1116
Anaconda, MT, USA
59711
406-563-7216
Bob Labert

Point of Rocks Guest Ranch
Box 680 Route 1
Emigrant, MT, USA
59027
406-848-7278
Max Chase

Rawhide Guide Service
Box 252
Livinston, MT, USA
59047
406-333-4756
Cougar Lee Fatouros

Ray Perkins & Son
1906 Main Street
Miles City, MT, USA
59301
406-232-4283

Reynolds Hollow Top Hide-Away
3050 Highway 91 North
Dillon, MT, USA
59725
406-683-5066

Rock N' H Packers
West Fork, Route 1
Darby, MT, USA
59829
406-821-3815
R.L. Stewart

Ron Mills Outfitting
Box 2
Augusta, MT, USA
59410
406-562-3335

Rugg's Outfitting
Box 50G Route 1
St. Ignatius, MT, USA
59865
406-745-4160
Ray Rugg

Rush's Lakeview Guest Ranch
2905 Harrison
Butte, MT, USA
59701
406-494-2585

Rus Willis & Associates
Heron, MT, USA
59844
406-847-5523

Saddle Mtn. Outfitting Co., Ltd.
Box 286
Hamilton, MT, USA
59840
406-363-2356
J. Spear

Schell, Jim
Box 775
Livingston, MT, USA
59047
406-222-7584

Schilla, Jack
807 Cherry Avenue
Helena, MT, USA
59601
406-443-3755

Selway Magruder Outfitter
Box 135
Corvallis, MT, USA
59828
406-961-4323
Dan Habel & Sons

Simons' Outfitters
84 Mullan Gulch Road
St. Regis, MT, USA
59866
406-649-2329

63 Ranch
Box 979B
Livingston, MT, USA
59047
406-222-0570
Sandra Cahill

Stanek, Joe
515 3rd Street
Victor, MT, USA
59875
406-642-3881

Stockton Outfitters
Wise River, MT, USA
59762
406-832-3138
Bill Stockton

Story Cattle Co. & Outfitting
Box 55
Emigrant, MT, USA
59027
406-333-4739
Mike Story

Sun Canyon Lodge
Box 327
Augusta, MT, USA
59410
406-562-3654
Lee Carlborn

Sun River Outfitters
Star Route 2476
Condon, MT, USA
59826
406-754-2228
Lloyd Hahn

T Bar 7 Guest Ranch
Star Route
Darby, MT, USA
59329
406-349-2499
Gerald Richie & Son

The Bear's Den Outfitters
Box 941
Livingston, MT, USA
59047
406-222-0746
Bruce C. Delorey

Trail Creek Outfitters
Box 63 NA
Garneill, MT, USA
59445
406-374-2398
Demorise E. Allen Jr.

Triple Tree Ranch
5520 Sourdough Road
Bozeman, MT, USA
59715
406-586-4821
B. Meyers

Trophy Guide Service
Box 287
Livingston, MT, USA
59047
406-222-2229
Dan Bowlin

Twisted Pine Ranch
Box 84
Merriman, NE, USA
69218
308-684-3482
K. Moreland

Venture West
4217 Timberlane
Missoula, MT, USA
59802
406-728-1673/800-348-2729
Cathy Ream

Big Game Outfitters Directory

North America

West Fork Outfitters
Box 258
White Sulphur Springs, MT, USA
59645
406-547-2226
Ron Corr

West Fork Outfitters
Box 644
Darby, MT, USA
59829
406-349-2816
Dave Walker

Whitetail Ranch
Ovando, MT, USA
59854
406-793-5666
Jack Hooker

Wildlife Outfitters Guest Ranch
992 Pleasant View Drive
Victor, MT, USA
59875
406-642-3262
Jack Wemple

Wilkes, Tim & Tom
9354 Nash Road
Bozeman, MT, USA
59715
406-586-9455

Yaak River Outfitters
Rte. 1
Troy, MT, USA
59935
406-295-4003
Clint Mills

Yellowater Outfitters
Box 836
Grass Range, MT, USA
59032
406-428-2195
R. Olsen

Yellowstone Outfitters
15100B Rocky Mountain Road
Belgrade, MT, USA
59714
406-388-4463

Zikan, Bob
Bridge Road
Darby, MT, USA
59829
406-821-4541

N. Carolina

Chestnut Hunting Lodge
Box 236 Dept. NH Route 2
Taylorsville, NC, USA
28681
704-632-3916
Jerry Rushing

Nevada

Agua Fria Guide Service
1 - 1001 South Third Street
Las Vegas, NV, USA
89101
Mike Bucks

Hurtado Desert Bighorn Guide
Service
8310 Fisher Avenue
Las Vegas, NV, USA
89129
702-645-1855
M. Hurtado

New Mexico

Agua Fria Guide Service
Box 844
Angle Fire, NM, USA
87710
Mike Bucks

B & A Outfitters
226 Uracca
Raton, NM, USA
87740
505-445-2298/9225

Back Country Hunts
1029 Haston Road
Carlsbad, NM, USA
88220
505-887-6178
Steve Jones

Baldy Mountain Outfitters
Box 386
Cimarron, NM, USA
87714
505-376-2566
Fritz Sturges

Ball, Ron
Box 362
Eagle Nest, NM, USA
87718

Bar X Bar Ranch
PO Drawer 2
Pecos, NM, USA
87552
505-757-6088

Beaverhead Ranch
Beaverhead Route
Magdalena, NM, USA
87825
505-772-5795
Jack Diamond

Black Range Guide & Outfitting
Box 97
Winston, NM, USA
87943
Sterling Carter

Broidy, Kenneth
Box 429
Mountainair, NM, USA
87036

Cactus Hunting Service
304 Sinimole Road Route 3
Roswell, NM, USA
88201
505-623-7208
Jon Corn

C Bar Land & Cattle Co.
Box 117 Route 4
Victoria, TX..USA
77904
512-573-2667
Malcolm Calaway

Chama Land & Cattle Co.
Box 476
Chama, NM, USA
87520
505-756-2133
Leo Smith

Cougar Mountain Guide Service
Box 31
Corona, NM, USA
88318
505-849-7700
Doug Cobbs

DeMasters, Ronnie
Box 472
Chama, NM, USA
87520
505-756-2492

Diamond E Outfitters
Box 807
Las Vegas, NM, USA
87701

Dirk Neal's Guide & Outfitting
Box 193
Red River, NM, USA
87558
505-754-2729

El Rio Guide Service
Box 23
Questa, NM, USA
87556
505-586-0652
Cecil Glines

Gringo Hill Outfitters
Box 2
Glorieta, NM, USA
87535
505-757-6036
George Stumpff Jr.

High-Lonesome Outfitters
Springerville, AZ, USA
89538
602-333-4309
Kerry Sebring

High Mountain Outfitters
Box 244
Eagle Nest, NM, USA
87718
505-377-2240
Pancho Trujillo

Horizon Guide & Outfitters
Box 1765
Socorro, NM, USA
87801
505-835-0813
K.P. Dow

Hulse, Quentin
Beaverhead Route
Magdalena, NM, USA
87825
505-772-5778

Jackalope Adventure Unlimited
Box 215
Chama, NM, USA
87520
505-588-7414
Lance Andrews

Jim Bobb Guide & Outfitter
Box 601
Capitan, NM, USA
88316
505-354-2998

Lobo Outfittes
Box 9A Route 2
Pagosa Springs, CO, USA
81147
303-264-5546
Dick Ray

Kit Carson Outfitters
Box 2366
Bloomfield, NM, USA
84718
Darrell Bays

M&B Cattle Co.
13521 Terrogon NE
Alberquerque, NM, USA
87112
505-294-3593

Mimbres Outfitters
Box 47
Mimbres, NM, USA
88049
505-536-9470
Owen Fowler

Moreno Ranch
Box 135
Eagle Nest, NM, USA
87718
505-377-6581/6555
Bob & Dean Butler

Mount Taylor Ranch
Box 229
Cubero, NM, USA
87014
505-822-3867
Perry Handyside

36

Big Game Outfitters Directory

North America

Mundy Ranch
Box 386
Cimarron, NM, USA
87714
F. Sturges

New Mexico CS Ranch
Eagle Nest Dam
Eagle Nest, NM, USA
87718
505-377-6521/6878
L. Brooks

Pecos Wilderness Outfitters
Box 12
Tererro, NM, USA
87573
505-757-6193
H.H. Ley

Reserve Outfitters & Guides
Box 637
Reserve, NM, USA
87830
505-533-6788
Bill Jernigan

Ric Martin Trophy Adventures Inc.
Box 20 Mountain Route
Jemez Springs, NM, USA
87025
505-829-3897

Rio Costilla Park Ranch
Box 111
Costilla, NM, USA
87524
505-586-0542

Rocky Mountain Big Game Hunts
Box 356
Regina, NM, USA
87046
505-289-3394
Jan Brown

Ross Johnson Guide & Outfitter
Box 194
Hillsboro, NM, USA
88042
505-895-5600
Ross Johnson

Runnels' Outfitters & Guide Service
Box 596
Capitan, NM, USA
88316
505-354-2778
Robert Runnels

San Francisco River Outfitter
Box 179C Route 10
Glenwood, NM, USA
88039
Tom Klumker

Sierra Grande Outfitters
Box 307
Chama, NM, USA
87520
505-756-2318
Les Ezell

Tierra Encantada Guide/Outfitter
Box 994
Socorro, NM, USA
87801
505-835-3198
Roger Gabaldon

Turkey Track Outfitters
Box 818
Espanola, NM, USA
87532
505-685-4483
Charles Cockerell

United States Outfitters, Inc.
Box 532
Ranchos de Taos, NM, USA
87557
505-758-9774
Frank Simms

UU Bar Ranch
Box 42 Route 1
Cimarron, NM, USA
87714
505-376-2643

Zia West, Inc.
Box 1146
Raton, NM, USA
87740
505-445-5309

New York

Global Outdoors
85 Johanna Lane
Staten Island, NY, USA
10309
718-317-7895
A. Cito

Rieder, Rory
44 Kane Avenue
Larchmont, NY, USA
10538
914-834-5611

Wilderness Trek
4417 Grandview Avenue
Hamburg, NY, USA
14075
P. McDonnell

Wildtrack Inc.
Box 500S
Honeoye, NY, USA
14471
716-229-2700

New Hampshire

Wilderness Adventures
17 Woodlawn Ridge
Concord NH, USA
03301
603-224-7578

New Jersey

Orion Trophy Expeditions Outfitters
Box 472 R.D. E3
Phillipsburg, NJ, USA
08865
201-859-1584

Ventures International
76 Weldon Road R.D. 4
Lake Hopatcong, NJ, USA
07849
201-663-1723
Donald Mulson

Wilderness Expeditions
Box 344
Allendale, NJ, USA
07401
800-852-HUNT

Ohio

Basset, D. Lee
30201 Aurora Road
Cleveland, OH, USA
44139

Grants Cabins
191 E. Washington Avenue
Marion, OH, USA
43302
614-387-5571

S.W. Safaris North
1917 Sugar Run Trail
Dayton, OH, USA
45305
513-848-4447

White Oak Exotic Hunting Preserve
Box 287
Senecaville, OH, USA
43780
614-685-6063

Whitetail Outfitters
75117 Johnson Run Road
Guernsey, OH, USA
43749
614-498-6443
A. Prisbe

Oklahoma

Neal Hunting Company
7901 South Sheridan
Tulsa, OK, USA
74133
918-492-1653

Texoma Hunting Wilderness, Inc.
2301 Hidden Lake Drive
Norman, OK, USA
73069
405-329-8933

Oregon

Anderson Land & Livestock
HCR Box 9
Pilot Rock, OR, USA
98768
503-443-9213
Terry Anderson

BR Guide Service
Kiamath Falls, OR, USA
503-882-1549
Brooks McDowell

Cabin Creek Outfitters
Box 308
Stayton, OR, USA
97383
503-581-4600

Cornucopia Wilderness Pack Station
Box 50 Rte. 1
Richland, OR, USA
97870
503-893-6400/742-5400
Eldon Deardorff

Divide Wilderness Outfitters
14 W., Jackson Street
Medford, OR, USA
97501
503-773-5983
Paul Brown

Eagle Cap Wilderness Pack Station
Box 416 Rte. 1
Joseph, OR, USA
97846
503-432-4145
Manford Isley

Eagle Creek Outfitters
Box 702 Dept. B Rte. 1
Sommerville, OR, USA
97876
503-534-4555/800-852-2768

Handrich Guides & Outfitters
6474 Stagecoach Road
Santa Barbara, CA, USA
93105
805-964-2965
Dave Handrich

High Cascade Stables & Pack Station
70775 Indian Ford Road
Sisters, OR, USA
97759
503-549-4972

High Country Outfitters
Box 26
Joseph, OR, USA
97846
503-432-9171
Calvin Henry

Hunters Rendezvous
Long Creek, OR, USA
97856
503-421-3684
John Cole

Big Game Outfitters Directory

North America

Joe Miller Guide Service
94771 Indian Creek Road
Gold Beach, OR, USA
97444
503-247-6762/6067

JP Pack Station
Box 101
Lostine, OR, USA
97857
503-569-2204
Jim Pyeatt

Moss Springs Packing
Box 104
Cove, OR, USA
97824
503-568-4823
Charlie Short

North-West Hunting Consultants
70744 Apiary Road Dept. SC
Rainier, OR, USA
97048
503-556-9661
Duane Bernard

Old Oregon Land & Livestock
Box 373
Pendleton, OR, USA
97801
503-443-6861

Oregon Guides & Packers Assoc.
Box 3797
Portland, OR, USA
97208
503-234-3268

Outback Ranch Outfitters
Box 384
Joseph, OR, USA
97846
503-426-4037
Ken Wick

Outdoor Adventures Plus
4030 W. Amazon Drive
Eugene, OR, USA
97045
503-344-4499
Larry Kirkpatrick

Pallette Ranch
Box B
Joseph, OR, USA
97846
503-432-9191
R.D. Schenk

Quarter Circle Eleven Ranch
Box 8003
Boise, ID, USA
83707
208-362-5515
Marty Rust

Snake River Packers
1329 Elm
Forest Grove, OR, USA
97116
503-357-5397
Robert Piland

Steen Mountain Packers
General Delivery
Diamond, OR, USA
97722
503-493-2403/2825
John & Carmen Witzel

Steen's Wilderness Adventures
Box 73 Rte. 1
Joseph, OR, USA
97846
503-432-5315
Jim & Connie Steen

Wapiti Outfitters, Inc.
Star Route
Echo, OR, USA
97826
503-376-8462
Barb Seager

Wapiti River Guides
Route 1
Cove, OR, USA
97824
Gary Lane

Wildland Resource Enterprises
Box 259
Lagrande, OR, USA
97850
503-963-3266

Pennsylvania

Boar Hollow Hunting Preserve
Road 1
Mohrsville, PN, USA
19541
215-926-4410
Gene Sarafino & Sons

Foulkrod's Archery Camp
Box 140 RD#1
Troy, PN, USA
16947
717-297-4367/3806
B. Foulkrod

Hemlock Acres
RD#3
Benton, PN, USA
17814
717-458-5143

Jim McCarthy Adventures
4906 Creek Drive
Harrisburg, PN, USA
17112
717-652-4374/748-1535

Martz's Game Farm
Box 85 RD#1
Dalmatia, PN, USA
17017
717-758-3307/1535
Harold & Don Martz

Outfitters Unlimited Inc.
Box 11940 General Square Stn.
Harrisburg PN, USA
17108
B. Dunn

Safaris Africa
3995 School Road South
Jeannette, PN, USA
15644
412-733-2878

Tioga Boar Hunting Preserve
R.D.#1
Tioga, PN, USA
16946
717-835-5341

Webb Quaivvik Ltd.
441 Church Road
Lansdale, PN, USA
19446
215-362-1510

World Hunts Inc.
Box 777
Latrobe, PN, USA
15650
412-537-7668
800-4-HUNTING

S. Dakota

Dakota Safaris
Box 518
Wall, SD, USA
57790
605-457-2682
Jerry Kjerstad

Fair Chase Adventures
Box 630
Piedmont, SD, USA
57769
800-843-8800 x. 22
Bo Hauer

Haensel Ranch
Box 17 RR#2
Montrose, SD, USA
57048
605-363-3402
Jerry Haensel

Sioux Land Hunting Inc.
Box 64 RR#1
Naples, SD, USA
57271
605-628-2987/2200
Rick Holiday

Texas

Adobe Lodge Hunting Camp
Box 5055 Route 5
San Angelo, TX, USA
76901
915-949-6885/942-8040
S. Duncan

CC Bar Land & Cattle Co.
Box 117, Route 4
Victoria, TX, USA
77904
512-573-2667
Malcolm Calaway

Corazon Ranch
Box 588
Bracketwille, TX, USA
78832
512-563-2390
W.A. Belcher

Dallas Safari Club
770S Twin Towers 8484 Stemmons
Dallas, TX, USA
75247
214-630-1453

Dolan Creek Ranches
Box 420069
Del Rio, TX, USA
78842-0069
512-775-3129
John Finnigan

Game Conservation International
Box 17444
San Antonio, TX, USA
78217

Game Conservation International
444 Fort Worth Club Building
Fort Worth, TX, USA
76102
817-335-1942
H. Tennison

Gilchrist, Dooley
Box 67
Spring Branch, TX, USA
78070

Greenwood Valley Ranch
Box 75 Route 1
Mountain Home, TX, USA
78058
512-683-3411
J. Hunt

High Sierra Outfitters
Box 2042A Route 2
Kempner, TX, USA
76539
512-556-2453
B. Glosson

Hoffmann, G. L.
Box 1458
Sonora, TX, USA
76950

Big Game Outfitters Directory

North America

Hunters Africa
5800 - 6 Desta Drive
Midland, TX, USA
79705-5510
915-682-6324

Indianhead Ranch, Inc.
Box 2 RR#1
Del Rio, TX, USA
78840
512-775-6481

International Prof. Hunters Assoc.
Box 17444
San Antonio, TX, USA
78217
512-824-7509

Nunley Brothers Ranches
Box 308
Sabinal, TX, USA
78881
512-988-2752

Outdoor Expeditions
4026 Westheimer
Houston, TX, USA
77027
713-621-7342
D. Petersen

Piemons, Scott D.
801 West Vickery
Fort Worth, TX, USA
76104
817-332-1598

Real Hunting
Box 536 WS
Marfa, TX, USA
79843
915-467-2902

Rio Grande Rancho
Box 914 Route 2
Adkins, TX, USA
78101
512-947-3647
Jeffrey Myers

Safari South Sporting International
504 - 7701 Wilshire Place Drive
Houston, TX, USA
77040
713-785-6681/744-3527

777 Ranch
Box 45297 Dept. HG
San Antonio, TX, USA
78280-8297
512-675-1408

Tadlock, Paul
Box 850 Route 8
New Braunfels, TX, USA
78130
512-625-4346

Texotic Wildlife Inc.
Box 181
Amarillo, TX, USA
79120
806-352-1106
G. Conner

Top of Texas Hunting, Inc.
Box 30504
Amarillo, TX, USA
79120
806-352-1106
Gary Conner

Trans-Pecos Guide Service
Box 599
Sanderson, TX, USA
79848
915-345-2629
G. W. Zachary

West Tex-New Mex Hunting Services
Box 69
Ozona, TX, USA
76943
915-392-2923
J. Rankin

Westminster Safaris Ltd.
B - 3200 Louis Court
Plano, TX, USA
75023
214-964-2213
J. A. Chaffee

Williamson, Col. Bill
Box 27241
Austin, TX, USA
78755
512-345-4891

Y.O. Ranch
Dept. SCI
Mountain Home, TX, USA
78058
512-640-3222

York, Darrell
Box 536
Maria, TX, USA
79843
915-467-2902

Young, Ron
6011 South Staples Street
Corpus Christi, TX, USA
78413
512-993-1200

Utah

Adventure Unlimited
Box 17
Hurricane, UT, USA
84737
801-635-2340
B. Branham

Diamond Ranch Outfitters
Box 209
Provo, UT, USA
84603
801-377-3100
Wade Lemon

Elk Ridge Outfitters & Guides
8221 East 599 South
Huntsville, UT, USA
84317
801-745-2569
Steve McFarland

Howard's Hunts
2929 Kenwood Street
Slc., UT, USA
84106
801-466-8830
Lee Howard

J.G. Guides & Outfitters
Box 41 Dept. SCI
Munroe, UT, USA
84754
801-527-4107

Pine Ranch Outfitters
100 North 300 West
Spanishfork, UT, USA
84660
801-798-7805
Bill Alldredge

Piute Creek Outfitters, Inc.
Rte. 1A
Kansas, UT, USA
80436
800-225-0218

Rick LaRocco & Associates
175 North Center Suite 13
Wellsville, UT, USA
84339
801-752-7774/245-3252

Safron, Bob
324 - 25th Street
Ogden, UT, USA
84401

Sleeping Deer Outfitters Inc.
Box 1232
Kanarraville, UT, USA
84742
801-586-9203
Scott Berry

Tri W Outfitters
97 - 1700 West 2700 North
Ogden, UT, USA
84404
Bobby Wright

Wasatch Outfitters & Guides
3336 Gramercy Avenue
Agden, UT, USA
84403
801-394-4262
Fred John

Virginia

Abrams Creek Outfitters
Box 790 140 North 21st Street
Purcellville, VA, USA
22132
703-338-5848
G. Abrams

Nathan, Tink
Box NN
McLean, VA, USA
22101

Washington

Bolwes, Ed
7022 West Fourth
Kennewick, WA, USA
99336

Caswell, Jess
Box 432
Montesano, WA, USA
98583
206-249-5687

Klineburger Worldwide Travel
3627 Ist Avenue South
Seattle, WA, USA
98134
206-343-9699
C. Klineburger

Martin, Craig
Box 428 Route 3
Dayton, WA, USA
99328
509-382-4930

High Country Packers Inc.
Box 108
Issaquah, WA, USA
98027

St. Joe Hunting & Fishing Camp Inc.
10405 Newport Highway
Spokane, WA, USA
99218
509-467-5971
Don E. Dixon

Susee's Skyline Packers
1807 East 72nd Street
Tacoma, WA, USA
98404
206-472-5558

Wisconsin

Buckhorn Ridge Guide Service
Box 294
Oak Creek, WI, USA
53154
414-425-1838
Gary Genaw

Big Game Outfitters Directory

North America

Hunts West
139 Hwy. 10 West
Stevens Point, WI, USA
54481
715-344-HUNT

River Country Consultants
4437 Brockman Road
Vesper, WI, USA
54489
715-423-7016
Dan Brockman

Wilderness Adventures
E13735 Hwy. 33
Baraboo, WI, USA
53913
608-356-3874
Bill Weitzel

Wyoming

AA Ranch
Big Piney, WY, USA
83113
307-276-3244
Ronald Ball

Absaroka Ranch
Fremont County, Star Route
Dubois, WY, USA
82513
307-455-2275
Robert Betts, Jr.

Adams, T.T.
Box 2470
Jackson, WY, USA
83001
307-733-2961

Allen Brothers Outfitting
Box 243
Lander, WY, USA
82520
307-332-2995
J. Allen

Arizona Creek Outfitters
Box 716
Jackson, WY, USA
83001
307-733-3129
Roy & Linda Bonner

Arrowhead Outfitters
Box 3252
Jackson, WY, USA
83001
307-733-5223
Robert B. Lowe

Astle Hunting Camp
Box 121
Beford, WY, USA
83112
307-883-2750
F. B. Astle

Atkinson, Dale
Box 108
Moran, WY, USA
83103
307-543-2442

Bald Mountain Outfitters
Box 754
Pinedale, WY, USA
82941
307-367-6539
Terry Pollard

Barkhurst, Dick
Box 13 Star Route
Saratoga, WY, USA
82331
307-327-5350
D. Barkhurst

Battle Mountain Outfitters
1235 Johnson Avenue
Thermopolis, WY, USA
82443
307-864-2620
J.W. Lumleu

Bear Creek Hunting Camp
Box 222 Teton County
Wilson, WY, USA
83014
307-733-4314
P.G. Gilroy

Bear Track Outfitters
2303 Southfork Road
Cody, WY, USA
82414
307-527-7815
Ron Dube

Beaver Creek Outfitters
Box 673
Big Piney, WY, USA
83113
307-276-5372/3748
Keith Manning

Bernard, Tim
Wildrose Ranch, Box 737
Dubois, WY, USA
82513

Big Horn Mountain Outfitters
5060 Coffeen Sheridan County
Sheridan, WY, USA
82801
307-672-2813
T. Johnson

Billings, John R.
Box 3127
Cody, WY, USA
82414
307-587-5609

Bitterroot Ranch
1 East Fork
Dubois, WY, USA
82513
800-545-0019
Bayard Fox

BJ Outfitters
5510 Alcova Route
Casper, WY, USA
82604
307-472-7956
Mr. Hollingsowrth

Black Mountain Outfitters
412 East Burkitt Sheridan County
Sheridan, WY, USA
82801
307-674-7369
J. Yeager

Blacktooth Mountain Outfitters
Box 405
Buffalo, WY, USA
82834
307-684-2701
O.B. Caudle

Blizzard Creek Trophy Hunts
Box 2015 Park County
Cody, WY, USA
82414
307-587-5011
Bill Smith

Bolton Ranch Outfitters
7000 Valley View Place
Cheyenne, WY, USA
82009
307-637-6017/635-8066
John Anderson

Bondurant Creek Hunting Camp
1515 South Park Route
Jackson, WY, USA
83001
307-733-5069
E.G. Wampler

Boulder Lake Ranch
Box 1100 Dept. NAH
Pinedale, WY, USA
82941
307-367-2961

Boxelder Ranch
Bx 3720
Ten Sleep, WY, USA
82442
M. Bush

Box K Ranch
Teton County
Moran, WY, USA
83013
307-543-2407
W. Korn

Box R Ranch
Box 23 Sublettee County
Cora, WY, USA
82925
307-367-2291
Irv Lozier

Box Y Lodge
ROute 1 Lincoln County
Afton, WY, USA
83110
307-886-5459
K. Clark

Boysen Outfitters
Box 66
Shoshoni, WY, USA
82649
307-876-2636
B. Weaver

Bridger Wilderness Outfitters
Box 561
Pinedale, WY, USA
82941
307-367-2268
Tim Singewald

Bud Nelson;s Big Game Outfitters
Box 409
Jackson, WY, USA
83001
733-2843

Cabin Creek Outfitters
1313 Lane 10 Route 1
Powell, WY, USA
82435
307-754-9279
Duane Wiltse

CJ Outfitter/Guide
1010 S. Washington
Casper, WY, USA
82601
307-235-1975
J. Dye

CK Hunting & Fishing Camp
Box 458
Big Piney, WY, USA
83113
307-276-3723/3471
D. & R. Copeland

Cleav. Creek Outfitter
Box 177 Sheridan County
Clearmont, WY, USA
82835
307-758-4388
R.R. Smith

Cloud Peak Outfitters
Box 4032
Casper, WY, USA
82604
307-265-0334
Kenneth McCants

Colony Outfitters
Alzada Star Route
Belle Fourche, SD, USA
57717
307-896-6214
Jim Dacar

Big Game Outfitters Directory

North America

Coulter Creek Outfitters
Box 504
Jackson, WY, USA
307-733-6557
B. Johnson

Coy's Yellow Creek Outfitters
Box 3055 Park County
Cody, WY, USA
82414
307-587-6944
B.J. Coy

Crittenden, Paul
Box 185 Sublette County
BOndurant, WY, USA
82922
307-733-6740

Cross Mill-Iron Ranch
Fremont County
Crowheart, WY, USA
82512
307-486-2279
L.C. Miller

Crossed Sabres
PArk County
Wapiti, WY, USA
82450
307-587-3750
F.A. Norris

Crystal Creek Outfitters
Box 44 A Star Route
Jackson Hole, WY, USA
83001
307-733-6318
Gap & Peg Puche

Dan's Outfitting
5 Hill Drive
Wheatland, WY, USA
82201
D. Artery

Darby Mountain Outfitters
Box 632
Marbleton, WY, USA
83113
307-276-3934
John Harper

David Ranch
Sublette County
Daniel, WY, USA
83115
307-859-8228
Melvin or Todd David

Deadman Creek Outfitters
Box 232
Alpine, WY, USA
83128
307-654-7528
G. Fischer

Diamond D Ranch Outfitters
Box 211 Teton County
Moran, WY, USA
83013
307-543-2479
R. Doty

Diamond J Outfiiters
Box 1347 Carbon County
Saratoga, WY, USA
82331
307-326-8259
J. Stuemke

Dick Page Inc.
1625 Holly
Casper, WY, USA
83604
307-237-7866

Dodge Creek Ranch
402 Tunnel Road Albany County
Rock River, WY, USA
82083
307-322-2345
J. Kennedy

Double R Ranch Outfitters
Box 2166
Cody, WY, USA
82414
307-587-6016
Ron Lineberger

D.T. Outfitting
Box 891 Route 63
Lander, WY, USA
82520
307-332-3123
R. Focht

Dvarishkis, Ramul
Hot Springs County
Hamilton Dome, WY, USA
82427
307-867-2262

Eagle Creek Outfitters
Box 562
Evansville, WY, USA
83636
307-237-7673
Bruce Hillard

East Table Creek Hunting Camp
15 Rustic Hills Road East
Rozet, WY, USA
82727
307-682-4196\8107
F. Donaldson

88 Ranch Outfitters
1937 Ross Road
Douglas, WY, USA
82633
307-358-5941
Mike & Rob Henry

Elk Mountain Safari, Inc.
Box 188
Saratoga, WY, USA
82331
307-326-8773
E. Beattie

Elk Mountain Outfitters
Wheatland, WY, USA
82201
307-322-3220
M.J. Wakkuri

Finley Ranch
Fremont County
Dubois, WY, USA
82513
307-455-2494
O.F. Finley

Fir Creek Ranch
Box 190 Teton County
Moran, WY, USA
83013
307-543-2416
P. Finch

Fleming, Warren
Box 2033 Teton County
Jackson, WY, USA
83001
307-733-2493

Flitner, Dave
Greybull, WY, USA
82428
307-765-2961

Flying H Ranch
598 Hunter Creek Road
Cody, WY, USA
82414
307-587-2089

Flying V Hunting Lodge
Box 158
Newcastle, WY, USA
82701
307-746-2096

Gardner, Low
Lincoln County
Smoot, WY, USA
83126
307-886-5665

Garst, Russell
Box 400 Trailcreek Road
Weston, WY, USA
82731
307-682-0119

Ghost Town Outfitters
4020 Bretton Drive
Casper, WY, USA
82601
307-265-4658
Bill Arnold

Gibbs, Donald J.
Box 216 Park County
Cody, WY, USA
82414
307-587-4198

Grand & Sierra Outfitters
Box 312
Encampment, WY, USA
82325
307-327-5200
G. Knotwell

Grand Slam Outfitters
Box 1098
Saratoga, WY, USA
82331
307-326-5508
Mark Condict

Grandstrom Outfitters
Box 283 Kaycee Route
Buffalo, WY, USA
82834
307-684-7363

Grant Ranch Outfitters
Box 199 Elder Route
Glenrock, WY, USA
82637
307-436-2421
Richard Grant, Jr.

Grassy Lake Outfitters
Box 853 Teton County
Jackson, WY, USA
83001
307-733-6779
B.J. Wilson

Green River Guest Ranch
Cora, WY, USA
82925
307-367-2314
Lyle Pendergast

Green River Outfitters
Box 727
Pinedale, WY, USA
82941
307-367-2416
Bill Webb

Greer, Randy C.
404 Prairieview Drive
Gillette, WY, USA
82716
307-682-5781

Grey Horse Outfitters
Box 428 Natrona County
MIlls, WY, USA
82644
307-265-5669
Morris L. Carter, Jr.

Greybull River Outfitters
Box 1431
Evanston, WY, USA
82930
307-789-7126
Craig Griffith

Big Game Outfitters Directory

North America

Grizzly Ranch
Park County
Cody, WY, USA
82414
307-587-3966
R. Felts

Haderlie Outfitting & Guide Service
Box 126
Freedom, WY, USA
83120
208-873-2353
Vaughn Haderlie

Hagen, Duane K.
153 Hidden Valley Road
Cody, WY, USA
82414
307-587-5090

Heart 6 Ranch
Box 70 Teton County
Moran, WY, USA
83103
307-543-2477
C. Garnick

Hidden Basin Outfitters
Box 7182
Jackson, WY, USA
83001
307-733-7980
N. Meeks

High Country Outfitters
Box 33E Route 1 Big Horn County
Deaver, WY, USA
82421
307-664-2241
R. Olson

Highland Meadows Ranch
Fremont County
Dubois, WY, USA
82513
J. Detimore

Hollingsworth, William
5510 Alcova Route
Casper, WY, USA
82604
307-472-7956

Horse Creek Ranch
Box 3878
Jackson, WY, USA
83001
307-733-6566
Ray Billings

Indian Creek Outfitters
Box 2882 Teton County
Jackson, WY, USA
83001
307-733-9207
B. Moyer

Irv Lozier's Trophy Hunts
Cora, WY, USA
82925

J & B Outfitters
Box 4246 1812 Fremont
Natrona Co. Casper, WY, USA
82604
307-237-5363
James Fritz

Jackson Hole Country Outfitters
Box 20102
Jackson, WY, USA
83112
307-883-2999
M. Jones

Jenson Hunting Camp
ROute 1 Lincoln County
Afton, WY, USA
83110
307-886-3401
K.C. Jensen

Johnson, Dean
Box 1535 Park County
Cody, WY, USA
82414
307-587-4072

Llano Outfitters
630 Trigood Drive Natrona County
Casper, WY, USA
82609
307-235-4865
J. Savini

Magic Mountains Outfitters
Box 248
Cokeville, WY, USA
83114

M.F. Hunting
Box 724 Teton County
Jackson, WY, USA
83001
307-733-2271
L. Feuz

Mankin Wildlife
Box 1239 Campbell County
Gillette, WY, USA
82716
307-682-3007
R.Mankin

McNeel & Sons Inc.
Rural Route Teton County
Alpine, WY, USA
83128
307-886-5508

Meadow Lake Outfitters
Box 146
Boulder, WY, USA
82923
307-537-5278
Hank Snow

Metzger, Dean
Box 734
Dubois, WY, USA
82513
307-455-2938

Morning Creek Outfitter
Box 2712 Park County
Cody, WY, USA
82414
307-587-4647
B. Reid

Mountain View Ranch
Box 248
Moran, WY, USA
83013
307-543-2458
Lewis Price, Jr.

Open Creek Outfitting
Box 3123
Cody, WY, USA
82414
307-543-2458
John Billings

Oxner, Floyd
Box 897
Pinedale, WY, USA
82941
307-367-2736

Page, Dick
1625 Holly Natrona County
Casper, WY, USA
82604
307-237-7866

Pass Creek Outfitters
Box 14 Fremont County
Arapahoe, WY, USA
82510
307-856-6812
R. K. Miller

Pathfinder Outfitter & Guides
Box 3581 Dept. NAH
Casper, WY, USA
82602
307-235-1453

P Cross Bar Outfitters
8586A North Hiway 15-16
Campbell Co. Gillette, WY, USA
82716
307-682-3994
M. Scott

Pennoyer, Stanley
Owl Creek Route Hot Springs Co.
Thermopolis, WY, USA
82443
307-867-2407

Peterson, Charlie Jr.
Box 1074 Teton County
Jackson, WY, USA
83001
307-733-3805

Peterson Outfitters
Box 725
Pinedale, WY, USA
82941
307-367-4627
Greg Peterson

Peterson's Hunting Camps
Box 1156
Aafton, WY, USA
83110
307-886-9693
Everett Peterson

Pilgrim Creek Hunting Camp
Box 1443 Teton County
Jackson, WY, USA
83001
307-733-3476
J. Davis

Platt, Ron
Box 49 Star Route Carbon Co.
Encampment, WY, USA
82325
307-327-5539

Ponderosas Lodge
Box 832 Sublette County
Pinedale, WY, USA
82941
307-367-2516
Gary & Sue Weiss

Powder River Outfitter
Box 37A 603 Sourdough
Buffalo, WY, USA
82834
307-684-2793
L.R. Brannian

Rand Creek Outfitter
Box 128
Wapiti, WY, USA
82450
307-587-5077
D. Blevins

Randle, Don
Box 911 Fremont County
Dubois, WY, USA
82513
307-455-2351

Red Desert Outfitters
Box 1201
Green River, WY, USA
82935
307-675-6199
V. Dana

Rimrock Ranch
2728 Northfork Route
Cody, WY, USA
82414
307-587-3970
G. Fales

Robinson, William
Box 1124 Teton County
Jackson, WY, USA
83001
307-733-3308

Big Game Outfitters Directory

North America

Rockin DBL R Outfit
2760 Robertson RD 38
Casper, WY, USA
82604
307-234-7732
L.F. Beekley

Rose, Don
Box 352 Fremont County
Dubois, WY, USA
82513
307-455-2467

Rough Country Outfitters
Box 973 Converse County
Glenrock, WY, USA
82637
307-436-2304
J.D. Schell

RR Haecker Outfitte
Box 818 Teton County
Jackson, WY, USA
83001
307-733-6195
Randy Haecker

Saddle Pocket Ranch
143 Mazet Road Fremont County
Riverton, WY, USA
82501
307-856-1720
G. Fuechsel

Safari Outfitters
16 Musser Road
Cody, WY, USA
82414
307-587-3888
Gretchen Stark

Sand Creek Ranch Outfitters
General Delivery
Alcova, WY, USA
82620
J. Collins

S & S Outfitters & Guide Service
1818-H S. Washington
Casper, WY, USA
82601
307-266-4229

Sanger, Chuck
Box 745 Carbon County
Saratoga, WY, USA
82331
307-326-5696

Savage Run Outfitter
49 Pahlow Land Albany County
Laramie, WY, USA
82070
307-745-5958
Jim Talbot

Sheep Mesa Outfitters
121 Road 20
Cody, WY, USA
82414
307-587-4014/4305
Dale & Ron Good

Siggins Triangle X Ranch
3400 Southford Road
Cody, WY, USA
82414
307-587-2031
Stan Siggins

Silver Star Ranch
148 Road Route 6
Cody, WY, USA
82414
307-587-2036
Bob Loran

Skinner Brothers Wilderness Camps
Box 859
Pinedale, WY, USA
82941

Spear-O-Wigwam Ranch
Box 328 Sheridan County
Story, WY, USA
82842
307-683-2226/674-4496
A. MacCarty

Spearhead Ranch
3493 Ross Road Route 3
Douglas, WY, USA
82633
307-358-2694
F.N. Moore

Spotted Horse Ranch
Teton County
Jackson, WY, USA
83001
307-733-2097
Dick Bess

Spring Creek Outfitters
Box 1033
Bondurant, WY, USA
82922
307-733-3974
Steve Robertson

Star Valley Outfitters
Box 143 Lincoln County
Smoot, WY, USA
83126
307-886-9585
R. Clark

Stearns Outfitting
51 Red Rock Drive
Douglas, WY, USA
82633
307-358-6580
Gary & Jane Stearns

Stephens, Press
Box 29 Big Horn County
Shell, WY, USA
82441
307-765-4377

Stetter General Outfitter
Box 695 Fremont County
Dubois, WY, USA
82513
307-455-2725
L.F. Stetter

Stevenson Outfitting
940 North Center Natrona Co.
Casper, WY, USA
82601
307-237-6176
J. Stevenson

Sweetwater Gap Ranch
Box 26 Sweetwater County
Rock Springs, WY, USA
82901
307-362-2798
B. Wilmetti

Sweetwater Outfitterrs
Box 4188 Natrona County
Casper, WY, USA
82604
307-266-1424
R. Dennis

Table Mountain Outfitters
Box 2714N
Cheyenne, WY, USA
82003
307-632-6352

Tass, Leo
Box 14 K.C. Route Johnson County
Buffalo, WY, USA
82634

Taylor, Glenn B.
Box 37 Teton County
Kelly, WY, USA
83011
307-733-4851

Taylor, Ridge W.
Box 2356 Teton County
Jackson, WY, USA
83001
307-733-9041

Teton Country Outfitters
Box 7434
Jackson, WY, USA
83001
307-733-6817
D. Lloyd

Teton Outfitters
Box 355 Star Route
Wilson, WY, USA
83014
307-733-5414
E.A. Linn

Teton Trail Rides, Inc.
Box 1350 Teton County
Jackson, WY, USA
83001
307-733-6409
C. Rudd

Teton Wilderness Outfitting
Box 442 Sheridan County
Ranchester, WY, USA
82839
307-655-2451
N. Vance

The Last Resort
Box 38
Daniel, WY, USA
83115
307-859-8294
Dru Roberts

Thompson, Dick
Box 17 Sublette County
Cora, WY, USA
82925
307-367-4551

Thorofare Outfitting
Box 604
Cody, WY, USA
82414
307-587-5029
D. Schmalz

Thunder Ridge Outfitters
849 South Spruce
Casper, WY, USA
82601
307-237-3329/266-1919
J. Galles

Timberline Outfitter
1202 West 32nd Street
Cheyenne, WY, USA
82001
307-635-7288
C. Oceanak

Tjomsland, Cy
Fremont County
Dubois, WY, USA
82513

T Lazy T Outfitting
Box 1288 Teton County
Jackson, WY, USA
83001
307-733-4481
T. Toolson

Trapper Galloway Ranch
Box 1222 Big Horn County
Shell, WY, USA
82441
307-765-2971
F.K. Smith, Jr.

Triangle C Ranch
Box 691 Fremont County
Dubois, WY, USA
82513
307-455-2225
J.L. Pavlik

Big Game Outfitters Directory

North America

Triangle X Ranch
Teton County
Moose, WY, USA
83012
307-733-3612/2183
Don & Harold Turner

Triple X Ranch
Park County
Cody, WY, USA
82414
307-587-2031
S. Siggins

Turpin Meadow Ranch
Box 48
Moran, WY, USA
83013
G. Wocicki

Tri W Outfitters
1700 W. 2700 N. #97
Ogden, UT, USA
84404
Bobby Wright

Two Ocean Pass Outfitters
Box 2322
Jackson, WY, USA
83001
307-733-5962
G. A. Rickman

Two Ocean Pass Outfitter
Box 472
Wright, WY, USA
82732
307-464-0189
J. Robidoux

Ullery, Brad J.
3045 East 4th Street
Natrona County Casper, WY, USA
82604
307-233-5453

Ullery, Dick
Box 1218 Natrona County
Casper, WY, USA
82602
307-235-5453

Ullery, Harold
Box 9680
Casper, WY, USA
82609
307-265-9051

Wallace Brothers Outfitters
Box 3366 Teton County
Jackson, WY, USA
83001
307-733-2591
J.T. Wallace

Wilderness Outfitters
Box 1072
Dubois, WY, USA
82513
307-455-2463/235-1759
R. Hansen

Wilderness Trails
Box 1113 Teton County
Jackson, WY, USA
83001
307-733-9051
G. Clover

Winter, John R.
Box 1922 Route 1
Cody, WY, USA
82414
307-587-4021

Wolf Lake Outfitters
Box 9
Pinedale, WY, USA
82941
307-367-2580
Mike Nystrom

Wolf Mountain Outfitters
Route 1
Afton, WY, USA
83110
307-886-9317
G. Azevedo

Wolverine Creek Outfitter
Box 9 Sublette County
Pinedale, WY, USA
82941
307-367-2580
M. Nystrom Sr.

Wyoming Peak Outfitters
Afton, WY, USA
83110
307-886-3936/279-3344
Billy Peterson

Wyoming Safari, Inc.
Box 1126
Saratoga, WY, USA
82331
307-327-5530/5502
W.G. Condict

Wyoming Wilderness
2051 Road 11 Park County
Powell, WY, USA
82435
307-754-4320
Jake Clark

Wyoming Wilderness Outfitters
Box 4311 Natrona County
Casper, WY, USA
82604
307-235-4511
D. Simpson

Wyoming Wilderness Outfitters
1051 Rd. 11, Rt. 1
Powell, WY, USA
82435
307-754-4320
Jake & Kay Clark

Yellowstone Country Outfitters
32 Creek Lane Park County
Cody, WY, USA
82414
307-587-3596
M.C. Coast

ZK Outfitters
Box 284 Fremont County
Dubois, WY, USA
82513
307-455-2210
G.J. Rice

Big Game Outfitters Directory

South America

Argentina

Safaris Del Neuquen
Gral. Roca 1028,
Neuquen, Argentina
South America
944-7616

Brazil

Almeida, Antonio De
Caixa Postal 840
Sao Paulo, Brazil
South America
227-0922

Venezuela

Lobo Outfitters (Venezuela)
Box 9A Route 2
Pagosa Springs, CO, USA
81147
800-248-0109

YES, I WANT TO SUBSCRIBE TO HUNTERS GUIDE To PROFESSIONAL OUTFITTERS

Send me my first copy right away! I understand that this subscription will be automatically renewed annually, and that I will receive my full-colour, hardcover book every February at the low subscription price of $19.95 US plus $5.00 postage and handling. Should I wish to cancel my subscription, I will notify *Hunters Guide* in writing.

Name _____

Address _____

City _____ Province/State _____ Code _____

☐ Bill me later ☐ Cheque Enclosed ☐ Charge VISA Acct. No. _____

Please allow 8 - 10 weeks for delivery. Expires _____ Signature _____

YES, I WANT TO GIVE HUNTERS GUIDE TO PROFESSIONAL OUTFITTERS TO A FRIEND

☐ Perpetual Subscription -- Automatic Renewal*   ☐ One-time Gift -- No Renewal

Name _____

Address _____

City _____ Province/State _____ Code _____

Bill to   Address
☐ Bill me later ☐ Cheque Enclosed ☐ Charge VISA Acct. No. _____

Please allow 8 - 10 weeks for delivery. Expires _____ Signature _____

* I understand that this subscription will be automatically renewed annually, and that my friend will receive his book every February at the low subscription price of $19.95 US plus $5.00 postage and handling. Should I wish to cancel this gift subscription, I will notify *Hunters Guide* in writing.

YES, I WANT TO GIVE HUNTERS GUIDE TO PROFESSIONAL OUTFITTERS TO A FRIEND

☐ Perpetual Subscription -- Automatic Renewal*   ☐ One-time Gift -- No Renewal

Name _____

Address _____

City _____ Province/State _____ Code _____

Bill to   Address
☐ Bill me later ☐ Cheque Enclosed ☐ Charge VISA Acct. No. _____

Please allow 8 - 10 weeks for delivery. Expires _____ Signature _____

* I understand that this subscription will be automatically renewed annually, and that my friend will receive his book every February at the low subscription price of $19.95 US plus $5.00 postage and handling. Should I wish to cancel this gift subscription, I will notify *Hunters Guide* in writing.

**HUNTERS GUIDE TO
PROFESSIONAL OUTFITTERS**
**17 Prince Arthur Avenue
Toronto, Ontario, Canada
M5R 1B2**

**HUNTERS GUIDE TO
PROFESSIONAL OUTFITTERS**
**17 Prince Arthur Avenue
Toronto, Ontario, Canada
M5R 1B2**

**HUNTERS GUIDE TO
PROFESSIONAL OUTFITTERS**
**17 Prince Arthur Avenue
Toronto, Ontario, Canada
M5R 1B2**

YES, I WANT TO SUBSCRIBE TO HUNTERS GUIDE To PROFESSIONAL OUTFITTERS

Send me my first copy right away! I understand that this subscription will be automatically renewed annually, and that I will receive my full-colour, hardcover book every February at the low subscription price of $19.95 US plus $5.00 postage and handling. Should I wish to cancel my subscription, I will notify *Hunters Guide* in writing.

Name

Address

City   Province/State   Code

☐ Bill me later   ☐ Cheque Enclosed   ☐ Charge VISA Acct. No.

Please allow 8 - 10 weeks for delivery.   Expires _____ Signature _____

YES, I WANT TO GIVE HUNTERS GUIDE TO PROFESSIONAL OUTFITTERS TO A FRIEND

☐ Perpetual Subscription --
   Automatic Renewal*

☐ One-time Gift --
   No Renewal

Name

Address

City   Province/State   Code

Bill to   Address

☐ Bill me later   ☐ Cheque Enclosed   ☐ Charge VISA Acct. No.

Please allow 8 - 10 weeks for delivery.   Expires _____ Signature _____

* I understand that this subscription will be automatically renewed annually, and that my friend will receive his book every February at the low subscription price of $19.95 US plus $5.00 postage and handling. Should I wish to cancel this gift subscription, I will notify *Hunters Guide* in writing.

YES, I WANT TO GIVE HUNTERS GUIDE TO PROFESSIONAL OUTFITTERS TO A FRIEND

☐ Perpetual Subscription --
   Automatic Renewal*

☐ One-time Gift --
   No Renewal

Name

Address

City   Province/State   Code

Bill to   Address

☐ Bill me later   ☐ Cheque Enclosed   ☐ Charge VISA Acct. No.

Please allow 8 - 10 weeks for delivery.   Expires _____ Signature _____

* I understand that this subscription will be automatically renewed annually, and that my friend will receive his book every February at the low subscription price of $19.95 US plus $5.00 postage and handling. Should I wish to cancel this gift subscription, I will notify *Hunters Guide* in writing.

**HUNTERS GUIDE TO
PROFESSIONAL OUTFITTERS**
17 Prince Arthur Avenue
Toronto, Ontario, Canada
M5R 1B2

**HUNTERS GUIDE TO
PROFESSIONAL OUTFITTERS**
17 Prince Arthur Avenue
Toronto, Ontario, Canada
M5R 1B2

**HUNTERS GUIDE TO
PROFESSIONAL OUTFITTERS**
17 Prince Arthur Avenue
Toronto, Ontario, Canada
M5R 1B2